Automatic Flight Control

Automatic Flight Control
Third Edition

E. H. J. Pallett TEng (CEI), AMRAes, FSLAET

BSP PROFESSIONAL BOOKS

OXFORD LONDON EDINBURGH

BOSTON PALO ALTO MELBOURNE

First published by
Granada Publishing Ltd, 1979
Second Edition 1983
Third Edition published by
BSP Professional Books 1987

British Library
Cataloguing in Publication Data
Pallett, E.H.J.
Automatic flight control.—3rd ed.
1. Automatic pilot (Airplanes)
I. Title
629.135′2   TL589.5

ISBN 0-632-01856-9

BSP Professional Books
Editorial offices:
Osney Mead, Oxford OX2 0EL
   (*Orders*: Tel. 0865 240201)
8 John Street, London WC1N 2ES
23 Ainslie Place, Edinburgh EH3 6AJ
52 Beacon Street, Boston
   Massachusetts 02108, USA
667 Lytton Avenue, Palo Alto
   California 94301, USA
107 Barry Street, Carlton
   Victoria 3053, Australia

Set by V & M Graphics Ltd
Aylesbury, Bucks
Printed and bound in Great Britain
by Billing & Sons Ltd Worcester

Contents

Preface to First Edition

At the present time there is hardly an aircraft in either civil or military operation without some form of automatic flight control system comprising part of its standard operational equipment. The systems available are as diverse as the aircraft themselves, varying from a simple roll stabiliser or 'wing-leveller' in a single-engined private aircraft, to the sophisticated flight-guidance systems capable of automatically controlling the flight paths of large transport aircraft from take-off to touchdown and roll-out. It is then a little difficult perhaps to realise that the development of such systems has arisen from foundations laid years before man himself took to the air to become the controller of his own 'flight path destiny'.

The early inventors of 'heavier-than-air flying machines' were, of course, faced with many problems, the most prominant of which was the one associated with the attainment of stabilised flight. Although there was an awareness that stability should be inherent in the basic design of a machine, little was known of the separation of stability into dynamic and static elements in relation to the various degrees of freedom possessed by a machine. As a result, and as recorded history indicates, efforts were directed more towards keeping a machine straight and level and free from the effects of external disturbances, and to derive the requisite stability by applying some form of artificial stabilising device.

It is of interest to note that possibly the first machine to use such a device was an unmanned glider designed by the Frenchman Charles Renard in 1873. The device consisted of a transverse pendulum coupled to two 'steering wings', the idea being that if the machine turned from its intended flight path, the pendulum would raise one wing and lower the other, and thereby straighten the machine's path. The first flight test indicated that such a device could work, but that lateral instability would have to be much less than that exhibited by Renard's machine to be really successful! Apart from the pendulum, the stabilising properties of a gyroscope were also considered, and a noteworthy 'first' in this connection was the stabiliser patented in 1891 by Sir Hiram Maxim and installed in his steam-powered machine. The design concept was somewhat ahead of its time in that it also comprised a servo control loop and other features which are basic to today's automatic flight control systems. Maxim's flying machine unfortunately, came to an untimely end before the stabiliser could be tested under 'live' conditions.

When later pioneers took up the challenge of designing machines in which they themselves ventured to fly, the possibility of manoeuvring their machines away from straight and level flight was realised. However, this was to present another problem; namely, how to cater for the changes in stability which would result when control for initiating a manoeuvre was applied. Thus, 'controllability' was to become an important feature of flying machine design, and one which the Wright brothers were to incorporate in the machine which gained for them the distinction of making that historic flight in 1903. The Wrights' approach to aerodynamic and in-flight problems was more advanced than that of their predecessors, and although the machines built and flown by them were not completely stable, the incorporation of the controllability feature permitted a number of successful flights to be made without artificial stabilisation.

The introduction of control systems by the Wright brothers and subsequent pioneers in their aeroplanes (as they were becoming known) was to establish an additional role for stabilisation devices to play because, if a device could be coupled to the controls, then it alone could correct any departure from a stabilised condition. This was not to go unchallenged of course, and the first practical demonstration of a coupled gyroscopic two-axis control device was given by Lawrence Sperry during his historic flight in Paris in 1914. Thus, it can be said that the foundation for automatically-controlled flight was laid in the early years of this century. By the mid-twenties and in the 'thirties', the development of systems in the United States, the United Kingdom and Europe, became a separate field of engineering technology, and a number of 'automatic pilots' and 'gyropilots' demonstrated their capabilities in commercial and military aircraft operations, and in several historic long-distance record flights. As the technology has continued to develop, system designs have been influenced not only by the advances made in aerodynamics and aircraft controllability characteristics, but also by the advances taking place in other technological fields. For example, the changeover from pneumatic operation of gyroscopes to electrical operation; the processing of control signals by electron tubes and magnetic amplifiers; the introduction of the semiconductor, and perhaps the greatest influence of all at this moment in time, the vast potential of digital processing technology.

The diversity of present-day automatic flight control systems arises principally because they need tailoring to suit the aerodynamic and flight handling characteristics of individual types of aircraft. It is possible to compromise, and by virtue of this, many of the systems installed in aircraft designed for operation in the general aviation sector are, in fact, highly versatile in their applications; however, there are limitations particularly where the more complex types of transport aircraft are concerned. Thus, any attempts at describing the range of systems and their operating fundamentals would be a mammoth task involving the writing of several volumes. However, any one automatic flight control system may be considered as being composed of four principal elements, which although differing in design and construction, perform functions common to all other control systems. The element functions concerned are progressively: attitude sensing, error signal sensing, signal processing, and conversion of processed signals into powered control, and they set a convenient pattern for a general study of control fundamentals. The material for this book has, therefore, been structured accordingly, and it is hoped that the selected examples of devices performing such functions, will usefully illustrate how relevant principles are applied.

A basic understanding of the priciples of flight and aircraft stability, and of servomechanisms, is a pre-requisite to a study of the main subject and they are therefore covered in the opening chapters. With the development of flight director systems and of the concept of integrating basic attitude and navigational data, it became logical to share data and servomechanism links such that a director system could provide guidance commands to an automatic flight control system. Thus, manufacturers develop and make available a wide range of complementary systems, the basic principles of which have also been included in this book. The concluding chapter deals with what may be termed the ultimate in automatic flight control evolution, namely automatic landing.

In preparing the material on systems, I have been greatly assisted by data and illustrations supplied by manufacturers, and would in particular, like to express grateful thanks to Collins Radio Company of England Ltd, Smith's Industries, Marconi Avionics Ltd, and Sperry Rand Ltd, for their permission to use certain of the data, and to have photographs reproduced. My thanks are also extended to friends and colleagues for useful suggestions, comments and assistance in proof reading, and finally to the publisher's editoral staff for their patience.

Copthorne   E.P.
Sussex

Preface to Second Edition

The publisher's invitation to prepare a second edition of this book has been gratefully accepted reflecting as it would seem, a continuing demand for knowledge of the subject at the introductory level. During the period in which the book has been in existence, I have had the pleasure of meeting many of its readers both in the UK and overseas, and I am indebted to them generally for their interest, and in particular to those who provided useful comments and suggestions. All of these have proved to be valuable in the preparation of material for this edition.

The sequencing of the chapters according to control element functions remains essentially as before, but the overall content has been expanded to accommodate a section in Chapter 1 on the fundamentals of helicopter flight, and a new chapter on the automatic control of helicopters. Other new features are the inclusion of a number of self-test questions at the end of each chapter, and also appendices summarising the combinations of control systems and aircraft currently in service.

Copthorne, Sussex

E.P

Preface to Third Edition

In this edition, the contents of a number of chapters have been expanded to provide more details of the operation of the appropriate systems and components. The sequencing of subjects adopted in earlier editions has been retained.

Information on electronic flight instrument systems has now been included, and forms an addition to the chapter on Flight Director Systems. Although it has been necessary to keep this information brief, it is nevertheless, hoped that it will provide a general understanding of one of the most interesting developments in the avionics field.

The application of signal processing by means of digital circuit techniques to automatic control systems requires a good understanding of logic gates and interpretation of associated circuit diagrams; for this reason therefore, a new chapter on the subject has been added.

I take this opportunity of thanking those readers of earlier editions who have submitted comments, suggestions and reference material, all of which have proved valuable in the preparation of this edition.

Copthorne, Sussex   E.P.

1
Principles of Flight

In order to understand the operating fundamentals of any automatic flight control system and its application to an aircraft, it is first necessary to have some understanding of how an aircraft flies, its stability characteristics, and of the conventional means by which it is controlled. There are two classes of aircraft with which we are concerned, namely fixed-wing and rotary wing or helicopter class, and the contents of this chapter are therefore set out under these appropriate headings.

A. FIXED-WING AIRCRAFT

Lift

It is a well-known fact from common experience that all material objects are attracted to the earth by a force which is in proportion to the mass of the object; such a force is called gravity. In order for an object to rise from the earth's surface, and to maintain itself in a continual ascent or at a constant height above the surface, the attraction which gravity has for the object must be opposed by the development of a force called lift. A variety of methods can of course be adopted, the choice being dependent on the object to be lifted. The method with which we are concerned, however, is the one applied to the wings of an aircraft. In this method, wings are designed so that they conform to specific plan forms, and aerofoil-shaped cross-sections, chosen on the basis of size, weight and performance requirements of the particular aircraft. The geometry of some typical wing plan forms, aerofoil cross-sections, and associated terminology are shown in fig. 1.1.

In order to generate the required lifting force there must be relative movement between the wing and the surrounding air. Theoretically, it makes no difference whether air flows over a stationary wing or whether the wing is moved through the air; in practice, however, the latter movement takes place as a result of the propulsive thrust from a propeller or turbine engine exhaust gases.

Referring to fig. 1.2 it will be noted that when the air strikes the leading edge of the wing, it divides into a flow over the upper and lower cambered surfaces of its aerofoil section. The mass of continuity of flow is constant, but

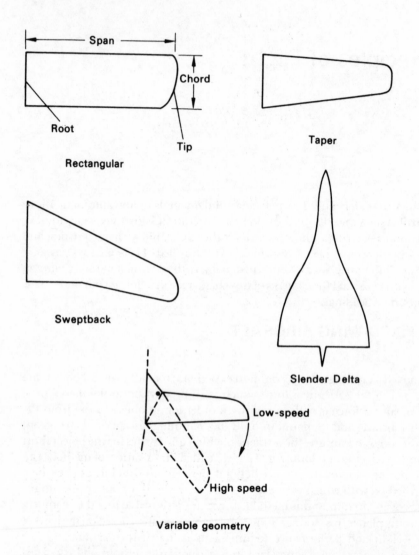

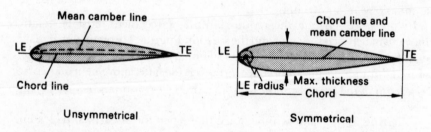

Fig. 1.1 Wing plan-forms and aerofoil terminology

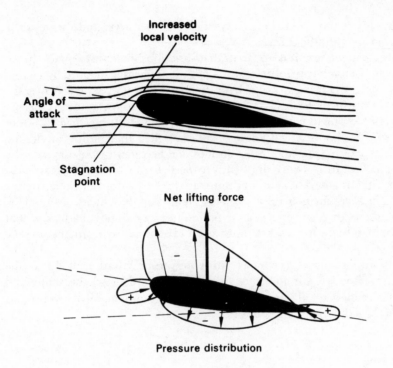

Fig. 1.2 Generation of lift

as a result of differences between the amount of upper and lower surface camber, and also because the wing is at an angle of attack, i.e. at an angle relative to the airflow, the velocity of the airflow over the upper surface will be greater than that of the air flowing along the lower surface. Since the pressure of fluid (liquid or gas) decreases at points where the velocity of the fluid increases, then for an aircraft wing at small angles of attack the pressures acting on both surfaces of the wing will decrease. However, the decrease is greater on the more highly cambered upper surface, and it is the resulting pressure difference across the wing aerofoil section which generates the net lifting force. The greatest pressures occur at the stagnation point, at points around the leading edge, and at the trailing edge.

The measurement of the pressures acting on the surfaces are in absolute values, and they are represented by vectors drawn perpendicular to the surfaces. The length of a vector is proportional to the difference between absolute pressure at a point and free stream static pressure. It is usual to convert this to a non-directional quantity called the pressure coefficient by comparing it with free stream dynamic pressure. The convention for plotting these coefficients is (i) measured pressure higher than ambient gives a positive coefficient, and the vector is plotted towards the surface; (ii) measured pressure lower than ambient, the coefficient is negative, and the vector is plotted away from the surface.

From the foregoing it is apparent that variations in angle of attack are an important factor in controlling the magnitude of the lift generated by a wing. For example, when angle of attack is increased the velocity of airflow over the upper surface increases at a faster rate than that over the lower surface, thereby changing the pressure distribution such that the net lifting force is further increased. At some critical angle of attack, called the stalling angle, the airflow separates from the upper surface and becomes turbulent, with the result that the lifting force is drastically reduced. In practice, the wings of each type of aircraft are fixed at an optimum angle of the chord line relative to a longitudinal datum (generally called the 'rigging angle of incidence') and the aircraft then flown within a small working range of angles of attack so that in combination the highest lift/drag ratio and economic performance may be obtained.

Other important factors which control pressure distribution and lift are the velocity of the free air flow, its viscosity and its density, the shape and thickness of the aerofoil section adopted for a wing, the wing plan form and its area, and condition of wing surfaces.

Delta wing

The lift coefficient (C_L) of a delta wing continues to increase up to very steep angles of attack because the system of leading edge vortices strengthens as angle of attack increases. The form of the vortex system of a wing with a large angle of sweep is shown in fig. 1.3.

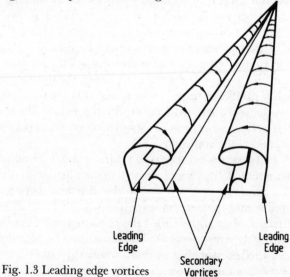

Leading
Edge

Leading
Edge

Secondary
Vortices

Fig. 1.3 Leading edge vortices

When the wing is at zero angle of attack, the airflow remains attached to both surfaces of the wing and no lift is generated. As soon as the angle of attack departs from zero, the flow separates along the entire length of the leading edges in the form of two free vortex layers joined to the leading edges and rolled up in the manner of two conically-shaped spiralling coils above the upper surface of the wing. The coils, or leading edge vortices, induce a suction on the upper surface which remains constant along the chord except in the neighbourhood of the trailing edge. The size of the vortices increases with angle of attack and they cover a progressively greater proportion of the wing surface. When the angle of sweep is sufficient, these vortices remain in a broadly similar form through a wide range of angles of attack and the flow is characteristically steady throughout the range appropriate to the required flight conditions. Secondary vortices flow between the leading edges and the cores of the main vortices, but because these also develop progressively they do not interfere with the stability of the main flow.

As the vortices increase with angle of attack, the suction force generated on the upper surface of the wing increases and thereby contributes to the total lift produced.

The slender delta plan form shown in fig. 1.1 is of the type adopted for the 'Concorde'. The curved shape of the wing is such that maximum sweepback is obtained at the inboard sections of the wing without destroying the best effects of the vortex system.

Centre of pressure

In connection with the pressure variations occurring across the surfaces of a wing, it is usual to consider the total lift force as acting from one point along the chord line; this point is known as the centre of pressure (CP). As will be noted from fig. 1.4 *a*, the total lift force is resolved into two principal components: (i) the lift component acting at right angles to the direction of the free airflow, and (ii) a total drag component acting in the direction of the free airflow. The ratio of lift to drag is a measure of the efficiency of any aerofoil section adopted for an aircraft wing.

The location of the CP is a function of camber and the factor known as the lift coefficient, and it varies with the angle of attack. As the angle of attack increases, there is a change in the distribution of pressure above and below the wing such that the magnitude of lift force increases and the CP moves forward. At a certain angle of attack, known as the stalling angle, there is a sudden decrease in the magnitude of the lift force and the CP moves rearward.

Aerodynamic centre

Movement of the CP with changes in angle of attack also causes the pitching

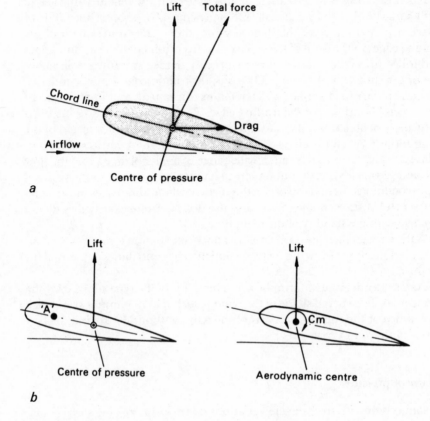

Fig. 1.4 Centre of pressure and aerodynamic centre

moment of a wing to vary, to an extent which depends on the position of the moment reference point 'A'. The pitching moment is equal to the product of the total lift force and the distance from the point 'A' to the CP (fig. 1.4 *b*). It is, however, possible to locate a reference point about which the pitching moment is constant (C_m) regardless of the angle of attack. Such a point is known as the aerodynamic centre, and for flight at subsonic speeds, it is usually located at or near 25% of the chord. In the mathematical treatment of stability and control of aircraft, allowance is made for the constant pitching moment and it is assumed therefore that the total lift force acts from the aerodynamic centre rather than the CP.

Drag

The movement of a body through a fluid, whether it is a liquid or air, always produces a force that tends to oppose the movement; such a force is known as

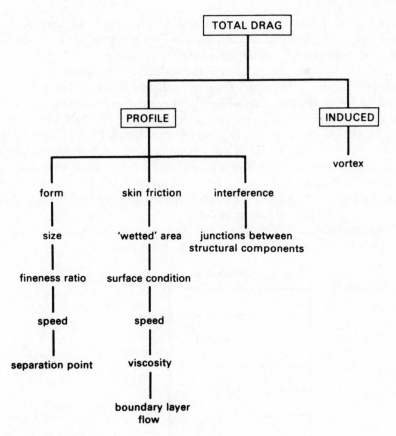

Fig. 1.5 Total drag of an aircraft

drag. Thus the wings of an aircraft, and all its other structural parts exposed to the airflow, experience components of a total drag which must be reduced to a minimum. The drag components arise in several different ways and they can be considered as constituting two principal types of drag, i.e. profile, and induced or vortex; these are summarised in tubular from in fig. 1.5.

Profile drag

Profile drag is composed of the drag components produced by the surface or skin friction created when a body is exposed to airflow, and also by the form or shape of the body. A controlling factor in determining, among other things, the nature of these components, is the very thin layer of air extending from the surface of the body, and referred to as the *boundary layer*. The whole surface area of an aircraft has a boundary layer and therefore has surface friction drag.

If the streamlines of an airflow over the wing of an aircraft are considered

7

as the boundary lines between layers of air, then because air has viscosity, variations in the velocity of each layer will occur as a result of viscous adhesion. Such variations are governed by the distance from the wings' surface, and also by the condition of the surface, i.e. whether it is rough or smooth. The layer adjacent to the surface will adhere to it and so its velocity will approximate to that of the wing. The viscous adhesion between this layer and the one above it will cause the second layer to flow in the direction of wing movement, but at a slightly lower velocity. Similarly, the velocity of the adjacent layers will be lowered until a point is reached where the movement of the wing causes no movement whatsoever of layers of air at some distance 'd' from the wing surface (see fig. 1.6 a). Thus, boundary layer may be more closely defined as the layer of air extending from a surface to the point where no viscous drag forces are discernible.

Boundary layer airflow may be either laminar, i.e. streamline, or turbulent as shown in fig. 1.6 b. Usually the airflow starts by being laminar over the

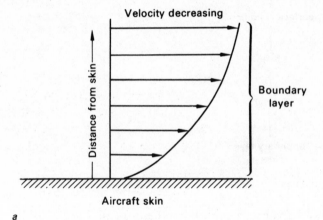

a

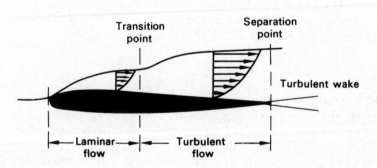

b

Fig. 1.6 Boundary layer

forward part of the surface, and then at some point, called the *transition point*, the layer tends to break away from the surface and becomes turbulent. The turbulent air mixes with the air above the boundary layer causing a thickening and spreading out of the layer and, as this increases the distance at which viscous drag forces can act, surface friction drag will accordingly increase. Eventually, at a point close to the trailing edge of the wing, the boundary layer separates from the surface resulting in a wake of turbulent air. The separation depends on the rate at which the pressure changes around the body, the rate of presssure change in turn depending on the shape of the body.

The position of the transition point in an airflow of a given density and viscosity depends on the velocity of the airflow and the thickness of the body in the airflow. When applied to a wing of a given thickness, an increase of velocity causes the transition point to move towards the leading edge with the result that more of the wing surface is covered by a turbulent boundary layer and so surface friction drag is further increased. However, a turbulent layer has more kinetic energy than a laminar layer and, since this has the effect of delaying boundary layer separation, the maximum value of lift coefficient is increased.

Form drag

This type of drag, as the name suggests, is dependent on the shape of the body exposed to the airflow and as noted earlier, the body shape governs the boundary layer separation and the rate at which the pressure around the body changes. For this reason, therefore, form drag is also referred to as boundary layer normal pressure drag. In order to appreciate the difference between surface friction drag and form drag, let us consider for a moment that the body exposed to the airflow is in the form of a very thin plate. When the plate is at zero angle of attack with respect to the airflow the direction of the airflow will not be materially changed and neither will the velocity or pressure. Thus the boundary layer in this case is purely laminar and the drag results solely from surface friction. When the plate is set at an angle of attack it will cause a change in airflow direction, velocity and pressure, so that the boundary layer now becomes turbulent and begins to separate from the upper surface of the plate. If the angle of attack is further increased such that the total surface area of the plate is presented to the airflow then there is a complete breakdown of the boundary layer and the drag is wholly form drag.

Interference drag

Interference drag is a result of disturbances to the airflow over an aircraft by the many junctions between major parts of its structure, e.g. between wings and fuselage, engine nacelles and wings. They can all cause changes in the pressure distribution and early separation of the boundary layer.

Induced drag

When a wing is producing lift, the airflow over both the upper and lower surfaces join at the trailing edge, and leave it in the form of a vortex motion the direction of which imparts a downward velocity component to the air. This downwash, as it is called, has the effect of inclining the lift force rearwards so that it will have a component acting in the direction of the drag force. This additional drag component is called the induced or vortex drag, and is affected by such main factors as plan form and aspect ratio of a wing, lift and weight, and speed of the aircraft.

One method of reducing vortex drag is to fit what are termed 'winglets' such that they are virtually wing-tip extensions turned through an angle compatible with the aerodynamic characteristics of the aircraft concerned. An example of the method as applied to a current type of swept-wing aircraft is shown in Plate (i).

Plate (i) Gulfstream III Corporate Jet (reproduced by courtesy of *Grumman Aerospace Corporation*)

Aircraft stability

Stability is the property of a system whereby the latter returns to a state of equilibrium after it has been displaced from a state of rest or a state of uniform motion. In applying this definition to an aircraft, it can be stated therefore, that following a displacement from an original steady flight path, an aircraft has stability if it returns to that path without movements of its flight control surfaces having to be applied.

In practice however, there are two types of stability to consider: static stability and dynamic stability (see fig. 1.7). Static stability refers to the immediate reaction of the aircraft and its tendency to return to equilibrium after displacement, while dynamic stability refers to the subsequent long-term reaction which is of an oscillatory nature about a neutral or equilibrium position. It is usual to classify both types of stability according to the nature of an aircraft's response to displacements from its original steady flight path: thus, stability is *positive* when, subsequent to the displacement, the forces and moments acting on the aircraft return it to its original steady flight path;

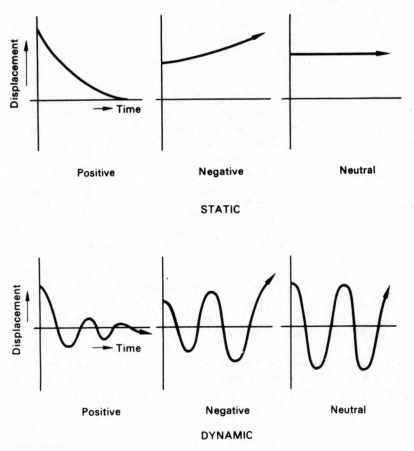

Fig. 1.7 Stability

neutral if the forces and moments cause the aircraft to take up a new flight path of constant relationship to the original; and *negative* if the aircraft is caused to diverge from the original steady flight path (an unstable condition). Static stability is a prerequisite for dynamic stability, although the converse is not true; it is possible to have a system which is statically stable, but dynamically unstable.

The displacements of an aircraft which, for example, result from an air disturbance, or by the operation of its flight control system, can take place in any one of three planes; known as the pitching, yawing and rolling planes. This also applies to the aircraft's stabilising motions in response to the displacements. The planes are not constant relative to the earth but, as indicated in fig. 1.8, they are always constant relative to the three body axes passing through the centre of gravity of the aircraft. Both forms of stability relate to the three axes in the following manner: longitudinal stability about the lateral axis, directional or 'weathercock' stability about the normal axis,

11

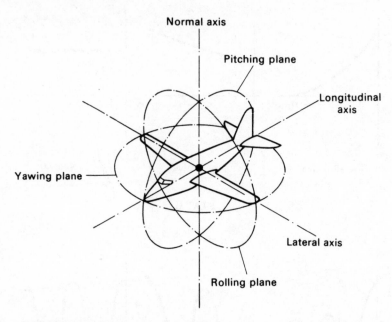

Fig. 1.8 Aircraft axes and displacement planes

and lateral stability about the longitudinal axis. In addition to the forces and moments set up by any displacement, forces are also set up as a result of the velocities of motion. These forces are a necessary contribution to the stability of an aircraft, and provide what is termed aerodynamic damping so that motions may be limited or eventually eliminated. The damping in roll, for instance, is the rolling moment due to angular velocity in roll and, since it acts in the opposite sense to the rolling velocity achieved by deflection of the ailerons, the velocity is limited. Damping also applies to pitch and yaw displacements. When this natural form of damping cannot be obtained, it must be furnished by artificial means, e.g. electrically-controlled yaw dampers (see page 215).

Longitudinal stability

Static

When an aircraft has a tendency to return to a trimmed angle of attack position following a displacement, it is said to have positive static longitudinal stability; it thus refers to motion in the pitching plane, and is influenced largely by the design of the horizontal stabiliser, and on the position of the aircraft's centre of gravity under the appropriate flight and load conditions.

The horizontal stabiliser together with the elevators in the neutral or streamlined position form an aerofoil which produces lift at varying angles of attack, the lift in turn producing either an upward or downward restoring moment to balance wing pitching moments about the aircraft's centre of gravity. The lift and restoring moments produced are governed by such factors as the area and planform of the stabiliser, the distance of its aerodynamic centre from the centre of gravity, i.e. the moment arm, and also by the effects of airflow downwash from the wings. When the elevators are maintained in the neutral or streamlined position, static stability is referred to as stick-fixed stability, as opposed to stick-free stability which refers to the condition in which the elevators are allowed to float in the airflow, i.e. 'hands-off' flight condition.

Assuming that in the stick-fixed position the aircraft is displaced nose up,

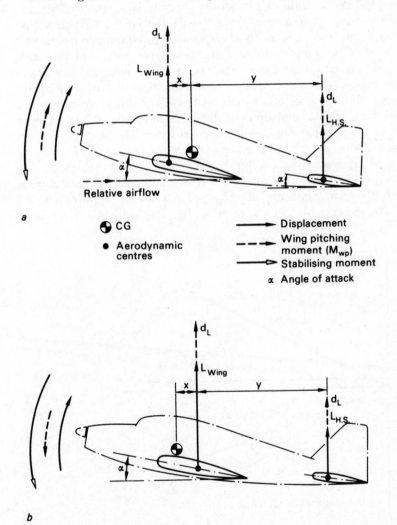

Fig. 1.9 Longitudinal stability

13

the angle of attack of the wings and, therefore, the lift produced, will be temporarily increased by an amount dL, resulting in an increase of the wing pitching moment about the aircraft's centre of gravity. Thus, if the aerodynamic centre is forward of the centre of gravity giving a moment arm of length x as shown at a of fig. 1.9, the wing pitching moment (M_{wp}) is increased by the amount dLx, the nose-up displacement is thereby worsened and the effect is a destabilising one. Since the nose-up displacement lowers the horizontal stabiliser, then its angle of attack and corresponding lift force will also be increased, but as the position of the aerodynamic centre with respect to the aircraft's centre of gravity provides the longer moment arm y, stabiliser lift force produces a stabilising nose-down moment. When the aerodynamic centre of the wings is to the rear of the centre of gravity (fig. 1.9 b) the increase in M_{wp} will be stabilising in its effect so that in conjunction with that produced by the horizontal stabiliser a greater restoring moment is provided.

For a given weight in level flight there is one speed and angle of attack at which an aircraft is in equilibrium, i.e. tail moments equal to wing moments. The speed and angle of attack depend upon the difference in rigging incidence between the chord lines of the wing and horizontal stabiliser; a difference known as the longitudinal dihedral angle. The angle of attack at which equilibrium is obtained is called the *trim point*.

It is thus apparent from fig. 1.9 that the ratio of the wing moment to stabiliser moment, and therefore the degree of longitudinal stability, is affected by the relative positions of both aerodynamic centres, and of centre of gravity. An indication of this is given in fig. 1.10, which is a graphical

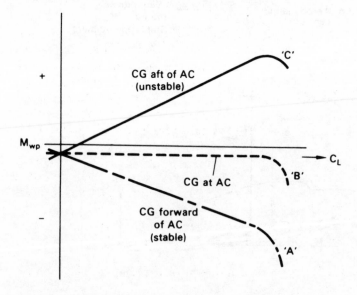

Fig. 1.10 Contribution of wing to longitudinal stability

representation of the conditions appropriate to the wing of an aircraft. Since stability is evidenced by the development of restoring moments, for the wing to contribute to positive static longitudinal stability the aircraft's centre of gravity must be forward of the aerodynamic centre. In this case, the wing contribution is a stable one, and the curve of M_{wp} to lift coefficient (C_L) would have a negative slope (curve 'A'). If the centre of gravity were located at the aerodynamic centre, all changes of lift would take place at the centre of gravity and so the wing contribution would be neutral (curve 'B'). An unstable contribution would be made with the centre of gravity to the rear of the aerodynamic centre, and the M_{wp}/C_L curve would then have a positive slope (curve 'C').

In addition to the wings and horizontal stabiliser, other major components of an aircraft such as the fuselage and engine nacelles can also influence the degree of longitudinal stability since, under varying angles of attack, the conditions of airflow and pressure distribution will produce individual pitching moments which can be either stabilising or destabilising in their influence. In plotting the total pitching moments against C_L, and the contribution of the major components to stability, curves similar to those shown in fig. 1.11 a are obtained (it is assumed in this example that the centre of gravity is at 30% of the mean aerodynamic chord). The contribution of the wing alone is destabilising as indicated by the positive slope of the curve, an effect which is further increased by the fuselage contribution. The large negative slope of the curve of the horizontal stabiliser contribution indicates its highly stabilising effect, which must be sufficient for the complete aircraft to exhibit positive static stability at the anticipated locations of the centre of gravity.

The typical effect of varying locations of the centre of gravity on static stability is indicated in fig. 1.11 b. As the centre of gravity moves rearward, the static stability decreases, then becomes neutral, and finally results in an unstable condition. The centre of gravity location which produces zero slope and neutral static stability is referred to as the *neutral point*. The distance of the centre of gravity at any time from the neutral point is known as the *static margin* and is an indication of the degree of longitudinal stability. Noticeable changes in static stability can occur at varying values of C_L, particularly when power effects contribute largely to stability, or when significant changes in downwash at the horizontal stabiliser occur. Such changes are illustrated in fig. 1.12. At low values of C_L, the slope of the curve indicates good positive stability, but this gradually starts decreasing with increasing C_L. With continued increase in C_L the slope becomes zero indicating that netural stability exists. Eventually the slope becomes rapidly positive indicating an unstable 'pitch-up' condition.

If the elevators are allowed to float free, they may have a tendency to float or streamline relative to the airflow, when the angle of attack of the horizontal stabiliser is changed. Thus, if the angle of attack is increased and the elevators

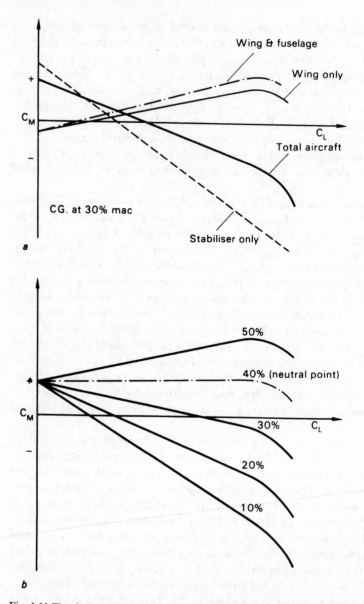

Fig. 1.11 Total pitching moments and effects of varying CG locations

tend to float up, the change in life produced by the horizontal stabiliser is less than if the elevator remain fixed; stick-free stability of an aircraft is, therefore, usually less that the stick-fixed stability. Elevators must therefore be properly balanced to reduce floating, and so minimise the difference between stick-fixed and stick-free stability. In the case of fully powered control systems

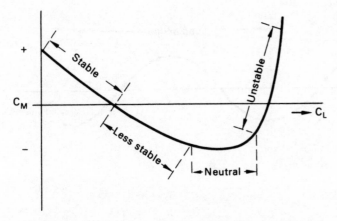

Fig. 1.12 Changes in longitudinal static stability

actuated by irreversible mechanisms, the elevators are not free to float and so there is no difference between stick-fixed and stick-free stability.

Dynamic
Longitudinal dynamic stability consists of three basic modes of oscillation, and these are illustrated in fig. 1.13. The first mode (diagram *a*) is of very long period and is referred to as a *phugoid* which involves noticeable variations in pitch attitude, altitude and airspeed. The period of oscillation is quite large, and may be counteracted by very small displacements of the elevator control system. The pitching rate is low, and as also only negligible changes in angle of attack take place, damping of the phugoid is weak and possibly negative.

The second mode (diagram *b*) is a relatively short period motion that can be assumed to take place with negligible changes in velocity. During the oscillation the aircraft is restored to equilibrium by the static stability, and the amplitude of oscillation decreased by pitch damping. If the aircraft has stick-fixed static stability, the pitch damping contributed by the horizontal stabiliser will usually assume sufficient dynamic stability for the short-period oscillation. The second mode, stick-free, has the possibility of weak damping or unstable oscillations, and for this reason elevators must be statically balanced about their hinge line, and aerodynamic control must be within certain limits. If instability were to exist in the second mode, 'porpoising' of the aircraft would result, and because of the short period of oscillation the amplitude can reach dangerous proportions with the possibility of structural damage resulting from the severe flight loads imposed.

The third mode occurs in the stick-free case, and is usually a very short-period oscillation. The motion is essentially one whereby the elevators flap about the hinge line and in most cases the oscillation has very heavy damping.

17

Automatic Flight Control

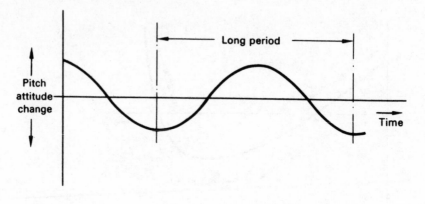

a PHUGOID

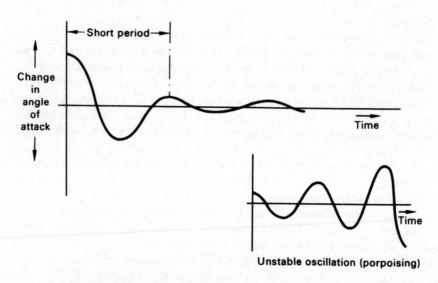

Unstable oscillation (porpoising)

b SHORT PERIOD OSCILLATION

Fig. 1.13 Longitudinal dynamic stability

Directional stability

Directional or 'weathercock' stability involves the development of yawing moments which will oppose displacements about the aircraft's vertical axis and so restore it to equilibrium. Unlike longitudinal stability, however,

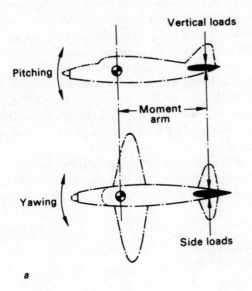

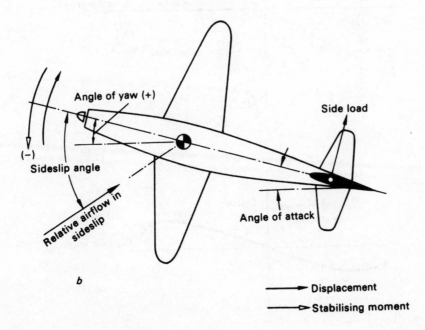

Fig. 1.14 Directional stability

directional stability is not independent in its influence on the behaviour of an aircraft, because as a result of what is termed aerodynamic coupling effect, yaw displacements and moments also producing roll displacements and moments about the longitudinal axis. Thus, directional motions have an influence on lateral motions and vice versa, the motions involved in each case being yawing, rolling, sideslipping or any combination of these.

As far as yawing displacement, forces, and moments only, are concerned conditions are, in fact, analogous to those relating to longitudinal stability but, whereas in the latter case a horizontal stabiliser has the greatest influence, directional stability is influenced by a vertical stabiliser. This may be seen from diagram *a* in fig. 1.14.

Assuming that with the rudder in neutral position the aircraft is yawed to starboard by a disturbance (diagram *b*), the vertical stabiliser will be at some angle of attack with respect to the airflow and a corresponding side force (lift)

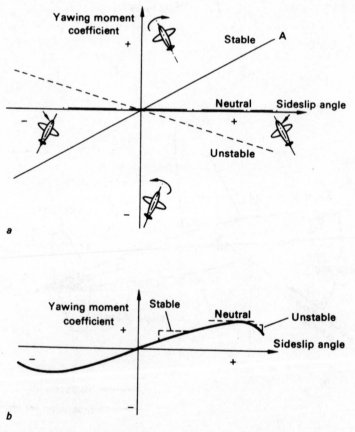

Fig. 1.15 Static directional stability

will be produced. Since the position of the aerodynamic centre of the stabiliser with respect to the aircraft's centre of gravity provides the longer moment arm, a stabilising yawing moment to port is created and equilibrium is restored. In addition to the stabiliser moment arm, other factors affecting the size of the stabilising moment are the area of the stabiliser, its aerofoil section, angle of attack, aspect ratio and sweepback. As in the case of longitudinal stability other major components of the aircraft can also influence the degree of directional stability, notably the fuselage and engine nacelles.

When an aircraft is at some angle of yaw, its longitudinal axis is considered as being displaced from a reference azimuth, and by convention, a displacement from this azimuth to starboard constitutes a positive angle of yaw, while a displacement to port constitutes a negative angle of yaw. In the yawed condition, and ignoring aerodynamic cross-coupling, the aircraft is maintaining a forward flight path so that, alternatively, the aircraft can be described as being in a condition of sideslip; thus from the example shown in fig. 1.14 and by convention, an aircraft yawed to starboard is sideslipping to port at a negative angle. The angle of sideslip, therefore, is minus the angle of yaw, and since it relates to the displacement of the aircraft's longitudinal axis from the relative airflow rather than a reference azimuth, it becomes a primary reference in directional stability considerations. This is illustrated graphically in fig. 1.15 a.

When an aircraft is subject to a sideslip angle (relative airflow coming from starboard in the case illustrated) static directional stability will be evident if a positive yawing moment coefficient results. Thus, a yawing moment to starboard would be created which tends to 'weathercock' the aircraft into the relative airflow. This is indicated by the positive slope of curve 'A'. If there is zero slope there is of course no tendency to return to equilibrium and so static directional stability is neutral. When the curve has negative slope the yawing moments developed by sideslip tend to diverge, thereby increasing sideslip such that the aircraft would be directionally unstable.

Diagram b serves to illustrate the fact that the instantaneous slope of the curve depicting yawing moment coefficient/sideslip angle will indicate the static directional stability. At small angles of sideslip, a strong positive slope depicts strong directional stability. Large angles produce zero slope and neutral stability; if the sideslip is very high the slope would indicate instability.

Lateral stability

Static
An aircraft has lateral stability if, following a displacement about the longitudinal axis (called a roll displacement), a rolling moment is produced which will oppose the displacement and return the aircraft to a wings-level condition. In practice however, and because of aerodynamic coupling,

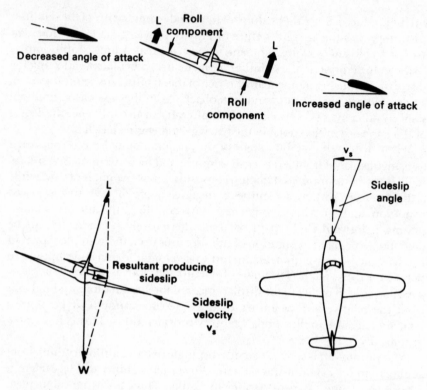

Fig. 1.16 Lateral stability

rolling moments can also set up yawing or sideslip motions so that the opposing of lateral displacements is not so simple as it seems.

When an aircraft experiences a roll displacement, the effective angle of attack of the down-going wing becomes greater than that of the up-going wing resulting in the appropriate changes in the lift produced (see fig. 1.16). These changes produce a rolling moment which although opposing the initial roll displacement will do no more that provide a damping effect proportional to the rate of displacement. In other words, the aircraft would possess netural static stability and so would remain in the rolled or banked position. However, the aircraft also experiences a sideslipping motion which is caused by the inclination of the lift vectors at the roll or bank angle. This motion, in turn, causes the airflow to exert forces on the different parts of the aircraft, and it is the rolling moment induced by sideslipping which establishes static stability reaction and return of the aircraft to a wings-level condition. This may be illustrated by a graph of rolling moment coefficient versus sideslip angle such as that shown in fig. 1.17. When the aircraft is subject to a positive sideslip angle, i.e. it sideslips to starboard, positive static stability will be evident if a negative rolling moment to port is produced; the curve will have

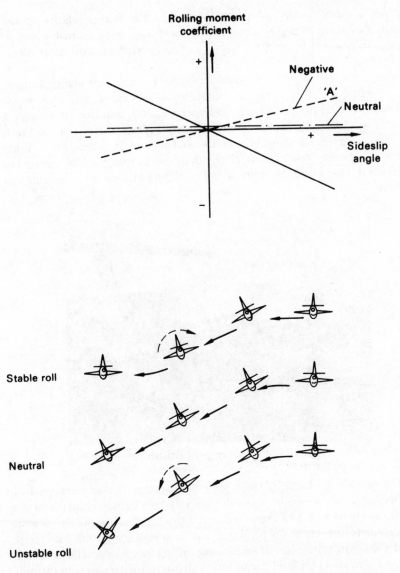

Fig. 1.17 Static lateral stability

a negative slope (curve 'A'). If the slope of the curve is zero, lateral stability is neutral, while a positive slope indicates lateral instability.

The overall value of the lateral static stability will depend on the effects contributed in varying magnitudes, by each different part of the aircraft, these in turn depending on the configuration of the aircraft and on the condition of flight. The principal contributions to overall lateral static stability are as follows.

1. *The dihedral angle* or upward setting of the wings relative to the horizontal. Dihedral angle is one of the most important contributions to lateral stability which, for this reason, is often referred to as dihedral effect.

2. *The angle at which the wings are swept back* relative to the longitudinal axis. Swept-back wings are a characteristic of many types of high-performance aircraft, producing additional lateral stability which has a greater effect in sideslip at low speeds. In some types of swept-wing aircraft, it may be necessary for stability to be reduced at low speeds, and this is done by setting the wings downwards relative to the horizontal, a setting referred to as *anhedral*. One example of an aircraft utilising anhedral is illustrated in Plate (ii).

Plate (ii) BAe 146 (reproduced by courtesy of British Aerospace)

3. *The vertical location of the wings with respect to the fuselage.* In a sideslip, air flows spanwise over the aircraft and causes changes in the effective angle of attack of the wings, such that in the case of a high-wing aircraft, the rolling moment produced will be a stabilising one, and in the case of a low-wing aircraft as de-stabilising rolling moment will be produced. There is a zero effect on lateral stability of an aircraft with wings in the mid-position.

4. *The keel surface.* The side load produced in a sideslip acts on an aircraft's fuselage and on the vertical stabiliser (fin) which together form the keel surface. This side load produces a rolling moment that is generally stabilising, but to a smaller degree than the moments produced in other ways.

5. *The flaps.* When flaps are lowered, they alter the spanwise distribution of pressure and lift, and since they are usually located at the inboard sections of

wings, the overall centre of lift is located closer to the fuselage centre line, i.e. the moment arm is reduced. Therefore, any changes of lift resulting from sideslip produce smaller rolling moments thereby reducing the overall lateral stability.

Dynamic
The relative effect of the combined rolling, yawing and sideslip motions produced by aerodynamic coupling, determine the lateral dynamic stability of an aircraft. If the stability characteristics are not satisfactory the complex interaction of the motions will produce three possible forms of dynamic instability: (i) directional divergence, (ii) spiral divergence, and (iii) an oscillatory mode termed Dutch Roll.

Directional divergence

This form of instability is a simple divergence in yaw which may occur if the aircraft is statically unstable about the vertical axis: thus, if the aircraft is flying straight and level and it experiences a small displacement in yaw to port, say, the result will be a yawing moment in the same direction thereby increasing the displacement. In addition, a side force will act on the aircraft in the yawed attitude, so that it will curve away from its original flight path. If the aircraft has lateral static stability directional divergence will occur without any significant degree of bank angle, and the aircraft would still fly a curved path with a very large amount of sideslip.

Spiral divergence

This form of instability exists when the directional static stability is very large compared with lateral stability. Assuming once again that a yaw displacement to port is experienced, because of the greater directional stability the yaw would be quickly eliminated by a stabilising yaw moment set up by the keel surface. A rolling moment to port would also have been set up by the yaw displacement and if it were strong enough to overcome the restoring moment due to lateral stability, and to the damping-in-yaw effect, the angle of bank would increase and cause the aircraft nose to drop into the direction of yawing. The aircraft then begins a nose spiral which gradually increases to a spiral dive.

Dutch roll

This is an oscillatory mode of instability which may occur if the aircraft has positive directional static stability but not so much, in relation to the lateral stability, as may lead to spiral divergence. Dutch roll is commonly found to a varying degree in combinations of high wing loading, sweepback, and high altitude, and where weight is distributed towards wing tips, e.g. engines mounted in pods under the wings. Assuming yet again that the aircraft is yawed to port, it will roll in the same direction. The directional stability will then begin to reduce the yaw to the extent that the aircraft will overswing and start a yaw, and a roll, to starboard. Thus, every period of the continuing oscillations in yaw acts in such a manner as to cause further displacement in roll, the resulting motion being a combination of rolling and yawing oscillations which have the same frequency, but are out of phase with each other.

Controllability

In order that an aircraft may fulfil its intended operational role it must have, in addition to the varying degrees of stability, the ability to respond to requirements for manoeuvring and trimming about its three axes, so that all desired flying attitudes can be achieved and equilibrium be established; in other words, it must have controllability.

Controllability is a different problem from stability in that it requires aerodynamic forces and moments to be produced about the three axes of the aircraft, such forces always opposing the natural stability restoring moments and causing the aircraft to deviate from an equilibrium condition. There is, therefore, a clear relationship between the two which may be illustrated by the analogy of a ball placed on various surfaces (fig. 1.18). Diagram *a* represents the condition of positive static stability and, as we have already learned, any displacement in this condition will always be opposed by a tendency of the ball to return to equilibrium. If, however, it is required to control the ball, and so maintain it in the displaced position, a balancing force must be applied *in the direction* of displacement. When stability is increased a greater balancing force is required to control the ball to the same displaced position. A large degree of stability therefore tends to make for less controllability, so that for aircraft it can be stated that the upper limits of its stability are set by the lower limits of controllability.

In a neutrally stable condition (diagram *b*) there is no tendency for the ball to return to equilibrium from a displaced position, and since a new point of equilibrium is always obtained, then no control balancing force is required to maintain the displacement. As the static stability approaches zero, controllability increases to infinity and the only resistance to a displacement would result from damping effects, e.g. the viscosity of air is a damping factor which is proportional to the speed of the displaced body. Thus for an aircraft it can be stated that the lower limits of its stability may be set by the upper limits of controllability.

The effect of negative static stability, i.e. instability, is shown in diagram *c* of fig. 1.18. If the ball is displaced from equilibrium it will tend to continue

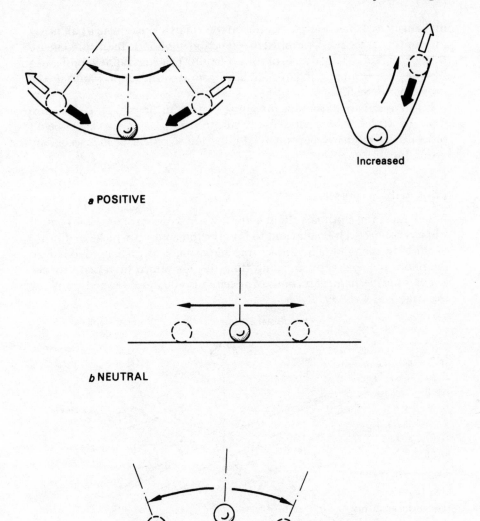

Increased

a POSITIVE

b NEUTRAL

c NEGATIVE

→ Displacement
➡ Return tendency
⇨ Control balancing

Fig. 1.18 Static stability and controllability

27

in the displaced direction and in order to control its displacement a balancing force must, in this case, be applied in a direction *opposite* to the displacement. In applying this reversed form of controllability to an aircraft it would mean that the pilot, in attempting to maintain a state of equilibrium, would also be providing the stability.

It will be apparent from the foregoing that for an aircraft, proper balance must be achieved between stability and controllability, the latter being provided by means of a primary flight control system, and a secondary 'trimming' system.

Primary flight controls

In its basic form, a primary flight control system consists of movable control surfaces connected by cables and rods to cockpit controls which are directly operated by the pilot. The surfaces are aerodynamically balanced to reduce the pilot's physical effort in controlling the aircraft. In high-performance aircraft, the mechanical sections of systems also include powered-actuators (see page 34).

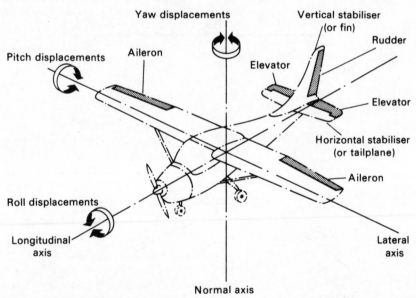

Fig. 1.19 Disposition of flight control surfaces

Conventionally there are three sets of control surfaces, and these are situated at the extremities of the wings and stabiliser units (see fig. 1.19) so as to obtain the largest possible controlling moments, consistent with stability, about the three principal axes and centre of gravity. Movement of a control surface causes a change in the aerodynamic profile and therefore a change in

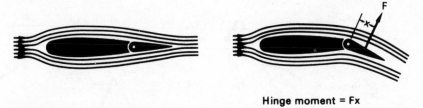

Hinge moment = Fx

Fig. 1.20 Control surface deflection

the forces produced as shown in fig. 1.20. The pressures acting through the centre of pressure of the control surface, produce a hinge moment which tries to return the surface to its neutral or 'faired' position. The size of the hinge moment is given by the produce of the force on the control surface and its distance x from the hinge point. In order to maintain the surface in its deflected position, the hinge moment is balanced by a control force applied to the control system either manually or automatically.

It is desirable that each set of control surfaces should produce a moment only about the corresponding axis. In practice, however, the cross-coupling effects, which arise from interaction between directional and lateral stability, apply equally to the flight control system; e.g. a yawing moment in addition to a rolling moment is produced when the ailerons are deflected. This will be described in more detail on page 39.

Ailerons

These provide lateral control, or roll displacements, about the longitudinal axis, the rolling moment produced being opposed by aerodynamic damping in roll. When the two are in balance the aircraft attains a steady rate of roll; ailerons are therefore essentially rate control devices. As will be noted from fig. 1.21 ailerons are, in most cases, operated by a control 'wheel' pivoted on a control column. They are always connected so that in response to instinctive movements of the control wheel by the pilot, they move in opposite directions thereby assisting each other in producing a roll displacement. Thus, when the control wheel is turned to the left, the left-wing aileron is raised and the wing lifting force is decreased, while the aileron of the right wing is lowered causing the lifting force of that wing to increase thereby initiate a roll displacement to the left. A similar but opposite effect occurs when the control wheel is turned to the right.

Elevators

Elevators provide longitudinal or pitch control about the lateral axis, and they also assist the horizontal stabiliser to maintain longitudinal stability. Elevators are usually in two separate halves and are normally mounted on a

29

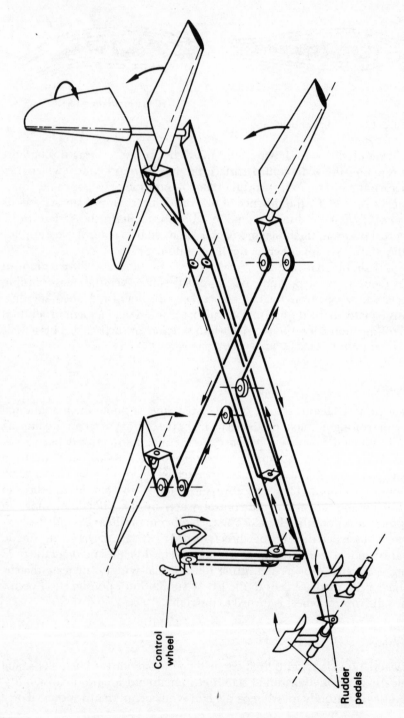

Control wheel

Rudder pedals

Fig. 1.21 Primary flight control system

common hinge line at the rear of the horizontal stabiliser. They are connected to the control column, which can be moved backwards and forwards.

When the column is moved backwards, the elevators are raised thereby decreasing the lift of the horizontal stabiliser so that the aircraft is displaced by a pitching moment about the lateral axis into a nose-up, or climbing attitude. Forward movement of the control column lowers the elevators to increase the lift of the horizontal stabiliser and so the pitching moment causes the aircraft to assume a nose-down or descending attitude. Pitch displacements are opposed by aerodynamic damping in pitch and by the longitudinal stability (see page 12) and as the response to elevator deflections is a steady change of attitude, elevators are essentially displacement control devices. It will also be noted from fig. 1.21 that control column and control wheel movements are independent of each other so that lateral and longitudinal displacements can be obtained either separately or in combination.

Rudder

This surface provides yawing moments or directional control about the normal axis of the aircraft, such control being opposed by damping in yaw, and by the directional stability. The rudder is operated in response to instinctive movements by the pilot of a foot-operated rudder bar or, more usually, of a pair of rudder pedals. Thus, if the left pedal is pushed forward the rudder is turned to the left and the force produced on the vertical stabiliser sets up a yawing moment which displaces the aircraft's nose to the left. A corresponding displacement to the right is set up when the right rudder pedal is pushed forward. The response to rudder deflections is a steady state of change of angle of attack on the keel surfaces and so, like the elevators, the rudder is a displacement control device.

Effectiveness of controls

The effectiveness of a control system, i.e. the moment produced for a given control surface deflection, depends on the magnitude of the force produced by the control surface and also on the moment arm, i.e. distance from the centre of gravity. The aerodynamic forces acting on an aircraft depend, among other important factors, on the airstream velocity, so the effectiveness of flight controls varies accordingly. At low speeds, large control surface movements are needed, while smaller ones are necessary at high speeds. Movement of a control surface alone may also alter control effectiveness, since the loads set up tend to twist and bend the aircraft's structure which has a certain amount of inherent flexibility.

In many types of large aircraft it is usual for control surfaces to be arranged in pairs, i.e. an inboard and an outboard aileron on each wing, an inboard and an outboard elevator, and an upper and lower rudder (see fig. 1.22 which illustrates the arrangements in the McDonnell Douglas DC - 10). The reasons for such arrangements are to ensure control effectiveness at both low and high speeds, particularly where lateral control is concerned, and also to ensure control in the event of any failures in the system. At low speeds, only the outboard ailerons provide lateral control, while at high speeds they are locked and lateral control is taken over by the inboard ailerons so that the deflecting forces act closer to the longitudinal axis thereby reducing wing twisting. The duplication of elevators and rudder is done primarily as a safety precaution. Each elevator and rudder is operated by an independent control system so that should a failure of a system occur one control surface of a pair can still be effective.

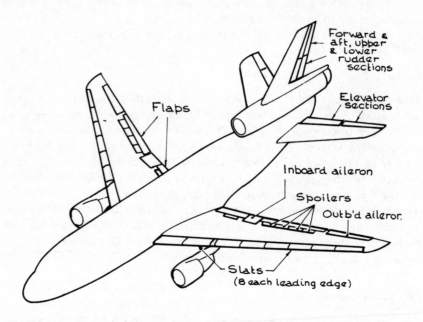

Fig. 1.22 Paired flight control surfaces

It will also be noted from fig. 1.22 that the rudder sections are in forward and aft pairs. The forward sections are actuated by the rudder pedals and associated hydraulic system, while the aft sections are hinged to the forward sections and are mechanically connected by pushrods to the vertical stabiliser. This arrangement provides for proportional displacements of the forward and aft sections and thereby an overall increase in rudder efficiency. The travel of each forward section is approximately 23° left or right of the neutral position, while the travel of each aft section is approximately 22° left or right relative to the forward sections.

Control gearing

Control gearing refers to the relationship between movements of the pilot's controls and the displacements of the corresponding control surfaces, and in the design of the flight control systems of any one type of aircraft, this relationship is a variable one so as to produce the required handling characteristics in all conditions of flight. The variation, or gear change ratio to be more precise, is effected through the mechanical linkages in the control circuits in such a way that when the the pilot's controls are moved a certain extent around their neutral position, a relatively small displacement of the control surfaces will be produced; the same extent of movement near the extremities of control movement range on the other hand, will produce a much larger displacement of the control surfaces.

The control gearing relationship can also be varied at different airspeeds by means of a dynamic, or 'q', pressure sensing gear change unit. In this case, the pressure/speed signals are fed to 'ratio changers' in hydraulic power actuators which operate so as to reduce control surface displacements as airspeed increases. This method is, for example, applied to the rudder control system of the Boeing 747.

Combined controls

In certain types of aircraft, the primary flight control system is arranged so that one type of control surface may combine its function with that of another; e.g. on a delta wing aircraft such as Concorde, a control surface at each trailing edge can perform the function of both ailerons and elevators; such a control surface is called an *elevon*. When the control column is moved either backwards or forwards both surfaces move together in the manner of elevators, but when the control wheel is turned, one elevon is raised and the other lowered as in the case of conventional ailerons. The interconnection between the two control systems is such that the surfaces can be deflected simultaneously to produce combined pitching and rolling moments.

Another example of combined controls is the one applied to some light aircraft having a 'V' or 'butterfly' tail. In this case, the control surfaces operate as either a rudder or as elevators, and for obvious reasons, they are known as *ruddervators*. They are connected to the control column and are moved up or down to produce pitching moments as in the case of conventional elevators. They are also connected to the rudder pedals, so that they move equal amounts in opposite directions to produce the required yawing moment. The control column and rudder pedal systems are connected to the surfaces through a differential linkage or gearing arrangement, so that combined pitching and yawing moments can be obtained.

In some aircraft, elevators are dispensed with and they are substituted with a movable horizontal stabiliser. Thus when the control column is moved the angle of attack of the stabiliser is varied such that a negative angle produces a nose-up attitude, and a positive angle produces a nose-down attitude. Such a stabiliser is known as a *stabilator*.

Powered flight controls

Powered flight controls are employed in high-performance aircraft, and are generally of two main types (i) power-assisted and (ii) power-operated. The choice of either system for a particular type of aircraft is governed by the forces required to overcome the aerodynamic loads acting on the flight control surfaces. In basic form, however, both systems are similar in that a hydraulically-operated servo-control unit, consisting of a control valve and an actuating jack, is connected between the pilot's controls and relevant

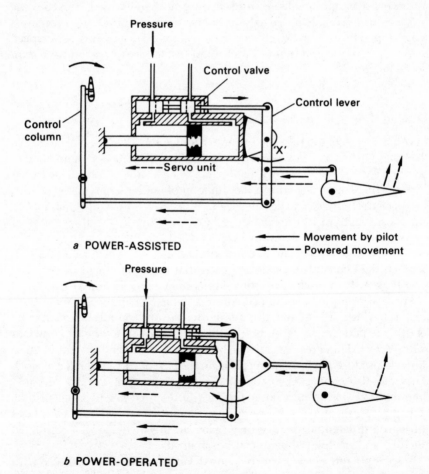

Fig. 1.23 Powered flight controls

control surfaces. The major difference, apart from constructional features, is in the method of connecting actuating jacks to control surfaces and this may be seen from fig. 1.23.

In a power-assisted system, the pilot's control is connected to the control surface, e.g. control column to elevators, via a control lever. When the pilot moves the control column to initiate a climb say, the control lever pivots about point 'X', and accordingly commences moving the elevators up. At the same time, the control valve pistons are displaced and this allows oil from the hydraulic system to flow to the left-hand side of the actuating jack piston, the rod of which is secured to the aircraft's structure. The reaction of the pressure exerted on the piston causes the whole servo-unit, and control lever, to move to the left, and because of the greater control effort produced the pilot is assisted in making further upward movement of the elevators.
the elevators.

In a power-operated system the pilot's control is connected to the control lever only, while the servo-unit is directly connected to the flight control surface. Thus, in the example considered, the effort required by the pilot to move the control column is simply that needed to move the control lever and control valve piston. It does not vary with the effort required to move the control surface which, as will be noted from the diagram, is supplied solely by servo-unit hydraulic power. Since no forces are transmitted back to the pilot he has no 'feel' of the aerodynamic loads acting on the control surfaces. It is necessary therefore, to incorporate an 'artificial feel' device at a point between the pilot's controls, and their connection to the servo-unit control lever.

A commonly used system for providing artificial feel, particularly in elevator and horizontal stabiliser control systems, is the one known as 'q'-feel. In this system, the feel force varies with the dynamic pressure of the air (i.e. $\frac{1}{2}$ ρV^2 or 'q') the pressure being sensed by a pilot-static capsule or bellows type sensing element connected in the hydraulic powered controls, such that it monitors hydraulic pressure, and produces control forces dependent on the amount of control movement and forward speed of the aircraft.

'Fly-by-wire' system

Another system which may be considered under the heading of powered flight controls, is the one referred to as a 'fly-by-wire' control system. Although not new in concept, complete re-development of the system was seen to be necessary in recent years, as a means of controlling some highly sophisticated types of aircraft coming into service. The problem associated with such aircraft has been one of designing conventional forms of mechanical linkage to suit the complex flight control systems adopted. Thus, a fly-by-wire system, as the name very aptly suggests, is one in which wires carrying electrical signals from the pilot's controls, replace mechanical linkages entirely. In operation, movements of the control column and rudder

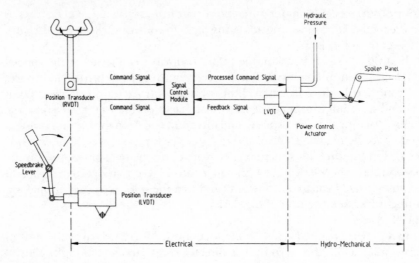

Fig. 1.24 Fly-by-wire system

pedals, and the forces exerted by the pilot, are measured by electrical transducers, and the signals produced are then amplified and relayed to operate the hydraulic actuator units which are directly connected to the flight control surfaces.

Figure 1.24 illustrates the principle as applied to the operation of the spoiler panels installed in the Boeing 767.

For lateral control, the deployment of the panels is initiated by movement of the pilot's control wheels to the left or right as appropriate. This movement operates position transducers, in the form of rotary variable differential transformers (RVDTs) via mechanical gear drive from the control wheels. The RVDTs produce command voltage signals proportional to control wheel position and these signals are fed into a spoiler control module for processing and channel selection.

The spoiler control module output signals are then supplied to a solenoid valve forming an integral part of a hydraulic power control actuator. The valve directs hydraulic fluid under pressure to one or other side of the actuator piston which then raises or lowers the spoiler panel connected to the piston rod. The actuator is mounted so that it pivots to allow for the required angular movement of the spoiler panel. As the actuator piston rod moves, it also actuates a position transducer of the linear variable differential transformer (LVDT) type, and this produces a voltage feedback signal proportional to spoiler panel position. When the feedback signal equals the command signal, a 'null' condition is reached and spoiler panel movement stops.

Deployment of spoiler panels for the purpose of acting as speedbrakes is initiated by movement of a speedbrake lever. The lever operates an LVDT

36

type of transducer which produces a command voltage signal for processing by the signal control module. The output signal operates the actuator in the same way as for lateral control except that the spoiler panels are deployed to their fullest extent. 'Nulling' of the command signal is also produced in the same way.

Lateral control and speedbrake signals are mixed in the signal control module to provide the proper ratio of simultaneous operation.

As a further advance in the 'fly-by-wire' concept, systems utilising fibre-optic cables for conveying flight commands have now been developed for use in aircraft coming into service in the very near future. The principal advantage of this method is its immunity to electromagnetic interference, and the consequent elimination of heavy shielding required to protect the more conventional 'signal wires'.

In a fibre-optic cable system, signals are transmitted in the form of light through a number of glass fibres, and where applications to aircraft are concerned, this has given rise to the term 'fly-by-light'. In relation to currently developed systems, however, the term is a misnomer because in these systems, light transmission applies only to command signalling and not to signal processing which is performed electronically within control system computers.

Manoeuvring and forces affecting an aircraft

The displacements resulting from the various movements of the flight control surfaces are those intentionally set up by the pilot in order to manoeuvre his aircraft into required flight attitudes. Such attitudes are: straight and level, climbing, descending, rolling, turning and a combination of these, e.g. a climbing turn. There are four principal forces affecting an aircraft in flight and the directions in which they act are shown in fig. 1.25. Lift, as we learned at the beginning of this chapter, acts at right-angles to the direction of the airflow from the centre of pressure, the position of which can vary with changing angle of attack. Weight acts vertically downward through the centre of gravity which can also vary in position with changing load conditions. Thrust is the forward propulsive force produced by either a turbine engine or a propeller to overcome the opposing total drag force.

Straight and level flight

To be in equilibrium in a straight and level flight attitude at constant speed, lift must equal weight, and thrust must equal drag, and it is arranged that these forces act from points which are not coincident, thereby producing couples which give rise to pitching moments. For example, because the relative positions of the centre of pressure and centre of gravity can vary

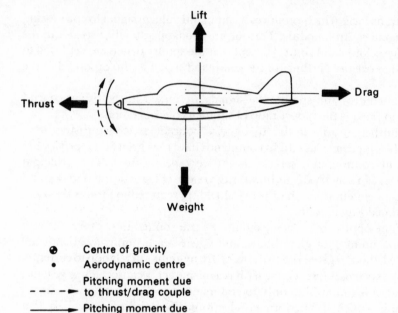

	Centre of gravity
	Aerodynamic centre
- - - ►	Pitching moment due to thrust/drag couple
──────►	Pitching moment due to lift/weight couple

Fig. 1.23 Balance of forces

during flight, the lift and weight forces produce couples which cause either a nose-up or a nose-down pitching moment. Similarly, pitching moments result from the displacement couples of thrust and drag. Ideally, the moments arising from these two couples should balance each other, and by design it is usual for a nose-down moment due to the lift/weight couple, to be balanced by a nose-up moment due to the thrust/drag couple as indicated in fig. 1.25. If the thrust is then decreased either by a deliberate reduction in engine power or by an engine failure, the lift/weight couple will overcome the reduced thrust/drag couple and cause a nose-down moment thereby putting the aircraft into a nose-down attitude.

Climbing and descending

These are pitch attitude manoeuvres which are set up by upward and downward movements respectively of the elevators. In the case of stabilators referred to earlier, the horizontal stabiliser is deflected to produce a negative angle of attack for the setting up of a climbing attitude, and a more positive angle of attack for a descending attitude. As an example of how the forces act we may consider the case of an upward deflection of elevators to produce a climbing attitude from straight and level flight as shown in fig. 1.26. When the elevators are deflected a pitching moment is produced to rotate the aircraft about the centre of gravity causing the lift vector to be inclined, and thereby

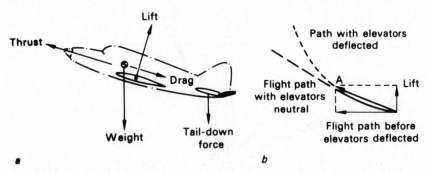

Fig. 1.26 Climbing

constitute an accelerating force at right angles to the direction of flight causing the aircraft to initially follow a curvilinear path. Diagram *b* is a vectorial representation of the conditions obtaining. The lift force in a climb is normally less than the weight, a component of which acts in the direction of drag; therefore, more power, i.e. greater thrust is required to lift the aircraft at a vertical speed, otherwise known as the rate of climb. At the required rate and angle of climb the elevators are returned to their neutral position, as at point A, and the aircraft will fly along a path tangential to the original curve.

Rolling and turning

Rolling of an aircraft takes place about the longitudinal axis, and is initiated by deflecting the ailerons in the required direction. As the effective angle of attack of each wing is thereby changed, then the down-going wing produces a greater lift than the up-going wing (see page 22) and so a rolling moment is established. The total lift vector (see fig. 1.27) rotates through the same angle as the aircraft and gives rise to two components, one vertical and equal to L cos θ and the other horizontal and equal to L sin θ. The latter component acts through the centre of gravity, and it establishes an inwards or centripetal force, thereby causing the aircraft to accelerate into a curvilinear flight path; thus displacing an aircraft into a rolled attitude also results in turning.

For any given airspeed and turn radius, however, turning of this nature would only occur at one correct angle of bank. At any other angle, and because of a cross-coupling response (see page 29), a yawing moment is produced which opposes the rolling moment. The yawing moment arises in this case, because the lift vector of the down-going wing is inclined forwards, while that on the up-going wing is inclined rearward. Furthermore, the up-going wing being further from the centre of the turn, has the greater angular velocity, and so it sustains more drag. The ailerons themselves, when in their deflected positions, can also create yaw (adverse aileron yaw) their effect being to alter the wing drag. This effect is reduced as much as possible by employing such methods as differential aileron deflection or, in some cases, by coupling the aileron control system to that of the rudder.

39

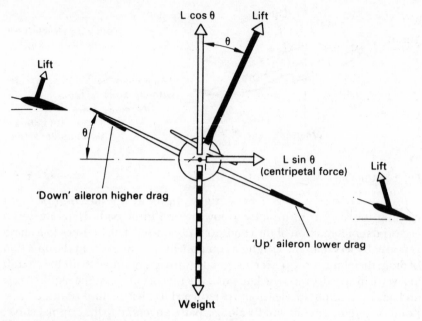

Fig. 1.27 Rolling and turning

A yawing moment also results in sideslip (see page 21) and this must be prevented if the aircraft is to be manoeuvred into a steady turn at any speed and roll angle; in other words, the turn must be a co-ordinated one. If an aircraft has a well-designed aileron system, a co-ordinated turn can be achieved by aileron deflection alone. As is more often the case however, the ailerons must be assisted by deflection of the rudder in the direction of its turn, thereby creating a side force on the vertical stabiliser to overcome adverse aileron yaw.

Trimming

The balancing of the aerodynamics forces and moments and the establishment of desired flight attitudes are continuous processes and, as we have already observed, are governed by the degree of inherent stability of an aircraft and by the manoeuvring capability afforded by its primary flight control system. In flight, however, control must also be exercised over changes in weight and centre of gravity locations which occur as a result of the consumption of fuel, disposition of passengers and cargo, flight under asymmetric power conditions, etc; in addition, the attitude changes resulting from the lowering of flaps must also be controlled. Although the required control could be maintained by repositioning relevant primary flight control surfaces, varying degrees of physical effort on the part of a pilot would be needed to keep the control surfaces in specifically displaced positions. It is usual, therefore, to provide a secondary control system which can be separately adjusted so that it will displace the primary control surfaces, thereby reducing the effects of aerodynamic loads on the primary control system, and so relieving the pilot of undue physical effort. The operation of such a system is referred to as 'trimming', and some typical methods by which it is operated are described briefly in the following paragraphs.

Trim tabs

In this method, which may be considered as the basic form of trimming, an auxiliary surface known as a tab is hinged at the trailing edge of a primary control surface and is connected via a cable, linkage and gearing system to a trim wheel in the cockpit. The wheel is arranged so that it can be rotated in the same sense as the required trim change.

As an example of tab operation, let us consider the case whereby balancing of forces and moments to maintain straight and level flight requires that the aircraft adopt a nose-up attitude. In order to obtain this the elevators must be displaced in an upward position, but for this to be done by movement of the control column the pilot would have to maintain a constant pull on the control column. However, by means of an elevator trim tab, the pilot can set up the required elevator displacement simply by rotating the trim wheel in the appropriate direction, in this case rearwards. As will be noted from fig. 1.28, the tab will move downwards, so that it is the airloads acting on the tab which will deflect the elevators upwards, and also move the control column to some rearward position. In terms of moments, the one produced by the elevators is $F_1 \times a$, and this is balanced by that produced by the tab, i.e. $F_2 \times b$.

Tabs may also be designed for purposes other than trimming, depending on the aerodynamic and flight control system characteristics appropriate to a

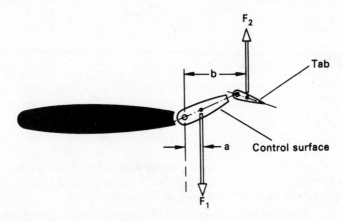

Fig. 1.28 Principle of a trim tab

particular type of aircraft. For example, they may be designed for (i) balancing the flight controls by varying the hinge moments produced by the controls; these are known as balance or geared tabs, (ii) reducing control loads at high speeds (spring tabs), and (iii) reducing control loads necessary to manoeuvre an aircraft (servo tabs).

Balance panels

In some types of aircraft, aerodynamic loads acting on ailerons and elevators are further reduced by means of balance panels that operate in conjunction with balance tabs. A typical arrangement as applied to an aileron is illustrated in fig. 1.29. The panel is interconnected to the leading edge of the aileron and the wing rear spar by hinged fittings, so that at the wing trailing edge it divides the area between the upper and lower surfaces into two vented compartments.

With the aileron and tab in their neutral positions, the pressure of the air vented into each compartment is in balance. When the aileron is displaced, e.g. upward, a higher pressure is developed in the upper compartment so that the resulting force acting on the balance panel, together with that acting on the downward displaced tab, assists in the application of aileron control.

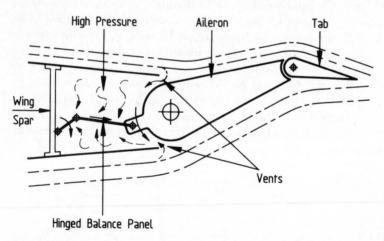

Fig. 1.29 Balance panel

All-moving tail

On many high-performance aircraft, trimming is effected by varying the angle of incidence of the horizontal stabiliser, the latter also operating in conjunction with elevators. This provides a much wider range of trim capability, and more precise manoeuvring in the pitching plane is possible because the full range of elevator movement is always available. Furthermore,

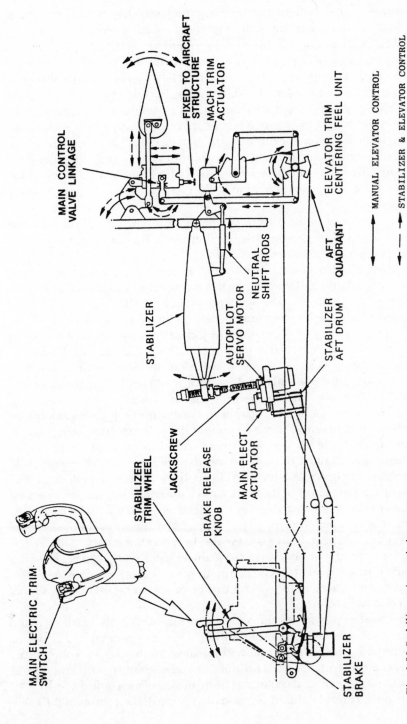

Fig. 1.30 Stabiliser trim and elevator system

this all-moving tail configuration overcomes the loss of effectiveness from which the use of elevators alone can suffer, especially at high speeds.

It is beyond the scope of this book to go into any detail relating to all the various methods of stabiliser operation, but the fundamental principles involved may be understood from fig. 1.30. The incidence of the stabiliser is varied by an actuator assembly which can be operated by any one of three methods: (i) by energising an electric actuator motor through switches on the control columns; (ii) by a trim servomotor (see page 206) which responds to signals from the automatic flight control system; if the latter is not in control, the servomotor can also respond to signals from a Mach trim system (see page 205), and (iii) by manually-operated trim wheels and control cables; this method is for emergency operation in the event of malfunction of the other two methods.

The actuator assembly consists of a jackscrew on which is threaded a ball nut connected to the leading edge section of the horizontal stabiliser. The lower portion of the assembly is connected to the fuselage structure by a gimbal which allows fore and aft angular movement of the actuator during stabiliser positioning. Similarly, the ball nut operates in a gimbal to prevent binding of the jackscrew. The operating range of the ball nut, and stabiliser movement, is limited by stop nuts at each end of the jackscrew.

The primary method of rotating the jackscrew is by means of a 115-volt three-phase motor connected to gearing which also forms part of the actuator. When the motor is energised via a switch on the pilot's control wheel, it rotates in one direction only, and its drive is transmitted to the jackscrew through either one of two electro-magnetic clutches which, on being energised, permit jackscrew rotation in either direction, corresponding to 'nose-up' or 'nose-down' trim. To prevent the stabiliser from being motor-driven onto either of the stop nuts, limit switches are provided, and on being mechanically operated by a striker on the stabiliser they de-energise the appropriate electro-magnetic clutch circuit. In the event that the actuator ball nut is driven onto either of the stops, a mechanical torque limiter is operated to prevent damage being done to the jackscrew actuator. When the trim system is not in operation, rotation of the jackscrew under the influence of air loads acting on the stabiliser is prevented by a braking system.

In the event of malfunction of the main actuator motor system, or of the automatic trim servomotor system, trimming may be carried out manually by means of trim wheels in the cockpit, and by cables connected to cable drums and a disconnect clutch.

The elevators provide for the control of manoeuvres in the pitching plane with the stabiliser in a trimmed position. They are operated by any one of four methods: (i) manually and by movement of the control column, (ii) stabiliser movement through a neutral shift rod mechanism, (iii) inputs from a Mach trim system, and (iv) inputs from an automatic control system.

When the control column is manually operated, then through the cable system the aft quadrant is rotated and this, in turn, operates a main control valve within the elevator power control unit, to admit hydraulic pressure into the unit's main actuator. The unit is thereby displaced to position the elevators in the manner of a power-operated system. The operation of a power control unit is described in more detail in page 204. A parallel input from the aft quadrant into the trim centring and feel unit provides the pilot with artificial feel.

The elevators are also displaced whenever the stabiliser is moved to a trimmed position, and as will be noted from fig. 1.30, this is effected through a neutral shift rod mechanism. The reason for elevator displacement, or neutral shift as it is called, is to augment the control authority of the stabiliser. The shift rod mechanism transmits its movement to the main control valve of the elevator power control unit via bodily displacement of the Mach trim actuator and the linkages from the aft quadrant of the control system. Fig. 1.31 illustrates the range of elevator neutral shift as the stabiliser is trimmed, and with the aircraft on the ground; in flight the range is slightly less due to aerodynamic loads acting on the stabiliser and elevators. It will be noted from the graph that the range also varies, dependent on whether the Mach trim actuator is extended or retracted.

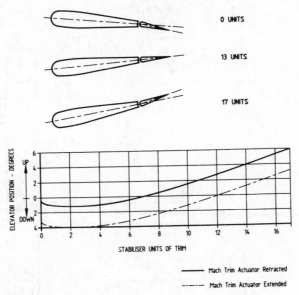

Fig. 1.31 Elevator neutral shift

The Mach trim actuator (see also page 225) is part of the neutral shift mechanism and at speeds below a set value, e.g. 0.7M, it is fully extended. As speed increases above this value, the actuator retracts to rotate the trim centring and feel unit, and through the aft quadrant and linkages the main

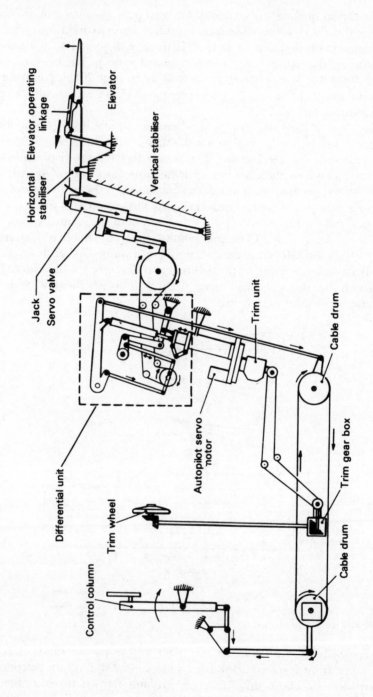

Fig. 1.32 Flying tail

control valve of the power control unit causes the unit to move down and so give an upward displacement of the elevators.

When the automatic control system is engaged the linkage to the main control valve of the power control unit is locked in its central position. Displacement of the elevators as required by a command signal from the pitch channel is carried out by supplying the signal to a transfer valve in the elevator power control unit. This admits hydraulic pressure to the unit's main actuator, and as in the case of manual control, the unit is displaced bodily to move the elevators to the commanded position.

Flying tail

A flying tail is one which controls both manoeuvring in the pitching plane, and trimming, by means of a variable-incidence stabiliser. Elevators are also provided but they can only be operated by direct movement of the stabiliser itself, thereby supplementing its control functions rather than serving as an independent pitch manoeuvring control surface. An example and its mechanical arrangement and operation under climb conditions are schematically illustrated in fig. 1.32.

Stabiliser incidence is varied either by appropriate movements of the control column, or by rotation of a pitch trim wheel. In each case, movements are finally transmitted via a common differential unit and a hydraulic power-assisted servomotor and actuator jack. The function of the differential unit is to vary the final control drive such that the trim control moves the stabiliser through a greater incidence range than that obtainable from the control column. When the autopilot is in control, stabiliser incidence is varied by a servomotor which, as can be seen from fig. 1.32, is connected to the pitch trim control system.

Mach trim

In aircraft which are capable of flying at high subsonic speeds, and of transition to supersonic speed, larger than normal rearward movements of the wing centre of pressure occur and in consequence larger nose-down pitching moments are produced; the attitude change being generally referred to as 'tuck under'. The attitude change is, of course, corrected and trimmed out by designing such aircraft so that they have the essential stability characteristics and trimming method, e.g. the variable incidence horizontal stabiliser already referred to. However, at a certain ratio of aircraft speed to the local speed of sound, or Mach number as it is called, compressibility effects arise which make the counteracting nose-up pitching moment produced by trimming the horizontal stabiliser to a negative angle of attack position, less effective as aircraft speed increases. Under manually controlled flight conditions, this would necessitate the pilot having to make prolonged trim

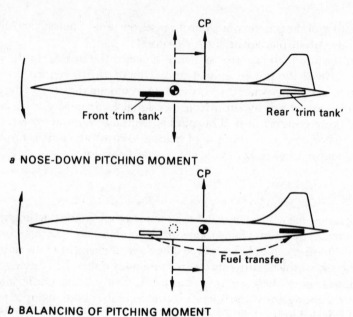

a **NOSE-DOWN PITCHING MOMENT**

b **BALANCING OF PITCHING MOMENT**

Fig. 1.33 Mach trimming

changes and to hold higher forces on the control column when displacing the elevators relative to a specific trimmed condition. It is usual therefore to install what is termed a Mach trim system (see also page 223) which automatically senses increases of speed above the appropriate datum Mach number and, by means of servo coupling, automatically re-adjusts the position of the horizontal stabiliser thereby maintaining the pitch trim of the aircraft.

Another example of Mach trimming is the one adopted for 'Concorde' and shown schematically in fig. 1.33. During transition from subsonic to supersonic speed, the nose-down pitch moment (diagram *a*) is counteracted by transferring fuel from a front 'trim tank' to a rear 'trim tank' so that the centre of gravity is moved rearwards thereby removing the couple introduced by the movement of the centre of pressure (diagram *b*).

Lift augmentation

During take-off, approach and landing, the speed of an aircraft corresponds to values in the low end of its overall speed range, and since there is a fixed relationship between these speeds and stalling speed (see page 41), then as high a maximum lift coefficient as possible is required at the lower speeds. In order to achieve this, secondary control devices are provided and when operated they augment the lift generated by the wings. The devices most commonly used are flaps, slats, and slots.

Flaps

Flaps are devices that form part of the trailing edge sections of the wings of an aircraft, and in such a manner that they can be lowered through selected angles and thereby increase the camber of the wing sections. In many cases, they can be extended simultaneously so that the wing area is also increased. Flaps vary in their configuration and methods of operation, dependent upon the type of aircraft in which they are installed. The split flap is the simplest type, deriving its name from the fact that it is part of the lower section of the wing, split from the remainder of it and deflected about a simple hinge arrangement by a mechanical linkage system throughout. The plain flap is a moveable section of a wing trailing edge deflected about its hinge access by a hydraulic actuator. The most widely used type is the Fowler flap, which not only increases the camber of the wing section but also increases the wing area. They are lowered and extended by hydraulic actuators although in some smaller types of aircraft, actuation is by means of an electric motor.

When flaps are lowered, the angle of attack under the prevailing conditions is reduced, and as a result of the change in wing section camber, there is a fixed and lower stalling angle for each increasing flap angle. The change in pressure distribution, and rearward movement of the increased lift-force also produces a nose-down pitching moment which is generally opposed by an increase in the downwash at the tail of the aircraft, this being an added effect of lowering flaps.

Although lift is increased by lowering flaps, drag also increases progressively but under approach and landing conditions this can be used to advantage, and for each type of aircraft flaps are lowered to corresponding angular positions. At the approach position, the increase of lift enables a lower approach speed to be made and since the stalling speed is decreased the aircraft can touch down at a lower speed. For landing, the flaps are fully lowered and a higher drag permits a steeper approach without speed becoming excessive; in other words, the flaps have a braking effect during approach and during the period an aircraft 'floats' before touch-down.

The increased lift coefficient when flaps are lowered, can also shorten the take-off run of an aircraft. Therefore, for each type of aircraft a recommended angle or 'take-off flap' position is always specified and which will give the correspondingly best lift/drag ratio.

The effectiveness of flaps may be considerably increased if the air is made to follow the lowered surface without a tendency to separate or become turbulent, particularly at high angles of attack and large flap angles. One method of achieving this is by designing flaps such that when lowered a slot is opened at their leading edges. This slot allows air to flow over the upper

49

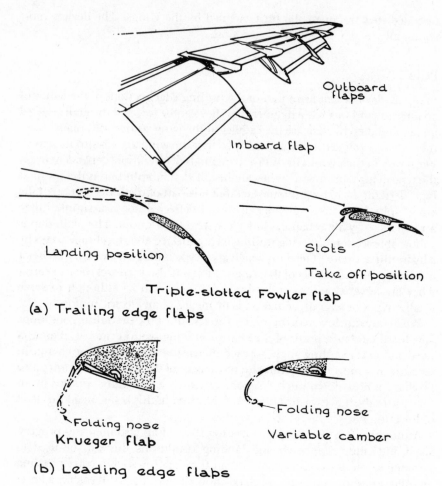

Outboard flaps

Inboard flap

Landing position

Slots

Take off position

Triple-slotted Fowler flap

(a) Trailing edge flaps

Folding nose

Krueger flap

Folding nose

Variable camber

(b) Leading edge flaps

Fig. 1.34 Flaps

surfaces of the flaps, thereby re-energising the air so that a smooth flow is maintained over the whole cambered surface formed by the wings and flaps. In Fowler type flaps, two or even three slots may be opened during lowering and extension as shown at (a) in fig. 1.34.

An example of the use of Fowler flaps in the take-off position is illustrated in Plate (iii).

In the case of swept-wing aircraft, a large increase in lift-dependent drag can occur at high angles of attack, mainly because of air-flow separation at the wing leading edge, and a spanwise flow of the boundary layer. These aircraft are therefore provided with leading edge flaps which are extended to increase the leading edge camber, the extension being in conjunction with that of the trailing edge flaps.

Plate (iii) Airbus A300 (reproduced by courtesy of *Airbus Industrie*)

The most common type of leading edge flap is the Krueger shown in fig. 1.34(b). Another type is the variable-camber flap which has a flexible surface made of fibreglass so that as it extends, the actuating linkage causes the surface to vary its contour in order to maintain a more efficient lift characteristic. In some aircraft, both may be used in combination; for example in the Boeing 747, Krueger flaps are located at the inboard leading edge sections, and variable camber flaps are at the outboard sections. Another method of increasing leading edge camber and of reducing air flow separation, is 'leading edge droop', the droop being obtained by lowering a section of the wing leading edge itself.

Slats

For some types of swept-wing aircraft, the alternative slat method of augmenting lift and of reducing spanwise flow of the boundary layer may be adopted. For example, both the McDonnell Douglas DC-10 and the 'L-1011 Tristar' have slat installations (see fig. 1.35) as opposed to leading edge flaps which, as already noted, are adopted in the Boeing 747.

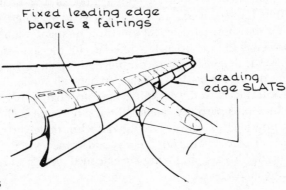

Fig. 1.35 Slats

Slats are cambered surfaces which, in the retracted position, lie flush with the upper surface of the leading edge section of a wing. They are arranged in sections along the leading edge and are extended and lowered by hydraulic actuators thereby providing an increase in leading edge camber and resulting increase in the lift coefficient. As will be noted from the diagram in figure 1.35 when a slat is in the extended position, a slot is formed between it and the upper surface of the wing leading edge. The air flowing through the slot is accelerated by venturi effect and this re-energises the boundary layer and prevents separation of air flowing from the wing. Since a number of slat sections are installed, then the combined effect of the airflow through each open slot is to prevent spanwise flow of the boundary layer, and any tendency for wing-tip stalling to take place.

Spoilers

Spoilers are flap-type control surfaces located in the upper surface of a wing in such a way that they can be raised to selected angular positions. As their name suggests they 'spoil' the airflow over the wing, and since this produces a change in both lift and drag they can be used to provide specific lift control features for the purpose of: improving lateral control, aerodynamic braking for vertical speed control during descent, and for reducing roll-out after landing. In order to illustrate the basic function and operating fundamentals of spoilers, we many consider the system as applied to the McDonnell Douglas DC–10 (see fig. 1.22). Five spoilers are located in each wing immediately forward of the trailing edge flaps and are used in conjunction with the ailerons. The commands for the various lift control functions are applied to lateral control mixer units, the outputs from which operate the spoilers via hydraulic actuators. During the lateral control mode of operation, displacement of the ailerons causes the mixer units to control the spoilers in such a manner that the spoilers on the down-going wing are raised thereby assisting the aileron on that wing. The spoilers on the up-going wing remain in the retracted position.

During descent, it is essential for both altitude and vertical speed to be closely monitored, and conventionally it is effected in the long-term by engine power, and in the short-term by the pitching moment established by the elevators. However, in aircraft such as the DC–10, the spoilers are used for altitude and vertical speed control during descent, since in the extended position they control lift by direct means. When this mode of operation is required, a control lever in the cockpit is operated manually and causes the hydraulic actuators to partially extend all the spoilers on each wing. If it is necessary to apply lateral control of the aircraft while under direct lift control, the ailerons are displaced in the normal way and by means of the mixer units, the spoilers on the down-going wing are extended further and those on the up-going wing are retracted.

Reduction of the landing run of the aircraft after it has touched down is achieved by fully extending the spoilers on each wing: this is generally known as the 'ground spoiler' or 'speedbrake' mode, and is also controlled by the control lever of the cockpit. The lever may be set in an 'armed' position so that the spoilers extend automatically when the main landing gear wheels spin on landing, or the lever may be positioned to provide direct manual control of the spoilers. In the armed position, the hydraulic actuators are controlled by signals from wheel-driven transducer units.

B. HELICOPTERS

Our study of principles of flight thus far, has been concerned with those types of aircraft which are propelled by thrust developed by propellers or by exhaust gases from turbojet engines, and which derive their lift capability from fixed wings. However, this study, and a study of automatic flight control principles would not be complete without some understanding of the mechanics of that type of aircraft which derives its lift capability from a device known as a rotor; namely, the helicopter.

The rotor, which employs two or more large blades of aerofoil section, is virtually a rotating wing, and this leads us to the more precise and accepted definition of the helicopter which is, 'a rotorcraft deriving lift from power-driven rotor(s) rotating about axes which are vertical, or nearly so, when the aircraft is in horizontal flight.'

As far as flight and its control are concerned, the helicopter is unique in that it is able to ascend and descend vertically, move horizontally in any direction, it can hover over a spot on the ground and while doing so can turn on to any heading.

General

The construction of a type of helicopter which is in common operational use, is shown in fig. 1.36 and this serves as a very useful example on which to base an introduction to helicopter principles of flight in general. As will be noted, it only vaguely resembles a conventional type of aircraft in that it has a fuselage; the main rotor, tail rotor, and other features are unique to helicopters.

The main rotor is particularly unique in that as a single system, it performs all three basic functions required for any type of aircraft to fly, i.e. propulsion, support, and controllability.

The engine is mounted in the upper part of the fuselage; it drives the main rotor through a gearbox, and the tail rotor by means of a long drive shaft (see fig. 1.37). The engine in this case, is of the turbine type but, in some

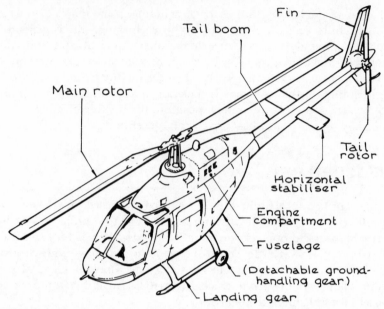

Fin

Tail boom

Main rotor

Tail rotor

Horizontal stabiliser

Engine compartment

Fuselage

(Detachable ground-handling gear)

Landing gear

Fig. 1.36

helicopters power may be derived from a piston engine. Helicopters of the twin-engined type are also in service and two examples are shown in Plates (iv) and (v). The number of blades forming a main rotor, and indeed the number of main rotors used, depends on the helicopter size and lift/weight requirements; in other words, these are comparable to the wing area, wing loading and performance requirements of fixed-wing aircraft. In the event of engine failure, rotor systems include a free-wheeling device to permit free rotation of the rotor.

In order to carry out their particular flight manoeuvres, helicopters must also have a flight control system which will produce similar effects to that employed in a fixed-wing aircraft, i.e. changes in pressure distribution and lift forces of the main aerofoil surfaces. However, in place of moveable flight

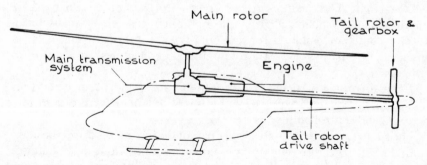

Main rotor

Tail rotor & gearbox

Main transmission system

Engine

Tail rotor drive shaft

Fig. 1.37 Rotor transmission system

54

control surfaces, these effects are obtained by varying the pitch of the main and tail rotor blades and three controls are provided for the pilot as follows:

(i) Collective Pitch Lever – changes pitch angle of main rotor blades collectively to provide vertical movement of the helicopter.

(ii) Cyclic Pitch Lever – tilts the main rotor disc by varying the pitch of the main rotor blades individually to provide horizontal movement.

(iii) Foot Pedals – change pitch angle of tail rotor blades collectively to provide directional control.

As already noted, a helicopter is able to ascend and descend vertically, to hover, fly horizontally in any direction and to turn on to any heading and as these sequences generally form a helicopter flight pattern, our study of the relevant principles of flight can also follow this pattern. However, as rotors are the primary aerodynamic elements involved, it is appropriate that we should first of all have an understanding of the types used and associated terminology.

Rotors

These may be classified as (i) articulated, (ii) semi-rigid and (iii) rigid.

An *articulated* rotor is one in which the individual blades are free to flap, drag and change pitch. This is made possible by mounting the blades on flapping and dragging hinges and pitch-change bearings.

A *semi-rigid* rotor is one which generally has no individual flapping and dragging hinges, and has only freedom to flap and change pitch by means of a gimbal mounting.

A *rigid* rotor has no flapping or dragging hinges but does have pitch-change bearings.

Certain terms used in connection with rotors and helicopter principles of flight generally, are described in the following paragraphs and their applications are indicated in fig. 1.38.

Shaft axis
This is the axis through the main rotor shaft and about which the blades are permitted to rotate.

Axis of rotation
This is the axis through the head of the main rotor shaft about which the blades actually rotate. This axis is not always the same as the shaft axis because under certain conditions of flight the rotor is permitted to tilt.

Plate (iv) Boeing BV 234 helicopter (reproduced by kind permission of *British Airways Helicopter Ltd*)

Plate (v) S61 helicopter (reproduced by courtesy of *Westland Helicopters*)

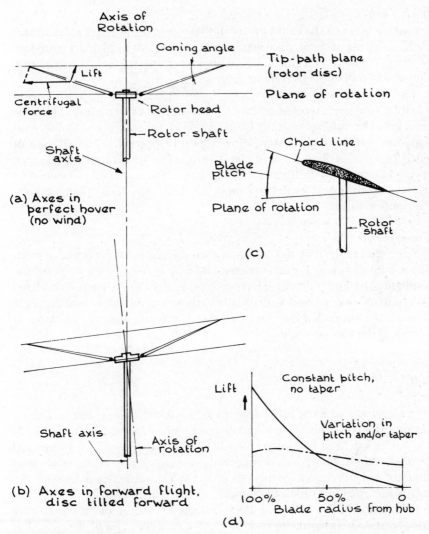

Fig. 1.38 Terminology

Plane of rotation
The plane of rotation is at right-angles to the axis of rotation at the head of the main rotor shaft and is parallel to the tip-path plane.

Tip-path plane (rotor disc)
This is the path described by the blade tips during rotation and is at right-angles to the axis of rotation. The area contained within the path is analogous to that formed by the tips of propeller blades and is, therefore, referred to as the 'rotor disc'.

57

Blade pitch

The angle between the chord line of the blade and the plane of rotation and the basic setting of the blades when attached to the rotor head. It may therefore be compared with the rigger's angle of incidence used for fixed-wing aircraft, and also to propeller blade angle (diagram (c)).

The lift produced by a fixed wing can vary along the span, depending on whether the wing is tapered or has a certain amount of 'wash out'. The same principle also applies to rotor blades in order to avoid considerable load variations which would otherwise occur if the blades had a constant value of pitch throughout their length (see fig. 1.38 (d)). The lift is increased at the root end and decreased at the tip and although it still has its greatest value near the tip, the blade pitch angle and taper selected provide a more uniform distribution of lift.

Coning angle

When a rotor is turning and producing lift, the blades are deflected upwards about their flapping hinges, and they take up a final position along the resultant of lift and centrifugal forces. Thus, in relation to the tip-path plane, they form an inverted cone with its apex at the main rotor shaft, and the angle between the tip-path plane and the spanwise centre line of the blades is known as the coning angle.

Lift

The lift produced from a fixed wing, as we already know, results from a combination of many factors and is commonly expressed by the formula $C_L \tfrac{1}{2} \rho V^2 S$. Lift from a helicopter rotor blade which is generally of symmetrical aerofoil section*, can usually be expressed in the same terms. However, we must bear in mind that changes in the velocity factor (V^2) and dissymmetry of lift can take place depending on the flight condition of the helicopter, e.g. whether it is hovering or in horizontal flight. These changes result from the fact that we are concerned with independent rotational velocity of the rotor blades as well as forward velocity of the helicopter.

Assuming that a helicopter is hovering in a 'no-wind' condition, the velocity of the relative airflow at the blade tips is the same throughout the tip-path plane, and it decreases at points closer to the rotor hub. When the helicopter moves into forward flight the relative airflow moving over each blade now becomes a combination of rotor rotational velocity and forward velocity of the helicopter. The advancing blade has a combined velocity equal to rotational velocity *plus* helicopter forward velocity, while the combined velocity of the retreating blade is equal to rotational velocity *minus* the

---

* In some helicopters, e.g. the Boeing BV 234 shown in Plate (iv) page 56, non-symmetric sections are used.

forward velocity of the helicopter. It is apparent therefore, that the lift over the advancing blade half of the rotor disc will be greater than that over the retreating blade half during horizontal flight. Similar dissymmetry of lift will occur with the helicopter hovering in wind conditions.

In order to equalise the lift of the rotor blades and thereby prevent any tendency for the helicopter to roll or pitch, the blades are free to flap about special hinges so that blade pitch angles, relative to the air flowing over them, change cyclically. Thus, assuming the helicopter is in forward flight and rotor blade pitch angle is constant, the increased lift of an advancing blade will cause it to flap upwards and decrease the angle of attack because the relative airflow will change from a horizontal direction to a more downward direction. The decreased lift on the retreating blade will cause it to flap downwards and so increase the angle of attack since the relative airflow is in a more upward direction. The amount that a blade flaps is the result of the cyclic change of balance between the lift, centrifugal force and inertia. While the rotor maintains any substantially fixed plane the resultant of these forces acting on each blade will be equal. It is only when the resultants are momentarily unequal that the plane of the rotor disc will alter.

Blade dragging

When a blade flaps it leaves its normal tip-path plane momentarily with the result that it must travel a greater distance (horizontally) than the other blade or blades; therefore, it has to travel at a greater speed for a very short period of time so that it can keep up with the other blade(s) and so maintain a constant speed. If the blades were rigidly fixed, a bending moment would be set up, causing fatigue and so result in a possible break-up of the blades. In addition, changes in the centre of gravity position of a blade can occur due to flapping causing oscillations in the plane of rotation and, in turn, vibration.

Therefore, in order to prevent the foregoing effects, the blades are mounted in hinges which permit a limited amount of backward and forward movement known as 'dragging'. To dampen out oscillations and vibration, to limit drag movement, and to maintain the geometric relationship of the blades, hydraulic or friction type dampers are fitted between blades and a part of the rotor hub.

Rotor thrust and drag

If the total reactive force acting on the aerofoil section of a rotor blade is split into lift induced drag components, the lift, which is at right-angles to the relative airflow, is not providing a force in direct opposition to the weight, as in the case of a fixed-wing aircraft. The lifting component of the total reaction must therefore be that part of it which is acting along the axis of rotation. This component is called *rotor thrust* (see fig. 1.39) and provided it

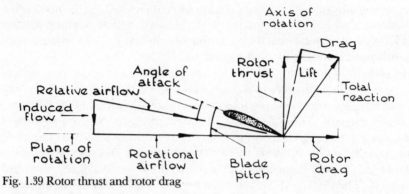

Fig. 1.39 Rotor thrust and rotor drag

is equal at each blade, the total thrust will act through the hub at right-angles to the plane of rotation. The other component of total reaction will be in the blade's plane of rotation and is called *rotor drag*.

Take-off and climb

As in the case of a fixed-wing aircraft, a helicopter can only take off when a lift force greater than the weight is produced.

For a fixed-wing aircraft, the thrust force is increased to a certain value, so that at some point along its take-off run a speed will have been attained at which the airflow over the wings, which are at some constant angle of attack, produces the required lift force.

The helicopter takes-off vertically, and to achieve the necessary lifting force an increase of thrust is also required. However, in contrast to a fixed-wing

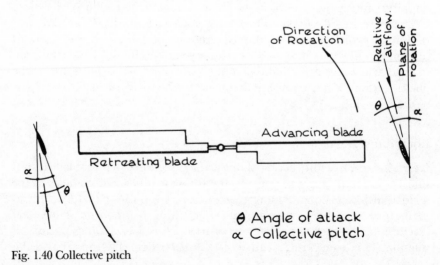

Fig. 1.40 Collective pitch

aircraft, the thrust increase and requisite lift from a rotary wing are both obtained by increasing wing angle of attack. This is achieved by means of a *collective pitch* system which enables the pilot to alter simultaneously the pitch angle of each and every blade, as shown in fig. 1.40. The basic arrangement of a system by which the pilot can do this by direct means is shown in fig. 1.41. In helicopters of substantial size, however, the feedback forces from the rotor system require considerable control forces to be applied by the pilot, and so to assist him hydraulic servos are incorporated in the control system (see pp. 229 and 235).

The swash plate assembly (a commonly use method) is connected by linkages to the collective pitch lever and is so designed that it not only rotates, but can also be moved up and down, and tilted. The lever movements are in the appropriate sense, i.e. upward movement increases pitch and lift, and

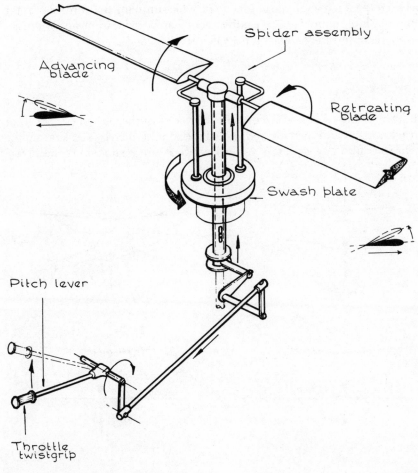

Fig. 1.41 Collective pitch control system

downward movement decreases pitch and lift. Thus, when the pilot pulls the collective pitch lever up as shown in fig. 1.41, the swash plate moves upwards and by means of the 'spider' assembly, it increases the pitch angle of each blade. With the pitch angle thus set, and at the requisite rotor speed, air is drawn in form above the rotor and displaced downwards, and the airflow relative to the blades causes them to lift upwards to the coning angle and thereby lift the helicopter from the ground.

Once the blades have a certain amount of pitch, the total thrust necessitates an increase in total reaction and this, in turn, will increase rotor drag. Engine power must therefore, be increased to maintain rotor rev/min when increasing total rotor thrust and vice versa. This means that the amount of lift can be varied by changing either the rev/min or the pitch angle of the blades. In practical cases generally however, lift is varied by collective pitch changing only, since it is usual to incorporate a cam-operated linkage between the pitch lever and engine to provide simultaneous control of rotor rev/min. Fine manual rev/min adjustments can be made by means of a twist-grip type of throttle handle on the pitch lever.

Hovering

If, after lifting-off, the collective pitch lever is further increased, the rotor thrust and lift will increase and exceed the weight, thereby accelerating the helicopter into a steady rate of vertical climb (assuming no-wind conditions).

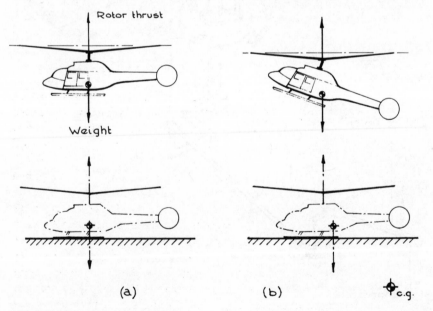

Fig. 1.42 Hovering

This is continued until the helicopter reaches an altitude at which it is required to make what is termed the 'transition' to horizontal flight.

In order to make the transition the helicopter must stop climbing; therefore, the collective pitch of the blades must be reduced until the thrust and lift forces equal the weight and main helicopter drag forces. The helicopter is thus made to take up the flight condition known as *hovering* as shown in fig. 1.42.

The total rotor thrust produced is taken as acting through the axis of rotation and at right-angles to the plane of rotation. In the perfect hovering condition the total weight of the helicopter will be acting vertically downwards through the centre of gravity, and if this is positioned immediately below the axis of rotation the attitude of the helicopter fuselage will be as indicated fig. 1.42 (a). If, however, the centre of gravity is not below the axis of rotation of the blades, then as soon as the helicopter leaves the ground a couple will exist between the total rotor thrust and the weight, and the fuselage will pitch until both forces are in line, as indicated in fig. 1.42 (b).

Ground effect

When a helicopter is hovering close to the ground the induced flow of air through the rotor disc meets resistance from the ground and the downwash is deflected into a flow radiating out from the helicopter. At the same time, some downwash is deflected inwards, underneath the helicopter and brought to rest thereby forming a cushioning or ground effect. This can be used to advantage when hovering under heavy load or low air density conditions.

Horizontal flight

A fixed-wing aircraft moves forward as a result of reactive thrust produced in the line of flight either by a propeller or by the high velocity gases exhausted from a turbojet engine. A helicopter on the other hand, moves forward by tilting the rotor disc and therefore, the total rotor thrust, in the forward direction.

Tilting of the rotor is effected by means of a second control system, known as *cyclic pitch* control and its basic function is similar to that of the collective pitch control system, i.e. it varies the pitch of the blades. However, there is one important difference; in a cyclic pitch control system the blades change pitch individually during the cycle of rotation, so that at any given time the pitch of one blade is increasing, while the pitch of the other blade(s) is decreasing.

Thus, to tilt the rotor forward for forward flight (see fig. 1.43) the blade which happens to be moving round to the rear of the disc (the retreating blade) must be caused to ride up about its flapping hinge, so as to be at its highest position at the rear of the disc. Conversely, the blade which happens

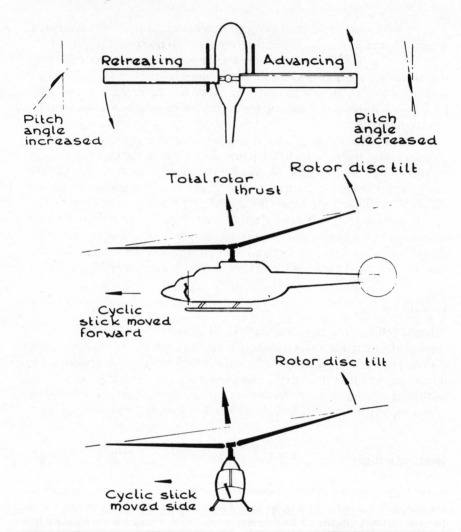

Fig. 1.43 Cyclic pitch

to be moving round to the front of the disc (the advancing blade) must ride lower so as to be at its lowest position when in front of the disc.

To keep the rotor disc in the tilted position, the rotor is designed so that the pitch angles are continuously changing throughout the 360° cycle of travel; hence the use of the term cyclic pitch change. Similarly, to make the helicopter fly sideways or rearwards the rotor disc and total thrust/lift vector are tilted in the appropriate directions.

The control system, shown in much simplified form in fig. 1.44 consists of a cyclic stick which is coupled to a lower swash plate having tilting freedom only. When the stick is pushed forward the lower swash plate is also tilted

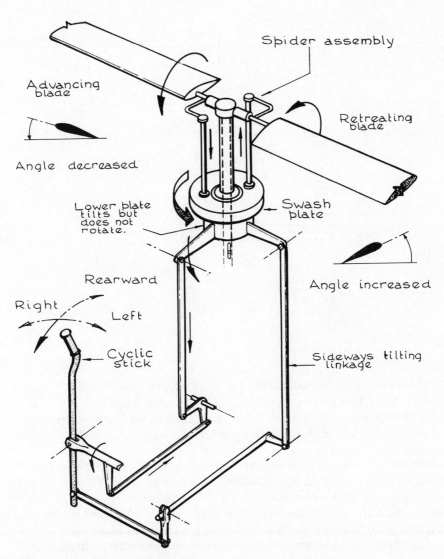

Fig. 1.44 Cyclic pitch control system

forward and thereby displaces the rotating plate which is the same one used for collective pitch changing. In this instance however, the retreating blade is made to increase its pitch angle while the advancing blade angle is decreased. Thus, from this we can see that cyclic pitch changes are always superimposed on the collective pitch changes and the total lift force remains substantially the same. Further study of fig. 1.44 will serve to indicate the movements and pitch changes which are obtained when the cyclic stick is moved sideways or rearwards.

65

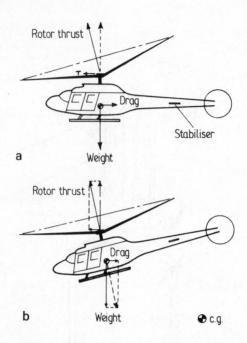

Fig. 1.45 Forces in horizontal forward flight

Mention was made earlier that the pitch angles of the blades change continuously throughout the 360° cycle of blade travel. This is due to the fact that as the rotating plate must always move against the lower swash plate fixed at some angle of tilt, the blade spider linkages consequently rise and fall during their rotation.

When an increase in pitch is given to a rotor blade, the blade does not rise immediately to a high flapped position, but does so up to 90° later in its revolution. Similarly, a blade is given a minimum pitch in a position 180° from where it received the maximum pitch, but only reaches its lowest flapped position 90° later. These variations are known as *phase lag*.

Let us now assume that the helicopter moves into forward flight from the hover and with the centre of gravity located ideally below the axis of rotation. The rotor disc will be tilted forward and the rotor thrust will produce a nose-down pitching moment about the centre of gravity as shown in fig. 1.45 (a). The vertical component of total rotor thrust and weight remain in line but a couple now exists between the thrust component (T) and fuselage drag as the helicopter gains speed. The fuselage is therefore pitched forward and the couple tries to bring the thrust and drag forces into line. As soon as the fuselage pitches forward an opposing couple will be produced between the vertical component of total rotor thrust and the weight. The fuselage therefore takes up a position at which the two couples are in equilibrium and the centre of gravity is again in line with the total rotor thrust as shown in fig. 1.45 (b). Thus, the centre of gravity is an important factor controlling the position of the fuselage in relation to the rotor disc.

As it is more desirable for the helicopter to fly with the fuselage level, various methods are adopted to achieve this. In some types of helicopter the design is so arranged that in hovering flight the fuselage is in a tail-down attitude and then assumes a fairly level attitude in forward flight. In other types, the one shown is fig. 1.36 for example, adjustable horizontal stabilisers are fitted in the tail boom and can be used to trim the aircraft attitude as required.

Directional control

When the main rotor of a helicopter is rotating there is always a tendency for the fuselage to rotate about the normal axis, in the opposite direction (see fig. 1.46 (a)). This is called torque reaction and is the same as that occurring in propeller-driven, fixed-wing aircraft where the fuselage tends to rotate about the longitudinal axis in the opposite direction to the propeller. Some means must therefore be provided to balance this torque and one of the most common methods adopted is the tail rotor which, as can be seen from fig. 1.46 (b) exerts a side thrust at the tail, thereby balancing the main rotor torque.

The tail rotor is driven by a shaft from the main rotor gearbox (see fig. 1.37) and always rotates when the main rotor is rotating. As the main rotor torque is not constant, it is necessary to vary the tail rotor thrust and this is achieved by altering the collective pitch of the blades in a manner somewhat similar to that of the main rotor. The pitch change mechanism is however, operated by foot pedals which in the operating sense are analogous to the rudder pedals of a fixed-wing aircraft.

It should now be apparent that since the tail rotor thrust can be varied to overcome torque reaction then such variations can also usefully serve as a means of changing the direction of the fuselage while hovering. If, in hovering flight the pilot wishes to turn the fuselage to the right he pushes on the right foot pedal and, assuming the direction of main rotor rotation to be as shown in fig. 1.46 (c), the pitch of the tail rotor blades and the thrust will be decreased. The fuselage will therefore turn as a result of the difference between tail rotor thrust and main rotor torque. If the pilot pushes on the left foot pedal the tail rotor thrust is increased (fig. 1.46 (d)) and will be greater than the main rotor torque so that the tail is pulled round to swing the fuselage nose to the left.

The tail rotor thrust produces two other effects which have to be corrected and these are tail rotor drift and tail rotor roll. The moment produced by the rotor in overcoming torque reaction causes a side pull on the pivot point or axis of rotation of the main rotor, resulting in a sideways drift of the

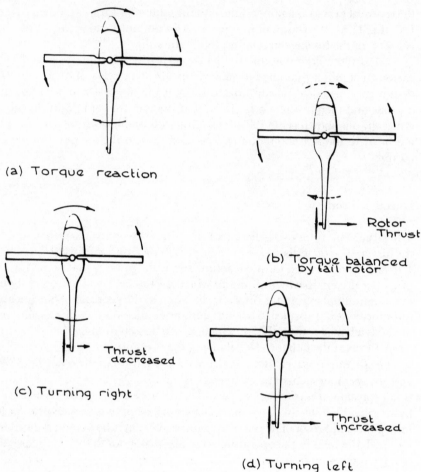

(a) Torque reaction

(b) Torque balanced by tail rotor

Rotor Thrust

(c) Turning right

Thrust decreased

(d) Turning left

Thrust increased

Fig. 1.46 Torque reaction and direction control

helicopter. It is corrected by designing the main rotor cyclic pitch linkage system so that the rotor is tilted to one side; its thrust therefore has a side component which will oppose the drift as shown in fig. 1.47 (a).

If the tail rotor is mounted on the fuselage below the horizontal level of the main rotor hub, the drift corrective force being produced by the main rotor will cause a rolling couple so that the helicopter will hover with the fuselage tilted to one side. This is shown in fig. 1.47 (b). It is usual therefore, for the fuselage to have a certain amount of upward sweep so that both rotors are on the same level or, in some cases, to have the tail rotor mounted on a pylon.

Turns

As in the case of fixed-wing aircraft, a helicopter in forward flight is turned

68

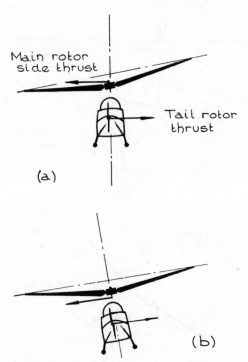

Main rotor
side thrust

Tail rotor
thrust

(a)

(b)

Fig. 1.47 Tail rotor drift and roll

on to any desired heading by banking. Bank is applied by moving the cyclic stick in the direction in which the turn is to be made and thereby tilting the rotor disc and the total lift/thrust force vector (see fig. 1.48). This force has two components; one acting vertically and in opposition to the weight, the other acting horizontally in opposition to centrifugal force. It is this horizontal component of lift that turns the aircraft in the banked direction. The tail rotor pitch control pedals are used during the turn, not to initiate it or assist it, but to compensate for added torque effect and so maintain longitudinal trim and turn co-ordination. If the angle of bank is increased, the total lift/thrust force vector will be tilted more towards the horizontal, thereby increasing the rate of turn. The vertical component of lift is decreased, and in order to compensate for this and the resulting loss of altitude, the collective pitch lever must also be operated to increase the angle of attack of the main rotor blades.

In forward flight, turning of a tandem-rotor type of helicopter as shown in Plate (iv) page 56 is achieved by moving a foot pedal in the direction of the turn so as to tilt the rotors laterally and in opposite directions to each other. At the same time, and by means of a differential control system, a cyclic pitch change also takes place in order to maintain the pitch attitude of the helicopter.

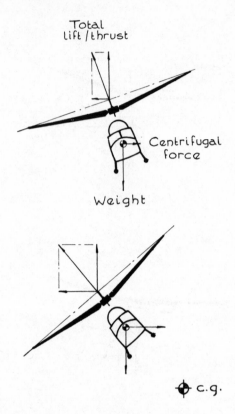

Fig. 1.48 Turning   ⊕ c.g.

Descent

A helicopter is made to descend by pushing the collective pitch lever down and in so doing to reduce the pitch and lift of each blade of the main rotor. When the descent is established an upward airflow component will be introduced and will directly oppose the 'downwash' induced by the rotating blades. In turn, this will alter the direction of the relative airflow along the blades. Vortices will also form at the blade tips.

If the collective pitch lever is lowered further, the rate of descent will be increased and a condition will eventually be reached whereby changes in the relative airflow and angle of attack of the blades produce a stalled condition at the root ends of the blades. At this stage rotor thrust will decrease at the root ends and also at the tips because of the vortices, leaving an area in between to produce the rotor thrust necessasry to control the descent. Any further downward movement of the collective pitch lever reduces the effective rotor thrust-producing area, causing the helicopter to descend rapidly and with the rotor operating in what is termed the *vortex ring state*. In addition to a rapid descent, the vortex ring state also causes juddering of the cyclic stick, random yawing, rolling and pitching.

Autorotation

Autorotation is the term used for the flight condition during which no engine power is supplied (e.g. an engine failure) and the main rotor is driven only by the action of air flowing upward through the rotor. The transmission system is designed so that when the engine stops, the main rotor is disengaged to allow it to rotate freely in its original direction.

TEST QUESTIONS

1 Briefly describe how the lift force is generated by a wing.

2 In what manner does a change in angle of attack affect the pressure distribution over a wing?

3 Apart from angle of attack, what other factors can affect pressure distribution?

4 The centre of pressure is the point:
   (a) about which the pitching moment is constant regardless of angle of attack.
   (b) from which total lift force acts.
   (c) at which the boundary layer airflow tends to break away from the wing surface.

5 Name the two principal types of drag, and state the components which constitute them.

6 What do you understand by the terms 'positive' and 'neutral' stability?

7 How does aerodynamic damping contribute to the stability of an aircraft?

8 As far as influence on the behaviour of an aircraft is concerned, in what manner does directional stability differ from longitudinal stability?

9 The static margin is:
   (a) the distance between the c.g. of an aircraft and the centre of pressure.
   (b) the c.g. location which produces neutral static stability.
   (c) an indication of the degree of longitudinal stability.

10 In which type of flight control system would there be no difference between stick-fixed and stick-free stability?

11 What would be the effect of a short-period of oscillation on an aircraft having longitudinal static instability.?

12 In connection with directional stability, what are the principal factors affecting the size of the stabilising yawing moment?

13 What do you understand by the term 'aerodynamic coupling'?

14 If an aircraft has directional static instability, displacements in yaw will cause:
   (a) spiral divergence.
   (b) directional divergence.
   (c) Dutch Roll.

15 What is meant by the effectiveness of a flight control system, and on what factors does it depend?

16 What are the primary differences between control systems which are power-assisted and power-operated?

17 Explain why rolling of an aircraft also results in turning.

18 Under the conditions referred to in Question 17, what other effect occurs, and how can it be minimised?

19 Why is a trim control system an integral part of the flight controls of an aircraft? State the principal methods commonly adopted.

20 Why is it necessary to provide lift augmentation systems?

21 The purpose of primary stops in a flight control system is to:
  (a) prevent damage to the system when the aircraft is parked in high wind conditions.
  (b) restrict the movement of the controls to their correct range.
  (c) act as a stop in the event of control flutter.

22 What is the purpose of slotted type Fowler flaps?

23 What is the primary difference in operation of leading edge flaps, and slats?

24 What is meant by the term 'direct lift control', and what methods are employed to achieve it?

25 Why are the blades of an articulated rotor allowed to flap and drag?

26 In terms of relative airflow and the lift produced, how do the rotor blades of a helicopter in forward flight, differ aerodynamically from a fixed wing?

27 The forces which give rise to the coning angle are:
  (a) thrust and centrifugal.
  (b) lift and centripetal.
  (c) lift and centrifugal.

28 When the collective pitch lever is operated, the pitch of each blade of the main rotor is:
  (a) either increased or decreased by the same amount.
  (b) either increased or decreased so that each blade is at a different angle.
  (c) increased by the same amount to provide lift only.

29 In what way does cyclic pitch differ from that of collective pitch?

30 What are the main functions of a tail rotor system, and how is it controlled by the pilot?

31 Briefly describe how a helicopter can be turned on to any desired heading?

2
Servomechanisms and Automatic Control Fundamentals

In manually controlled flight, the pilot and the flight control system of his aircraft together comprise what may be termed a closed-loop servo-system. Let us consider the simple case of an aircraft which after flying on a constant heading at a particular altitude is required to continue its flight on the same constant heading, but at a lower altitude. The pilot will move the control column forward to apply downward movement to the elevators, thus causing a nose-down attitude of the aircraft and initiation of the descent. Since the descent must be made at a certain angle and rate of change the pilot will also monitor those of his primary flight instruments which detect and indicate attitude changes; namely, gyro horizon, vertical speed indicator, altimeter and airspeed indicator, and then start returning the elevators to their neutral position by pulling back on the control column. In order to level out at the new altitude, the control column will firstly be pulled further back, thereby applying upward movement of the elevators to produce a nose-up attitude of the aircraft, and then will be moved forward again to position the elevators in neutral to fly into the new level flight attitude.

In the case of a helicopter, the pilot establishes the descent by lowering the collective pitch lever, adjusting the throttle to maintain engine speed, and operating the foot pedals to maintain heading. The cyclic control stick would also have to be operated to maintain descent attitude and airspeed. To level off from the descent the pilot starts raising the collective pitch lever such that he leads the desired level-off altitutde by an amount dependent on the rate of descent. At the same time, adjustments are made to the throttle, the foot pedals and the cyclic pitch, to obtain cruising speed and level-flight attitude as the desired altitude is reached.

From the foregoing, and much simplified, explanation of how an attitude change is effected, the particular point to be noted is that a pilot must always 'follow-up' his initial control inputs by applying secondary opposing inputs, thereby progressively removing control so that the attitude changes will be made as smoothly and as accurately as possible, and without exceeding those changes commanded by the input. Such a closed-loop servomechanism technique is applied to automatic flight control systems, the 'follow-up' action in his connection being referred to as 'feedback'.

73

Servomechanisms

A servomechanism may be broadly defined as a closed-loop control system in which a small power input controls a much larger power output in a strictly proportionate manner. In applying such a mechanism to the automatic control of an aircraft, the system must be capable of continuous operation and have the ability to (i) detect the difference between an input and an output (error detection); (ii) amplify the error signals; and (iii) control the closing of the servo loop by providing the feedback.

There are two main classes of servomechanism: (i) position control and (ii) speed control; both classes may be independently applied to automatic flight control systems depending respectively on whether they are of the displacement type or the rate sensing type. In some control systems they may also be used in conjunction with each other (see also p. 148).

Position control servomechanism

A block schematic diagram of a position control servomechanism is illustrated in fig. 2.1, and from this it will be noted that it is one in which a load has to be rotated through an output angle θ_o corresponding to an input

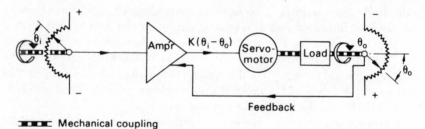

Mechanical coupling

Fig. 2.1 Position control servomechanism

angle θ_i of a controlling shaft. The controlling shaft is, in this example, mechanically coupled to the wiper arm of a potentiometer, the signal output of which is fed to a servomotor via an amplifier. The output angle of the load is measured by a second potentiometer whose wiper arm is mechanically coupled to an output shaft. The potentiometers are electrically connected such that when their wiper arms occupy corresponding angular positions the servomechanism is in a 'null' or zero signal condition. When it is requied to move the load to a particular angular position (θ_o) the controlling shaft is rotated through the appropriate number of degrees; thus the mechanism is no longer at 'null' and an error signal corresponding to angle θ_i is produced and fed to the amplifier. The amplifier has an amplification factor of K, and therefore the input to the servomotor is increased to $K\theta_i$. As the motor positions the load, the output shaft rotates the wiper arm of the second potentiometer to produce a signal corresponding to an angle θ_o. This signal is fed back to the amplifier thereby reducing the input error signal to the amplifier so that the real output from this unit to the servomotor is $K(\theta_i-\theta_o)$. When the load finally reaches the position required, the servomechanism will then be at a new 'null' condition.

Speed control servomechanism

A speed control servomechanism is one in which error signals are produced as a result of a difference between voltages corresponding to input and output speeds, such signals being used to control the speed of the servomotor and load. Referring to fig. 2.2, it will be noted that the system differs from that used

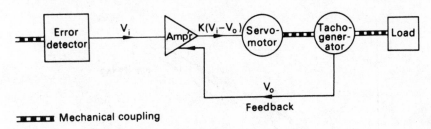

Mechanical coupling

Fig. 2.2 Speed control servomechanism

for position control in that the servomotor also drives a device known as a tachogenerator. When it is required to operate the load, the servomotor is driven by an amplified input error voltage, V_i, and the motor accelerates the load towards the required speed. At the same time, the motor drives the tachogenerator which produces an output voltage, V_o, in proportion to its speed of rotation. The output voltage is fed back to the amplifier thereby reducing the input error voltage and so producing a real output from the amplifier equal to $K(V_i-V_o)$. The servomotor in this class of servomechanism (sometimes called a velodyne) is therefore controlled by differences in voltages, and will speed up or slow down until the difference is zero.

Response of servomechanism

The response to servomechanism is the pattern of behaviour of the load when a change is made to the input condition, the most important factors being the form which the input change takes and the various restraints, friction, etc., which act on the output. There are two types of input change to be considered and these are referred to as step input, and ramp input, the names being derived from the shape of the curves of input against time as shown in fig. 2.3.

A *step input* is one whereby the input (e.lg. the controlling shaft of the system shown in fig. 2.1) is suddenly changed to a new angular position θ_i, from a

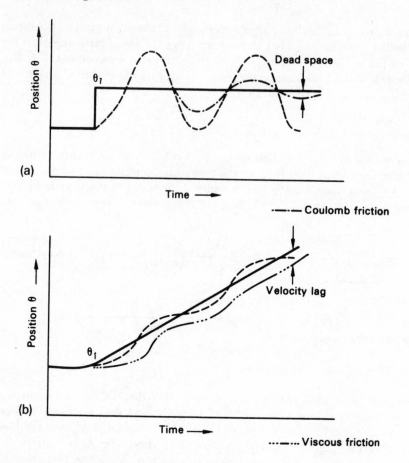

Fig. 2.3 Response of servomechanisms   *a* Step input   *b* Ramp input

null position. Because of the inertia of the load an angular change at the servomechanism output will not be able to follow exactly that at the input, with the result that a large error signal is produced initially. This causes the load to be accelerated to its required position, and thereby reduces the error to zero. At this point however, and although the acceleration is zero, the load has reached a steady rate of change, and so it overshoots resulting in an increase of error in the opposite sense to decelerate the load until it comes to rest in the opposite direction. By this time the error signal is equal to the original error signal but of opposite polarity, and so the load is accelerated back towards the required position and produces another overshoot. If the frictional losses in the system are negligible, a continuous oscillation is produced.

A *ramp input* is one whereby the input is suddenly moved at a constant speed. In the early stages of the input, and while the error signal is small, the load accelerates slowly and lags behind the input. The signal increases as the lag increases, thereby building up the acceleration. Eventually the input and load speeds are equal, but since a substantial position error exists, the load continues to accelerate, the acceleration is reduced, and the load attains a constant speed at zero position error with no error signal. Thus, as in the case of a step input, a continuous oscillation is produced.

Damping

Oscillatory or transient responses of a servomechanism from whatever cause are obviously undesirable, and so it is necessary to provide some form of damping by which a load can be brought to rest in its required position with the minimum of overshoot.

Varying degrees of damping can be applied (see fig. 2.4). Using only inherent friction *light damping* is achieved. If there is too much extra viscous

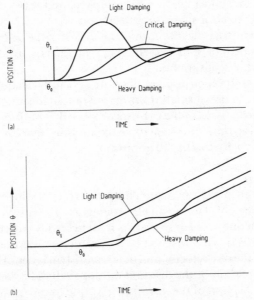

Fig. 2.4 Degrees of damping: (a) step input (b) ramp input

friction, the system is *heavily damped* and a very sluggish response is produced. The degree of damping which just prevents any overshoot is known as *critical damping*. Damping which allows one small overshoot and gives the smallest settling time is known as *optimum damping*.

Servomechanisms possess various inherent factors which, together, have the general effect of reducing the amplitude of each successive oscillation; such factors include static friction, kinetic friction, eddy current, lubricant viscosity, etc., and while contributing to damping requirements they do have certain detrimental effects, e.g. power is wasted, and errors can be introduced with the servomechanism operating in the steady state. The effects are partly due to a small force of constant magnitude known as *coulomb friction*, and to *viscous friction* which increases with speed.

Coulomb friction relates particularly to the response to a step input and this is illustrated in *a* of fig. 2.3. It has the tendency to downgrade the sensitivity of a servomechanism, since the torque required to overcome the friction must be generated before any movement of the load takes place. To provide this torque the load error must reach some finite size and any errors less than this will not be corrected. The load comes to rest somewhere within a band of error (the dead space), the width of the band depending on the amount of coulomb friction. The friction is, however, very small in most current types of servomechanism so that its effect can be neglected.

Viscous friction (fig. 2.3 *b*) produces a similar dead space effect, but as the friction varies with speed, the effect is associated with a ramp input. In the steady state the load moves with constant speed, and is therefore resisted by viscous friction. An error signal must be produced to overcome this and so a steady state error must exist, the error being known as *velocity lag*. Coulomb friction also contributes to velocity lag, but is is considered small in comparison with viscous friction.

The transient responses just described are generally adequate in applications requiring the use of small position servomechanisms, but when large loads are involved it is desirable to further reduce the number of oscillations, and the response time. Two methods commonly employed are *viscous damping* and *velocity feedback* damping.

Viscous damping

A device commonly used for viscous damping is one in which a disc is free to rotate between the pole faces of an electromagnet. The disc is coupled to the servomechanism output shaft so that, as it rotates, eddy currents are induced in the disc. The eddy currents are of a magnitude proportional to the field strength, and to the disc velocity, and they establish magnetic fields and forces which oppose rotation of the disc and output shaft. The damping effect is produced by absorption of the servomotor torque in the desired proportion.

The response achieved by additional viscous damping can be made adequate for the particular servomechanism function, but since it absorbs servomotor torque it has the disadvantage of wasting energy; furthermore, where a ramp input is concerned the velocity lag is increased.

Velocity feedback damping

Velocity feedback damping overcomes the wasting of energy by feeding back a voltage from a tachogenerator (see fig. 2.2), the voltage being proportional to the load velocity and in opposition to the error signal applied to the amplifier unit of the servomechanism. Thus, the net input to the amplifier is the error signal voltage (i.e. the difference between input and output voltages) minus the velocity feedback voltage and since the overall effect will result in a lowering of the amplifier output, the servomotor torque will also be lowered so that less energy will be expended. Velocity feedback also increases velocity lag in response to ramp input, but for a different physical reason. In this case, the steady state velocity of the load imposes a signal at the amplifier input which must be cancelled in some way if the steady state velocity is to be maintained. The cancellation can only be made by an equal error signal, which means that an error must exist. By suitably adjusting the feedback voltage it can be arranged that the error signal is reduced to zero and then reversed before the load reaches its new position. In this manner the momentum of the load acting against the reversed servomotor torque will bring the load to rest just as it reaches its new position, thereby reducing overshoots and subsequent instability. The principle of this form of damping is shown in fig. 2.5.

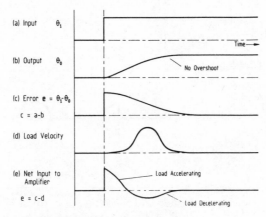

Fig. 2.5 Principle of velocity feedback damping

Error-rate damping
As already noted, in velocity control servomechanisms (ramp input) employing velocity feedback damping the transient response is improved but velocity lag is increased. This can be tolerated in certain applications, but where requirements for rotating a load at constant speed are to be met the lag must be reduced to zero in the steady condition. This may be achieved by adopting either of two methods which in each case produce the same result, i.e. cancelling the velocity feedback signal when the input and output velocities are equal. One method (see fig. 2.6 (a)) is to fit a second tachogenerator at the input so that it feeds a signal forward into the amplifier, thus making the net input an error voltage plus a voltage proportional to input shaft speed minus the velocity feedback voltage.

79

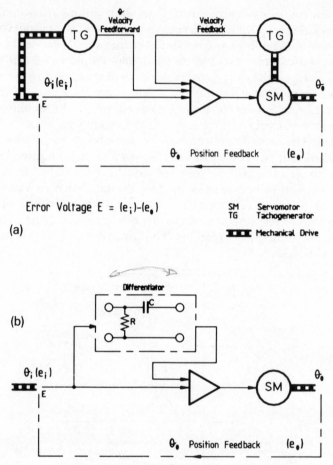

Fig. 2.6 Error-rate damping: (a) feedforward of input velocity (b) feedforward of error rate

During a ramp input a steady state is eventually reached in which the tachogenerators apply equal and opposite voltages to the amplifier; the net input is therefore zero. If any velocity lag exists at this stage, the position error signal will establish torques at the servomotor to reduce it.

The foregoing method, although eliminating velocity lag, presents the difficulty of ensuring that the voltage outputs of both tachogenerators will remain constant over a long period of time. Since the velocity of an error is equal to its rate of change, with respect to time, i.e. the differential of the error, then by combining a differential signal with the actual error signal at the amplifier input, the same final result will be obtained as when using two tachogenerators. In the second method, therefore, the tachogenerators are dispensed with and are replaced by a resistance-capacitance differentiating network as shown in fig. 2.6 (b).

Transient velocity damping

This type of damping also known as acceleration feedback, utilises a differentiating network connected in the velocity feedback signal line as shown in fig. 2.7. Thus, only the derivative of the load velocity reaches the amplifier, with the result that damping is effective only during the transient response period, i.e. when a rate of change of load velocity exists. Once the steady state is reached there is no further rate of change, the derivative is zero, and the feedback ceases thereby reducing velocity lag.

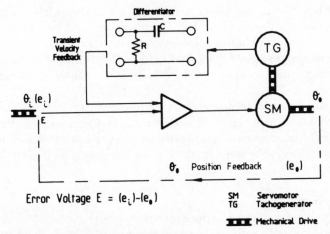

Fig. 2.7 Transient velocity damping

Phase advance damping

A suitable transient response in a remote position control system and a good steady state response in a velocity system can be obtained by inserting a resistance-capacitance network in the input to the amplifier, as shown in fig. 2.8. With this arrangement, the output signal is θ degrees in advance of the input signal.

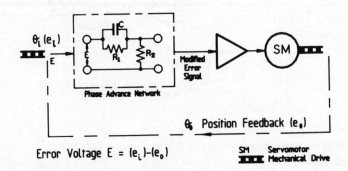

Fig. 2.8 Phase advance damping

When a position control system is subjected to a step function input, the error rises immediately to its maximum value because of the inertia of the system. Initially, therefore, since the capacitor 'C' cannot charge instantaneously (due to its time constant) the full error voltage is developed across R_2 and is applied to the amplifier, causing the motor to accelerate rapidly. As the capacitor is charged the voltage across it rises and the input to the amplifier falls, thus reducing the motor torque. As the load reaches the required position, the error voltage falls. However, if the values of the components of the phase advance network have been carefully chosen, the charge acquired by the capacitor during the initial period will cause the voltage across it to exceed the error voltage. Thus the voltage applied to the amplifier is now negative despite the slightly positive error voltage. This means that a retarding torque is applied to the load before it reaches its required position; overshooting is therefore prevented and stability during the transient period is improved.

For a ramp function input the phase advance network gives an almost zero error in the steady state, i.e. it virtually eliminates velocity lag. In the steady state there is neither acceleration nor deceleration and zero torque is required. For this condition to be satisfied, the input to the amplifier must be zero, i.e. zero error.

Integral control
The methods so far described reduce velocity lag, but have no effect on lag and 'dead space' caused by inherent friction. A commonly used method of dealing with these residual steady state errors is known as integral control. The arrangement as used in conjunction with feedforward of error rate is shown in fig. 2.9.

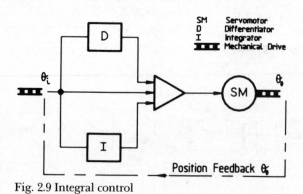

Fig. 2.9 Integral control

The differentiator operates in the same manner as that used for error rate and transient velocity damping, but the conditions are modified by the inclusion of an integrator which feeds the time integral of the error signal into the amplifier. The effect on the transient response is negligible, but as the error settles to its steady state so its integral increases, superimposing on the amplifier a signal which provides additional torque at the load. The load is moved by this torque towards the correct position.

Adjustment of the proportion of the integrator output can be made to ensure, when the error signal is zero, that the subsequent constant integrator output is just sufficient to counter the inherent friction. Thus, velocity lag is zero. For a step input the dead space error signal is integrated until large enough to zero the error, and adjustment of the damping differentiator output ensures stability.

Fundamentals of automatic control

Having briefly studied some of the fundamental operating principles of servomechanisms, we can now see how the closed-loop servo technique can be applied as a means of achieving automatic flight control of an aircraft. Fig. 2.10 is a functional diagram of a closed-loop system which is basic to all classes of automatic flight control systems, and from this we note that there are four principal elements which together are allocated the task of coping with what is generally termed 'inner loop stabilisation'. The individual functions of the elements are as follows:

(i) Sensing of attitude changes of the aircraft about its principal axes by means of stable reference devices; e.g. gyroscopes and/or accelerometers;
(ii) Sensing of attitude changes in terms of error signals and the transmission of such signals;
(iii) Processing of error signals and their conversion into a form suitable for operation of the servomotors forming the output stage;
(iv) Conversion of processed signals into movement of the aircraft flight control surfaces.

The number of control loops, or channels, comprising an automatic control system is dependent on the number of axes about which control is to be effected.

Note: Although certain of the automatic control fundamentals and applications of the above elements are appropriate to both fixed-wing aircraft and helicopter systems, it has none the less been considered convenient for purpose of explanation, to treat them separately. Thus, from this point on and through chapters 3 to 7, descriptions relate to fixed-wing aircraft systems, while helicopter systems and comparable features form the whole of chapter 8.

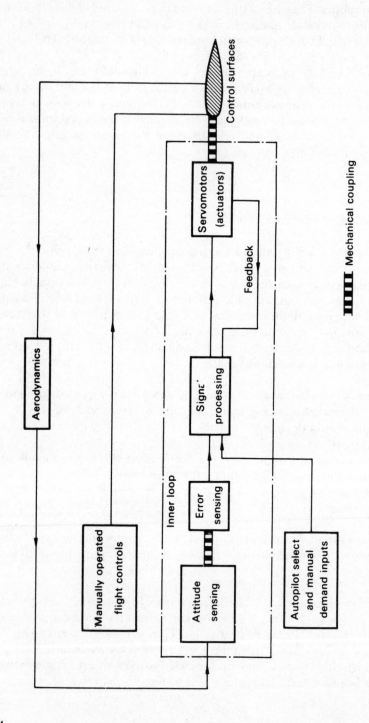

Fig. 2.10 Inner loop stabilisation

Classifications of systems

Based on the number of axes about which control is effected, it is usual to classify systems in the following manner:

Single-axis in which attitude control is normally about the roll axis only; the control surfaces forming part of the one and only control loop are, therefore, the ailerons. Such a control system is the most basic in concept, and it is used in a number of types of small fixed-wing aircraft for lateral stabilisation, or wing-levelling as it is frequently termed. The pilot can inject command signals into the control loop thereby enabling him to turn the aircraft automatically. In some cases, signals from a compass system and from radio navigation equipment are also injected into the loop so that magnetic headings, and tracking capability can be automatically maintained; such operating modes are known as heading-hold and radio-coupling respectively, and form part of the outer loop control described in chapter 6.

Two-axis in which attitude control is, in most cases, about the roll and pitch axes; the control surfaces forming part of the two loops are, therefore, the ailerons and elevators. Manual turn control, heading-hold and radio-coupling facilities are normally standard features in any one design with, in some cases, an additional facility for selecting and holding a specific altitude (see fig. 2.11).

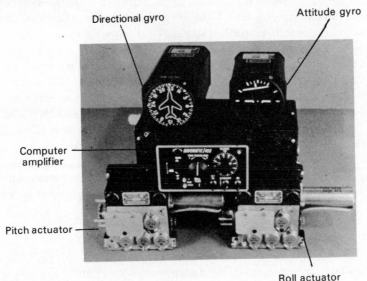

Fig. 2.11 Two-axis automatic control system

Fig. 2.12 illustrates the principal components of another example of a two-axis automatic control system which is integrated with an attitude director

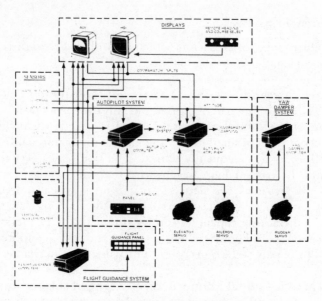

Fig. 2.12 Three-axis automatic control system

indicator (ADI) and horizontal situation indicator (HSI) of a flight director system. Such integration permits the sharing of common basic attitude and navigational data, and servomechansim loops, and by virtue of the indicators' display presentations it enables a flight crew to initiate precise flight guidance commands to the automatic control system. Flight director systems and their integration are described in more detail in chapter 9.

It will also be noted from fig. 2.12 that the rudder control is carried out by means of a yaw damper system. This does not imply that the automatic control system should therefore be classified as a three-axis one and not two as stated earlier. The reason for this is that a yaw damper system is always separate, and can be operated to apply rudder control regardless of whether or not the automatic control system is engaged (see page 214).

Three-axis in which attitude control about all three axes is carried out by specifically related control channels of an automatic flight control system.

Control

In its basic mode of operation, the function of an automatic control system is to hold an aircraft on a desired flight path, by detecting and correcting any departure from that path; in other words, it functions as a stability augmentation system (SAS). When a system is initially engaged via appropriate interlock circuits, clutch mechanisms are operated to provide mechanical coupling between the appropriate servomotors and the aircraft's primary flight control system, and the manually trimmed attitude existing at the moment of engagement is maintained.

Note: Many types of aircraft use hydraulically-powered flight control systems. In such cases, therefore, separate servomotors are not required since during its engagement, an automatic flight control system controls the flow of hydraulic fluid in power control units.

If the attitude of the aircraft changes as a result of, say, an air disturbance or an out-of-trim condition of the aircraft, the attitude sensing elements will detect this change and their associated command signal sensor elements will translate the change into an error signal. The signal is fed to the relevant control channel amplifier in the signal processing element and after amplification it is supplied to the servomotor so that it can apply corrective control. For example, if the error signal is caused by a change about the pitch axis, nose down as shown in fig. 2.13, the signal is processed by the pitch

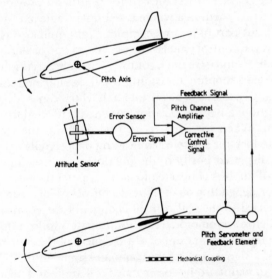

Fig. 2.13 Sensing and correction of an attitude change

control channel and fed to the pitch servomotor which repositions the elevators to correct the attitude change. The servomotor also repositions a feedback or follow-up element (see also pp. 157 and 213) the purpose of which is to reduce an input error signal and thereby limit the control applied. Thus, the feedback element produces a signal equal and opposite to that of the input error, thereby limiting servomotor operation until it stops with the elevators in the angular position required to return the aircraft to the level flight attitude. As the aircraft returns, the error signal decreases and the feedback signal, via the amplifier, now causes the servomotor to reduce the angular position of the elevators towards neutral. A similar sequence takes place when an error signal is caused by a change about either the roll or yaw axes.

In addition to the foregoing role of inner loop stabilisation, an automatic control system must have the capability of assisting the pilot in manoeuvring the aircraft so that its attitude can be changed in order to comply with required in-flight procedures. Such changes would, for example, be a turn on to a new heading, or an altitude change. Any attempt, however, by the pilot to make these changes by applying forces to the control wheel or rudder pedals in the conventional manner would (with the exception of a control wheel steering mode, see page 194) be resisted by the automatic control system since in performing its primary stabilising function it would interpret the changes as disturbances. It is, therefore, necessary to provide a flight control panel through which the pilot can inject command signals into the appropriate control channels and thereby initiate servo-control. The flight control panel may thus be considered as the primary element in the outer control loop (see chapter 6) and the control facilities it provides depend on whether the control system as a whole is a simple single-axis 'wing leveller' or whether it forms part of a more complex flight guidance system. In the basic form, however, control panels have two main control facilities and these are (i) a turn control, and (ii) a pitch control. There are exceptions to this, and they apply to systems adopting the control wheel steering mode (see page 194).

The turn control consists of a control knob which can be displaced to the left or to the right of a neutral position commonly referred to as the 'centre detent' position. When the knob is in this position, the control circuit provides an interlock for pre-selected heading data signals from a compass system. In the displaced position, the interlock circuit is interrupted, and since the control knob is connected to either a potentiometer or a synchro transmitter rotor, depending on the type of control system, a command signal circuit is completed to the roll control channel of the control system and thence to the aileron servomotor. Thus, the aircraft is rolled into a turn at an angle proportional to the amount of displacement of the control knob. The resulting feedback signal opposes the command signal until both signals are equal. In order to maintain the commanded roll angle and turn, the aileron control must be progressively 'taken off'. This is accomplished by the appropriate attitude sensor which, in sensing the roll command as a disturbance, will cause its associated command signal sensor to transmit a signal which is ultimately applied to the aileron servomotor causing it to return the ailerons to their neutral positions. The aircraft, therefore, is flown at the required roll angle until the turn control knob is returned to the detent position. When this is done, the roll command signals and the attitude sensor signals will be in the opposite sense, the ailerons being returned to neutral as the aircraft returns to the level flight attitude. Since the heading data system continuously operates in a follow-up mode, the return of the control knob to detent also permits the signals appropriate to the new heading to be applied to the roll control channel via the re-engaged interlock circuit.

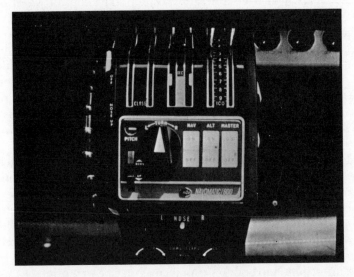

Control panel installed in a small twin-engined aircraft

Fig. 2.14 Control panels

The angle of roll must be limited to angles compatible with the aircraft's control characteristics, and this is effected by passing the command signals through a limiter network. The limiter output is also supplied through a cross-feed circuit to the rudder control channel so that the rudder is displaced by an amount sufficient to provide co-ordination of the turn (see page 120).

The pitch control comprises a control wheel which can be rotated in a vertical plane, and in the same sense required to establish a nose-down or nose-up displacement from a neutral position. The control wheel is also connected to either a potentiometer, or a synchro transmitter rotor, but in this case, the appropriate command signals are applied to the pitch control channel and elevator servomotor of the control system. Thus, the method of applying control, and of returning the elevators to their neutral position, is similar in operation to that applied to turn control. In systems which incorporate altitude-hold and glide path-coupling facilities (see chapter 6) the pitch control also includes an interlock circuit which disconnects these facilities whenever a pitch attitude change is selected, thereby preventing any opposition to the command signals.

In addition to turn and pitch control facilities, a control panel also incorporates a switch for engaging the servomotors to the aircraft's primary flight control system; and examples are shown in fig. 2.14.

In the majority of cases, and as already noted, it is the practice to integrate an automatic control system with a flight director system (FDS) to provide more precise automatic flight guidance. As the operating mode requirements for attitude, radio navigation and certain manometric data, e.g. airspeed and altitude, are common to both systems, then as may be seen from the example shown in fig. 2.15, the relevant control panels can be grouped together. In this

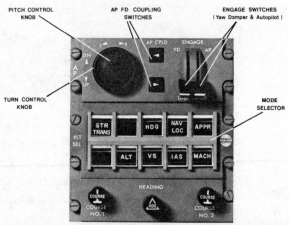

Fig. 2.15 Control and mode selector panels (autopilot/flight director system)

example, the left-hand and right-hand FDS indicators respectively are coupled to the automatic control system by operating the upper and lower coupling switches on the control panel.

There are, of course, many variations in the 'make-up' of panels depending on the operational requirements to be met by specific aircraft/automatic control/FDS combinations. The panel shown in fig. 2.16 is one applied to the

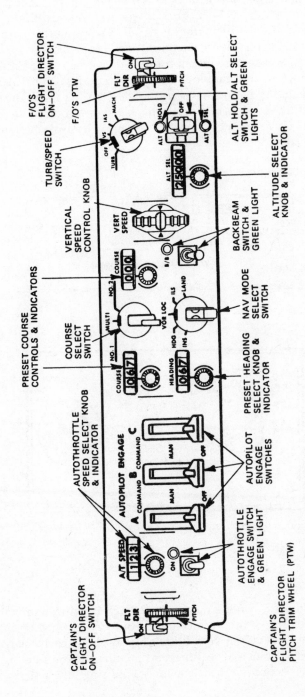

Fig. 2.16 Flight controller

Boeing 747 combination and contains all the switches and logic circuits for mode selection and control of both automatic control system and FDS channels. In addition to this panel, a separately located flight controller panel is provided and contains the pitch control wheel and turn control knob.

In some aircraft, the automatic control and FD systems, although utilising common data sources, are in fact controlled from separate control panels. The Boeing 737 is one example and the configurations of the panels used are illustrated in fig. 2.17. A further point of interest to note is that the automatic control system panel does not include pitch and turn controls, the reason for this being that in this type of aircraft the concept of control wheel steering (see page 194) is adopted.

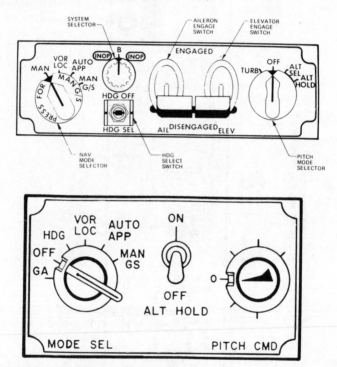

Fig. 2.17 Autopilot/flight director system control

Interlocks

Before an automatic control system can be engaged with an aircraft's flight controls, certain preliminary operating requirements must be fulfilled to ensure that the system is in a condition whereby it may safely take control of the aircraft. The principal requirements are that the connections between system power supplies, the elements comprising the system, and the appropriate signal and engage circuits are electrically complete. It is the practice, therefore, to incorporate within any automatic control system a series of switches and/or relays, known as interlocks, which operate in a specific sequence to ensure satisfactory engagement, and the coupling of input signals from outer loop control elements (see chapter 6).

The number of interlocks incorporated in any one system varies considerably according to the control capability of that system (see page 85) and space does not permit detailed description of the various functions and circuit combinations. However, the fundamentals of interlock operation in general, may be understood from fig. 2.18 which is a much simplified presentation of an engagement circuit based on that adopted in a current type of automatic control system. It will be noted that the contacts of switches and relays, in the main, form a series-connected circuit, i.e. each must be closed in order to complete the power supply circuits to the servomotor clutches via the engage switch.

When the aircraft's power supply is on, it is automatically supplied to the attitude sensing elements and signal processing elements of the control system, so that they are in a stand-by condition when the engage switch is in the 'off' position. Certain of the relays in the engage circuit are also automatically energised when the power supplies are on, namely, the d.c. and a.c. power monitoring relays and the Mach trim coupler relays. The vertical-axis gyroscope relay also energises automatically but only after the gyroscope has run up to operating speed, and the fast erection cycle has been completed. In order to complete the circuit to the engage switch, the turn control knob must be at its centre detent position, the mode selector knob at the 'manual' position, and as in the example shown, the automatic trim cut-out switch must also be on.

When the engage switch is placed in the 'Autopilot' position, direct current is supplied from the mode selector switch to the engage interlock relay, which on being energised completes the power supply circuit to the elevator and aileron servomotor clutches, and to the coil of an engage relay, which then completes a circuit to the engage switch, the circuit being in parallel with the turn control and mode selector switches. At the same time, of course, the rudder servomotor clutch is energised but in this particular example the circuit is completed via another set of contacts within the engage switch. This also applies to a coil circuit within the engage switch, the purpose of the coil being to hold the switch at the 'Autopilot' engaged position.

As noted earlier (page 88), when it is necessary to apply a turn command to the flight control system, the turn control knob is positioned to the left or right of its detent, and this action corresponds to an 'open interlock' condition. However, as reference to fig. 2.18 will show, this will not cause disengagement of the servomotor clutches, because the engage interlock relay coil then remains energised via the d.c. supply circuit in parallel with the turn control switch. The circuit functions in a similar manner whenever the mode

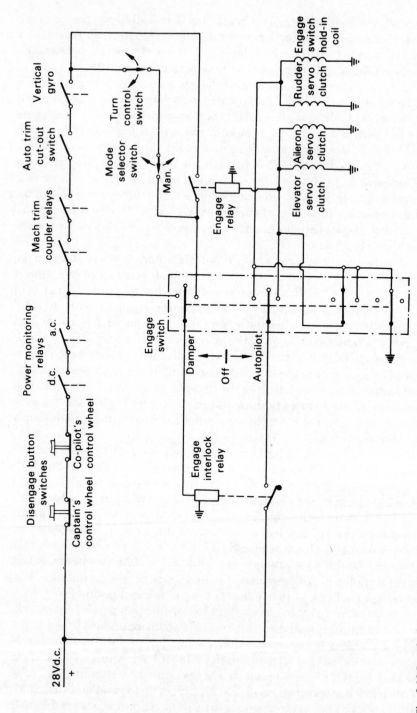

Fig. 2.18 Interlocks

selector switch is positioned out of the 'manual' position in order to apply appropriate outer loop control commands to the flight control system. The circuits relevant to the outer loop elements also incorporate interlocks, and their functions are described in the appropriate sections of this book.

The 'damper' position of the engage switch permits the selection of a yaw damping facility (page 214) which in the example shown in fig. 2.18, is provided by the rudder servomotor. When selected, the circuits through the turn control and mode selector, together with the aileron and elevator servomotor clutch circuits, are isolated from the engage switch, and the d.c. supply for the rudder servomotor clutch, and engage switch hold-in coil, is fed via the closed contacts of the engage interlock relay.

Disengagement of the automatic control system is normally effected by pressing one or other of the button switches on the control wheels. This action de-energises the engage relay and the engage interlock relay, and also interrupts the engage switch hold-in coil circuit thereby releasing the switch to the 'off' position. Similarly, disengagement will take place whenever any one of the other interlock switches or relays is opened.

Trimming and synchronisation

In addition to the pre-engage requirements that automatic control system circuits are electrically complete, it must also be ensured that on engagement the 'take-over' is effected smoothly and without 'snatching' of the aircraft's control system. In other words, the aircraft must be trimmed for the desired flight attitude before engagement, and the automatic control system must be synchronised to maintain that attitude on engagement.

When power is applied to the automatic control system, the attitude sensing elements are in operation so that they will always detect the aircraft's attitude, and therefore, supply any necessary control command signals to the servomotors. At the same time, any signals will be supplied to the appropriate channels of a trim indicating system, or out-of-trim light system (page 223). For example if, before control system engagement, the aircraft is in a climb, or has been trimmed to fly in a nose-up attitude, the pitch attitude sensing element will detect this, and will supply a signal to the elevator servomotor commanding it to rotate in a direction corresponding to 'elevator down', such as would be shown on the trim indicator. Because the signal in this case is a standing one, assuming for the moment that it has no opposition, the servomotor will continue to rotate, and if its clutch was engaged at any one moment the elevators would be snatched from their trimmed position and so cause a nose-down attitude change.

The aerodynamic load acting on the elevators would be felt by the servomotor, thereby helping to retard its rotation. As soon as the sensing element of the pitch attitude detector responds to the attitude change, the opposing signal produced would then eventually stop the motor and rotate it in the opposite direction. Thus, control would be of an oscillatory nature and the aircraft would take up the pitch attitude determined by the attitude detector and not that which it was desired the control system should maintain, i.e. in the example considered a climb or a nose-up trim condition. It is, therefore, necessary to oppose the standing signal and reduce it to zero before engaging the control system, so as to stop the servomotor in a position which is synchronised with the datum attitude detected by the sensing element, such position being indicated by the return of the trim indicator pointer to its central position.

The manner in which synchronising is effected depends on the type of automatic control system and the signal processing circuit arrangements adopted; some representative examples are described in chapter 5.

TEST QUESTIONS

1 What are the main requirements of a closed-loop control system?

2 Describe the operating principle of a typical servomechanism.

3 What is meant by the term 'response' of a servomechanism?

4 What are the main differences between a step input and a ramp input?

5 State the effects which coulomb friction and viscous friction have on servomechanism response, and the methods adopted to minimise them.

6 What is the difference between critical damping and optimum damping?

7 Describe one method adopted for reducing velocity lag.

8 What method is adopted to reduce the steady state error referred to as 'dead space'?

9 In applying the closed-loop servomechanism principle to an automatic flight control system, what main elements are required.?

10 Briefly describe the operation of an automatic flight control system when correcting a disturbance about an aircraft's pitch axis.

11 Which interlock circuits are associated with the turn and pitch controls of a pilot's control panel, and when are they interrupted.?

12 Why is it necessary for interlocks to be incorporated within a control system?

13 What would be the effect if a control system were engaged with 'standing' attitude command signals present, and how is it overcome?

3
Sensing of Attitude Changes

Under automatically controlled flight conditions, the sensing of all changes in aircraft attitude is accomplished by referencing them against some form of stabilised device comprising the primary element of inner loop stabilisation. The device most commonly adopted for this purpose is the gyroscope which, in some applications, is 'backed up' by a pendulous device that senses short-term attitude changes brought about by the effects of accelerations, vertical speed changes, and sideslip.

In the majority of current automatic control systems, gyroscopic and pendulous devices are contained in individual units that form part of a system. However, in aircraft utilising an inertial reference system for purposes of navigation (see page 186), attitude reference data for automatic flight control is derived from sensors on the stabilised inertial platform, and so individual gyroscopic or pendulous units for the automatic control system itself are not required.

The gyroscope and its properties

A gyroscope is basically a mechanical device, the essential element of which is a heavy metal wheel, or rotor, spinning at high angular velocity about a spin axis. In order to provide spinning freedom, the rotor shaft is pivoted in a ring which is, in turn, pivoted in a second ring; the rings are known as the inner and outer gimbal rings respectively. The whole assembly comprises what is known as the gimbal system of a *free or space gyroscope* in that the spin axis, XX, remains fixed in space. The gimbal system is pivot-mounted in a frame as shown in fig. 3.1. The foregoing pivoting arrangements of the gimbal rings permit the gyroscope to have two degrees of freedom: (i) tilting freedom of the inner ring and rotor about the horizontal axis YY_1, and (ii) veering freedom of the complete gimbal system about the vertical axis ZZ_1.

In operation, the gyroscope possesses two important fundamental properties: gyroscopic inertia or rigidity, and precession. Both these properties depend on the principle of conversation of angular momentum, i.e. the angular momentum of a body about a given point remains constant unless

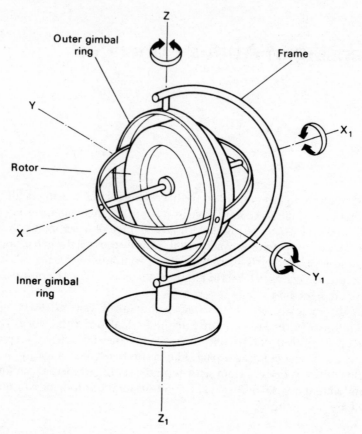

Fig. 3.1 Free gyroscope

some force is applied to change it; the properties form the subjects of the first and second laws of gyrodynamics respectively.

Rigidity

This property resists any force which tends to change the plane of rotation of the rotor of a gyroscope, and is dependent on three factors: (i) the mass of the rotor, (ii) the angular momentum of the rotor, and (iii) the distance at which the mass acts from the axis of rotation, i.e. the radius of gyration.

Precession

Precession is the angular rate of change in the direction of the plane of rotation under the influence of an applied force. The rate of change is proportional to the strength of the applied force, and inversely proportional to the moment of inertia of the rotor and the angular momentum of the rotor.

Fig. 3.2 *a* illustrates a free gyroscope, the rotor of which is assumed to be spinning, with constant angular momentum ω in an anti-clockwise direction. If a force F is applied upward at the inner ring then, as with any body which may be moved about some axis, the force will produce a torque T (equal to the produce of the force and the distance at which it acts from the centre of the rotor) about the axis YY$_1$. Since a gyroscope possesses rigidity,

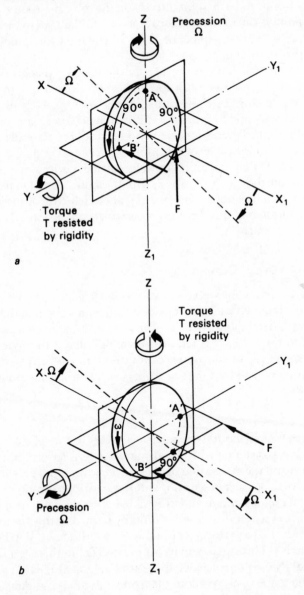

Fig. 3.2 Gyroscopic precession

any tendency for the torque to produce tilting of the inner ring and rotor about axis YY_1, is resisted. The complete gryroscope will, however, precess at a constant angular velocity about the axis ZZ_1, and in a direction at right-angles to the applied force.

A simple rule of thumb method of determining the direction in which a gyroscope will precess is to consider that the applied force acts at right-angles to the plane of spin, and at a point directly on the rotor rim (point 'A' in fig. 3.2 a). If the point is carried around the rotor and through 90° in the direction of rotation (point 'B') that will be the point at which the force and resulting torque are apparently acting.

The direction in which precession of a gyroscope takes place is dependent on the direction of rotation of its rotor, and on the direction of the applied force. This may be noted by comparing diagram b of fig. 3.2, with diagram a. As soon as the force and torque are withdrawn precession ceases, but if they are continually applied precession will continue until the plane of spin of the rotor is aligned with the plane of the applied force.

In connection with gyroscopic attitude sensing devices, it is usual to mutually associate the axes YY_1 and ZZ_1 with the spin axis and to relate them to input and output functions. Thus, the axis about which a torque is applied is termed the input axis and the one about which precession takes place is termed the output axis.

Limitations of a free gyroscope

The free or space gyroscope we have thus far considered would serve no useful purpose as an aircraft attitude sensing device, since an aircraft in flight is still very much an 'earth-bound' vehicle. Thus, all attitude references must be with respect to the earth. It is required therefore, that a free gyroscope be corrected in some way to take into account the effects of such factors as the earth's rotation and the transport of the gyroscope from one point on the earth to another.

Effects of the earth's rotation

Since the earth rotates about its axis 360° every day its rate of rotation is 15° per hour, and in association with gyrodynamics, this is termed the earth rate (ω_e). Depending on the orientation of the spin axis and input axis (as defined earlier) of a free or space gyroscope, it will sense various components of the earth rate as an angular input, and to an observer on the earth the gyroscope would appear to veer, or drift as it is normally termed in this context.

Let us consider first a gyroscope positioned at a latitude λ ('A' in fig. 3.3) so that its spin axis is horizontal, and its input axis (ZZ_1 in this case) is aligned with the local N–S component of the earth's rate at this latitude. To an observer at the gyroscope's position, the gyroscope rotor and gimbal system would appear to drift in a horizontal plane relative to the frame; the drift rate would be equal to 15° cos λ. Drift would also be apparent at position 'B', but since in this case the input axis is aligned with the earth's axis, the drift rate would be equal to the earth's rate, i.e. 15° per hour. When the input axis is

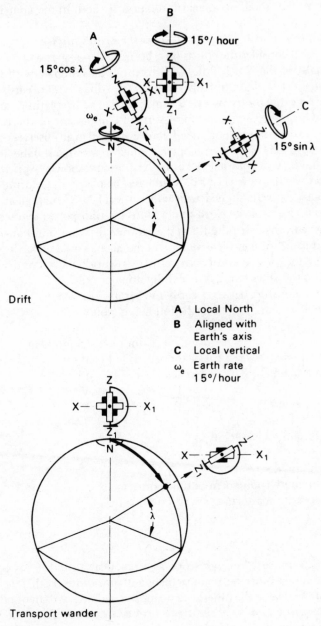

A   Local North
B   Aligned with
    Earth's axis
C   Local vertical
ω_e Earth rate
    15°/hour

Fig. 3.3 Drift and transport wander

101

aligned with the local vertical component of the earth's rate (position 'C'), the apparent drift would be equal to $15° \sin \lambda$. If the input axis were aligned with the local E–W component of the earth's rate, there would be no apparent drift since rotor rotation and earth rotation are both in the same plane.

Effects of transporting a gyroscope over the earth's surface
Let us again consider the effects on a horizontal axis gyroscope which is set up initially at the North Pole, with its input axis aligned with that of the earth then, as we have already observed, it would exhibit earth rate drift. Assume now that the gyroscope is transported to a lower latitude and with its input axis aligned with the local vertical component of the earth's rate. During the time of transport, it will have appeared to an observer on the earth that the spin axis of the gyroscope has tilted in a vertical plane, until at the new latitude λ it appears to be in the position shown. Apparent tilt, or transport wander as it is called, would also be observed if, during transport, the input axis were aligned with either a local N–S component or a local E–W component of the earth's rate. Since the transported gyroscope is also rotating with the earth the tilt and earth rate drift are simultaneous effects which, during one complete rotation of the earth, would make the gyroscope appear to trace out a conical path. A free gyroscope having a vertical spin axis would, on the other hand, only exhibit apparent tilt.

The relationship between earth rate, transport wander and input axis alignment are summarised in the following table.

	Input axis alignment		
	Local north	Local east	Local vertical
Earth rate	$\omega_e \cos \lambda$	nil	$\omega_e \sin \lambda$
Transport wander	$\dfrac{U}{R}$	$\dfrac{V}{R}$	$\dfrac{U}{R} \tan \lambda$

ω_e = earth's angular velocity
λ = latitude
R = earth's radius
V = north–south component of transport velocity
U = east–west component of transport velocity

Earth or 'tied' gyroscope

In order to utilise a free gyroscope as a practical attitude sensing element, compensations must be made which will minimise earth rate drift and transport wander to the fullest extent and, by so doing, will maintain the axis in the required mutual positions relative to the earth. Thus, the gyroscope must be converted into what is commonly termed an earth or 'tied' gyroscope.

Various compensation methods are adopted for this purpose, and their application is governed by sensing element design. Fundamentally however, they are based on gravity sensing and the utilisation of the property of precession.

Gimbal lock and tumbling

Gimbal lock is a phenomenon which can occur when the rotor spin axis of a two-degrees-of-freedom gyroscope, coincides with the outer gimbal ring axis, i.e. the inner ring has turned through 90°. Under such conditions the gyroscope no longer has two-degrees of freedom and, if it is turned, a force will be applied to the inner gimbal ring to precess the outer gimbal ring into a continuous spin. Once spinning has begun the gimbal rings remain locked regardless of the attitude assumed by the gyroscope thereafter. To prevent gimbal lock, mechanical stops are incorporated, e.g. in a vertical axis gyroscope freedom about the pitch axis is normally restricted to ±85° of motion.

The use of stops presents another problem. When they contact the outer ring it precesses through 180° about its axis, such motion being known as 'tumbling'. However, it is very seldom that the instrument pitch limits are exceeded under normal operating conditions.

Nutation

A two-degrees-of-freedom gyroscope is also susceptible to a phenomenon known as nutation, which is simply a wobbling of the rotor spin axis. It is, in effect, a self-sustaining oscillation which physically represents a transfer of energy from one degree of freedom and back again. In contrast to precessional motion, nutation needs no external torque to sustain it. It is minimised by having as large a rotor angular momentum as possible in conjunction with gimbal rings having low moments of inertia.

Gimballing errors

These errors occur when the angular motions of gimbal rings do not correspond to the actual motion about their reference axes. For example, when a horizontal axis gyroscope (as used for directional references) is tilted on inter-cardinal headings and then turned, the azimuth indication will be in error.

Attitude references established by gyroscopes

Gyroscopes establish reference data against which changes in an aircraft's pitch, roll, and yaw (or direction) attitudes may be sensed and for this purpose two types of earth gyroscope are adopted: the displacement gyroscope and the rate gyroscope.

Displacement gyroscope

A displacement gyroscope is one which has two degrees of freedom, and can be used for detecting angular displacements about the fixed datum established by the property of rigidity. For the establishement of a directional reference, a gyroscope having its spin axis horizontal is employed (fig. 3.4 a).

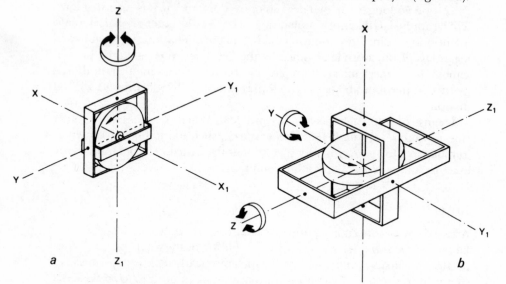

Fig. 3.4 Attitude references
a **Directional reference about axis ZZ_1**
b **Pitch attitude reference about axis YY_1. Roll attitude reference about ZZ_1**

A displacement gyroscope is also used for establishing pitch and roll attitude references, but as will be noted from diagram b the gyroscope spin axis is, in this case, vertical. The operating details of some typical attitude sensing devices employing displacement gyroscopes are given on pags 105 to 107.

Rate gyroscope

Unlike a displacement gyroscope, a rate gyroscope (fig. 3.5) is constrained to only one degree of freedom, and it detects the angular rate at which displacements about a selected input axis takes place. It utilises the property of precession for this purpose, the precession occurring in proportion to the rate at which displacements occur, equilibrium being established between precession and some form of controlled restraint (e.g. a spring). The operating principle of this type of gyroscope is described on page 110.

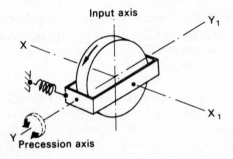

Fig. 3.5 Rate gyroscope

Displacement type sensing elements

The most common applications of horizontal-axis and vertical-axis displacement gyroscopes, relate to the standard flight instruments known as the directional gyro and the gyro horizon respectively. Since both these instruments are, in fact, adapted for use as directional, pitch, and roll attitude sensors in some basic automatic flight control systems (see fig. 2.11 for example), they also serve as a useful introduction to the operating principles employed in the independent gyroscopic sensing units associated with the more sophisticated flight control and flight director systems.

Directional gyro

This instrument provides a stabilised directional reference for maintaining a desired heading, and for turning on to a new heading. The outer gimbal ring of the gyroscope is pivoted about its vertial axis in the instrument case and has a circular card, graduated in degrees, secured to it. The card is referenced against a fixed lubber line, and is visible through a rectangular opening in the front of the instrument case. In some types of directional gyro the graduated card is in the form of a flat disc and geared to the outer gimbal ring so that it rotates in a vertical plane. With the instrument in operation, gyroscopic rigidity stabilises the gyroscope and card, and a certain heading is referenced against the lubber line. If the aircraft heading changes, the instrument case and lubber line turn with the aircraft about the gyroscope thus giving an indication of the number of degrees through which the aircraft turns. Since a directional gyro is non-magnetic, and is also subject to a long-term wander, its heading indications must be set to correspond with those of the magnetic compass. This is achieved by a setting knob at the front of the instrument. When the knob is pushed in, it engages a locking, or caging, mechanism with the gyroscope gimbal system which can then be rotated to the desired heading by turning the setting knob.

From this outline of how stabilised heading indications are obtained, it

105

will be apparent that by coupling an electrical pick-off element to the gimbal system of a directional gyro, directional sensing signals can also be obtained for the purpose of automatically maintaining desired headings, and turning an aircraft on to new headings. Details of how this is achieved will be given in chapter 6.

The rotors of the gyroscopes used in basic types of direction indicators are pneumatically operated either by connecting them to the vacuum side of an engine driven vacuum pump, or to the pressure side of such a pump. In each case air passes through a jet system in the gimbal rings and spins the rotor by impinging on 'buckets' cut in the periphery of the rotor. In directional gyro units applied to heading reference systems, e.g. remote-indicating compasses and flight directors, the rotors operate on the electrical induction motor principle.

Gyro horizon

The gyro horizon provides visual indications of any change of pitch and roll attitudes by the relative positions of two elements; one symbolising the aircraft itself, and the other in the form of a bar stabilised by a vertical-axis gyroscope and symbolising the natural horizon. The spin axis of the gyroscope is maintained in the vertical position by a gravity sensing device. Supplementary indications of roll are presented by the position of a pointer, also gyro stabilised, and a fixed roll angle scale. The gimbal system is arranged so that the inner gimbal ring forms the rotor casing and is pivoted parallel to the aircraft's lateral axis YY_1; and the outer gimbal ring is pivoted parallel to the aircraft's fore-and-aft axis ZZ_1. The outer gimbal ring pivots are located at the front and rear ends of the instrument case. The element symbolising the aircraft may be either rigidly fixed to the case or externally adjusted up and down for pitch trim setting.

In operation, the gimbal system is stabilised so that in level flight the three axes are mutually at right angles. When there is a change in the aircraft's attitude (it goes into a climb, say) the instrument case and outer gimbal ring will turn about the axis YY_1 of the stabilised inner gimbal ring. The horizon bar is pivoted at the side, and to the rear of the outer gimbal ring, and engages an actuating pin fixed to the inner gimbal ring, thus forming a magnifying lever system. In a climb attitude the bar pivot carries the rear end of the bar upwards causing it to pivot about the stabilised actuating pin. The front end of the bar and the pointer therefore move downwards through a greater angle than that of the outer gimbal ring and, since movement is relative to the symbolic aircraft element, a climbing attitude is indicated.

Changes in the lateral attitude of the aircraft, i.e. a roll to the left or right, turn the instrument case about the axis ZZ_1 and the whole stabilised gimbal system. Hence, lateral attitude changes are indicated by movement of the symbolic aircraft element relative to the horizon bar, and also by relative movement between the roll angle scale and the pointer. A background plate which symbolises the sky is fixed to the front end of the outer gimbal ring and carries a roll pointer which registers against the roll angle scale.

In applying this instrument to the automatic control of an aircraft suitable pick-off elements are mounted on the pitch and roll axes of the gimbal system (see chapter 4).

Gyro horizons may also be operated pneumatically, and in a manner similar to that adopted for directional gyros. However, in most applications the gyroscope is a 3-phase squirrel-cage induction motor which operates from a 115 volt, a.c. 400 Hz supply.

Electrically-operated gyroscopes

One of the essential requirements for any gryroscope is to have the mass of the rotor concentrated as near to the periphery as possible, thus ensuring maximum inertia. This presents no difficulty where solid metal rotors (as employed in air-driven instruments) are concerned, but when adapting electric motors as gyroscopes some rearrangement of their basic design is necessary in order to achieve the desired effect. An induction motor normally has its rotor revolving inside the stator, but to make one small enough for use as a gyroscopic sensing element, would result in too small a rotor mass and inertia. However, by designing the rotor and its bearings so that a section of it can also rotate on the outside of the stator, then for the same required size of motor the mass of the rotor is concentrated further from the centre, so that the radius of gyration, and the inertia, are increased. This is the method adopted not only in gyro horizons, but in all instruments and systems employing electrically-operated gyroscopes.

Vertical-axis gyroscope units

In more advanced types of flight control systems, displacements in pitch and roll are also referenced against a vertical-axis gyroscope, but instead of forming part of a panel-mounted instrument as hitherto described, the gyroscope is incorporated in a unit which is located at some remote point within the aircraft. Thus, the unit can serve as a central transmitting source of attitude information not only for a flight control system but also for attitude indicators which form part of an FD system (see chapter 9). An example of a vertical-axis gyroscope unit is shown in fig. 3.6.

The sensing of attitude changes about the pitch and roll axes of the unit is carried out by control synchro transmitters mounted on the appropriate axes of the gimbal system (see fig. 3.7). The stator of the roll synchro is secured to the unit frame, while its rotor is secured to the outer gimbal ring. The pitch synchro has its stator secured to the outer gimbal ring and surrounds its rotor which is secured to the inner gimbal ring.

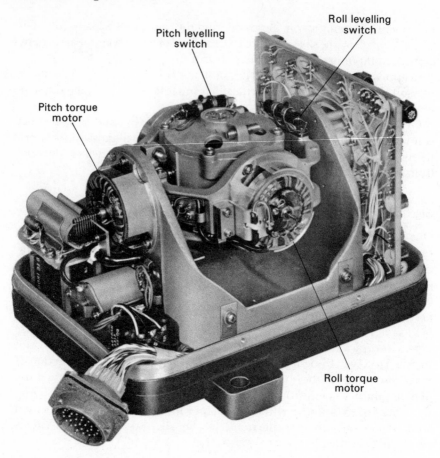

Pitch levelling switch

Roll levelling switch

Pitch torque motor

Roll torque motor

Fig. 3.6 vertical–axis gyroscope unit

Each rotor is supplied with an excitation voltage of 115 volts a.c., and the three-phase stators are connected to their respective channels of the FDS and automatic flight control system computers. When the gyro is operating and its axis is vertically stabilised, both synchros are in what is termed a 'null' position and so there are no output signals from their stators. If a displacement of the aircraft occurs about the roll axis, the unit frame and roll synchro will also be displaced about its stabilised rotor and this induces an error voltage signal in the stator. In the FDS roll channel this signal is supplied to the stator of a synchro receiving element (called a control transformer) contained in the attitude director indicator. An error voltage of a phase and magnitude appropriate to the direction and degree of roll synchro displacement is induced in the control transformer rotor. After amplification, the error voltage is fed to a motor which is mechanically coupled to the

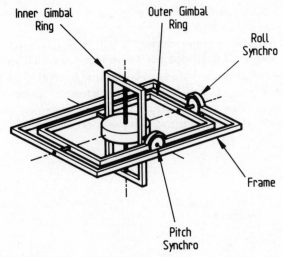

Fig. 3.7 Pitch and roll attitude sensing

control transformer and to the attitude-indicating element of the indicator. Thus, the rotor is driven to a position at which no further error voltage is induced, and the indicating element is positioned to display the direction of the aircraft's displacement about the roll axis. In the roll channel of the automatic control system, the error voltage signal induced in the roll synchro stator is supplied directly to the roll channel amplifier which then provides the servo control signal to oppose the displacement of the aircraft.

In the case of a displacement about the pitch axis, the unit frame carries the outer gimbal ring and pitch synchro about the stabilised inner gimbal ring to induce an error voltage signal for processing in the FDS and automatic control pitch channels in a manner similar to that just described.

A more detailed description of the operation of the type of synchro used in vertical-axis gyroscope units is given on page 134.

Rate type sensing elements

In serveral types of automatic flight control systems, the sensing of aircraft attitude changes is accomplished by rate gyroscopes which, as noted earlier are single-degree-of-freedom gyroscopes utilising the property of precession. The resultant movements of the rotor, and gimbal ring, position the moving element of an electrical signal pick-off element. Rotors are electrically driven, and the power supply required depends on the type of aircraft and the automatic flight control system applied to it. For example, in certain types of small aircraft employing a single-axis control system (see chapter 2), the power supply required is 28 volts direct current, while for larger aircraft employing more sophisticated systems, the gyroscopes operate from a 115 volt alternating current supply.

As an attitude change sensing device, a rate gyroscope has several advantages over a displacement gyroscope, the principal of which are (i) more rapid detection of small attitude changes since the time interval of the angular veloctiy is not involved, and (ii) smoother corrective action without 'overshoot' tendencies, because control signals are provided at a rate proportional to that at which attitude changes occur (called 'rate/rate control').

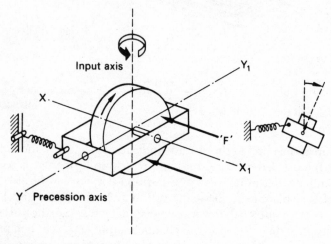

Fig. 3.8 Rate gyroscope principle

Rate gyroscope principle

It will be noted from fig. 3.8 that freedom of movement about the output or precession axis of a rate gyroscope is restrained, in this case, by a spring connected between the gimbal ring and casing. The spring, which may be of the linear or torsional type, has a characteristic which is calibrated to balance the precission produced at the appropriate rates of torque input. An alternative method of restraint adopted in some designs is one employing a force-balance, or force-feedback system, (see also page 114) whereby a torque is generated electrically to balance the precession, and by means of a torque motor the gimbal ring is restrained at a null position. The current flowing through the torque motor thus becomes a measure of the rate of torque input.

When a rate gyroscope is in its normal operating position the rotor spin axis will always be horizontal due to the spring restraint, and the moving element of the signal pick-off will be at the zero datum. With the rotor spinning, its rigidity will further ensure that the zero datum is maintained. When, however, the gryroscope is turned about a vertical input axis, the rigidity of the gyroscope resists the turning, but it tilts in one direction or the other about the precession axis YY_1 depending on the direction of the turn; the effects of a turn to the left are indicated in fig. 3.8. Precession continues until it is balanced by the restraining force created by the stretching of the spring. Since the precession of a rate gyroscope is equal to the product of angular momentum of the rotor, and the rate of turn, the spring force is then a measure of the rate of turn.

In practical applications, the gimbal ring deflection is generally limited by stops to not more that 2°, the reason for this being to reduce the cross-coupling error due to the rate-of-turn component not being at right angles to the spin axis during gimbal ring deflection.

It should be noted that a rate gyroscope requires no erecting device or correction for random drift, for the simple reason that it is always centred at its zero datum position by the appropriate system of spring restraint. Since precession plays such an important part in the operation of rate gyroscopes, it is essential for the rotor speed to be maintained constant. This is ensured by providing direct current powered gyroscopes with a centrifugal governing device, while in the case of gyroscopes powered by alternating current the power supply frequency is maintained constant.

Typical rate sensors

In the case of alternating current-operated rate sensors it is usual for the gyroscope to be in the form of a hysteresis motor. As is normally the case when adopting an electric motor as a gyroscope, the rotating element is designed so that the greatest possible radius of gyration and moment of inertia, compatible with the speed and rate measurements required, and the overall physical dimensions of the gyroscope, are obtained. The principle is illustrated in fig. 3.9. The rotor undergoes magnetisation and demagnetisation as the strength of the stator field changes; if the flux density B is plotted against the magnetising force H the result is the familiar hysteresis loop from which the motor derives its name (fig. 3.9 *a*). The area within the loop can be shown to be numerically equal to the energy consumed in the magnetisation/ demagnetisation cycle, and it is this energy that drives the rotor. Let us assume that at one particular instant the stator current induces magnetism of north polarity in stator pole 'A' (diagram *b*), magnetism will also be induced in the rotor, and a point 'x' immediately opposite pole 'A' will be of south polarity. During the next half-cycle of the magnetising current, the polarity of pole piece 'A' will change from north to south, and the adjacent pole piece 'B' will take on a north seeking polarity. The polarity at point 'x' on the rotor will at this stage be diminishing because of the polarity change taking place in pole piece 'A'. However, due to hysteresis effect, point 'x' will still be of south polarity while polarity changes are taking place in both pole pieces 'A' and 'B'. It will be seen therefore, (diagram *c*) that pole piece 'B' will now attract point 'x' causing the rotor to move in the same direction as the stator field. At

111

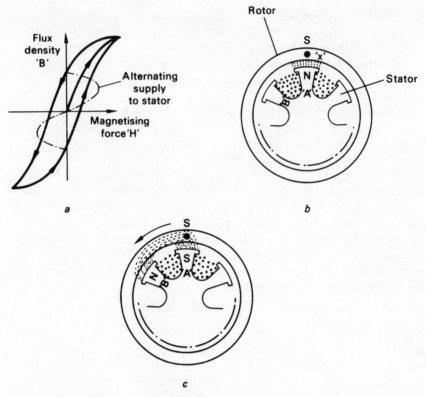

Fig. 3.9 Principle of hysteresis motor

the normal running speed, the rotation of the rotor and the stator field are in synchronism.

The emphasis on miniaturisation of airborne electronic equipment, and associated electro-mechanical components, has also significantly affected the design of rate gyroscopes, to the extent that miniature, sub-miniature and micro-miniature units are widely adopted to meet the attitude sensing requirements for specific types of control systems. An example of a miniature unit is shown in fig. 3.10. The gyroscope is also formed by a three-phase hysteresis motor operating at a speed of 24 000 rev/min from a 26 volt, 400 Hz a.c. supply. The rotor in this example is supported in precision type ball bearings but in some units the rotor runs in bearings formed by an inert gas, while in others the bearings are of the self-generating aerodynamic type. The gimbal ring is supported in ball bearings and is restrained by means of a torsion bar spring, the stiffness of which provides for a maximum rate of 60°/second. An electrical signal pick-off element is incorporated in the unit, and is also of the inductive variable magnetic coupling type, and consists of a rotor and a fixed stator.

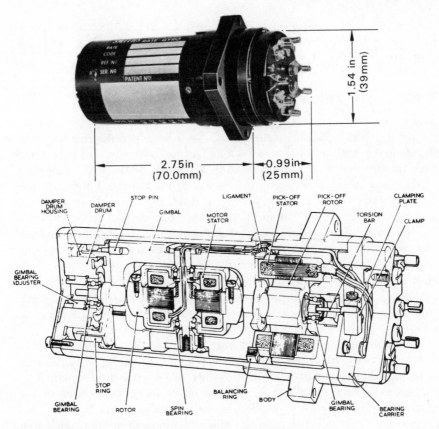

Fig. 3.10 Miniature rate gyroscope

An interesting example of a direct current operated rate gyroscope is that adopted in one of the 'Century' series of control systems developed by Edo-Aire Mitchell (see also page 117). The gyroscope serves as both a roll and yaw sensing element, and is unique in that the motor employs a photo-electric means of commutation as opposed to conventional brushes and commutator. The gyroscope rotor is magnetically polarised and housed within a coil assembly. One half of the rotor's peripheral surface is of reflective brass, while the other half is chemically etched to be non-reflective. When the power is off, the non-reflective half of the rotor is exposed to an incandescent light source, and a photo-transistor, both of which are directed towards the rotor. When power is applied to the rotor coil, the current flow through it turns the rotor, and when the reflective half of its surface is exposed to the light source, the current flow is isolated. Momentum of the rotor, however, carries it round until the non-reflective half is again exposed. At this point, the cycle will repeat and the rotor continues to rotate. As the rotor gains speed, a feedback voltage is developed across the rotor coil, and after mixing with a reference

113

voltage, it is applied to two switching transistors the functions of which are to regulate the rotor speed by switching the current on and off at a rate proportional to rotor rotation.

Damping of rate gyroscopes

In the design of rate gyroscopes it is also necessary to incorporate a system of damping restraint. Such a system should be as small as possible to ensure that the gyroscope will instantly respond to rate-of-turn changes, and at the same time, provide sufficient restraint to damp out any oscillations. The damping methods adopted vary between manufacturers, but in general, they fall into three principal classes (i) eddy current, (ii) fluid, and (iii) air dashpot.

Typically, the eddy current damping method utilises a copper disc mechanically linked to the gyroscope and positioned between the pole faces of a permanent magnet. When the gyroscope is deflected to one or other side of its zero datum position, the disc is rotated past the magnet pole faces. Eddy currents are thereby induced in the disc, the resultant effect of which is to oppose the motion of the disc and so provide a damped or 'dead beat' movement of the gyroscope. The effects of inertia on the copper disc are reduced by some form of friction loading between it and its shaft.

Fluid damping systems are used in certain types of miniature and sub-miniature rate gyroscopes, e.g. the one illustrated in fig. 3.10, and in operation, are dependent on the viscous shear of a silicone fluid contained in the space between a damper drum and its housing. Deflections of the gyroscope produce relative motion between the drum and housing, but owing to its viscosity the oil produces a force to oppose the motion. Although silicone fluid has a relatively low variation of viscosity with temperature, it is usually necessary to compensate for changes to ensure that the damping ratio is kept within acceptable limits over the operating temperature range of the gyroscope.

The air dashpot method of damping is based on that which has been in use for many years in turn-and-bank indicators. Pistons are linked to the gimbal ring, and whenever it is deflected they move in and out of their respective cylinders fixed to the gyroscope frame or casing. As the pistons move, air pases through small bleed holes in the cylinders, the size of which can be pre-adjusted to provide the required degree of damping.

Force-balance rate gyroscope

A force-balance, or force feedback, rate gyroscope operates on the same fundamental principle as its conventional counterpart, but instead of utilising spring balancing force as a measure of the rate of turn or torque input, balancing is achieved electrically by a torque motor acting on the gimbal ring. The torque motor is connected to the pick-off sensing element

114

via a high-gain amplifier; thus, when the gyroscope is turned about its input axis, precession of the gimbal ring is detected by the pick-off element, and a signal is transmitted to the amplifier. The amplifier signal is then transmitted to the torque motor in which an electromagnetic field is generated to produce a torque equal and opposite to the input torque so that the gimbal ring is restrained at its null position. In other words, the pick-off element serves only as a null detector, and the torque motor system functions as a stiff electrical spring. Since the torque is precisely related to the current flowing through the torque motor, the current may be used directly as a rate signal output to the appropriate control channel. Damping is achieved by incorporating suitable shaping networks in the feedback amplifier, thereby eliminating the need for any of the methods adopted for conventional spring-restrained gyroscopes.

In some types of force-balance gyroscope, the pick-off element is of the optical type consisting of a light emitting diode, two photo-electric cells, and a vane attached to the gimbal ring. The diode generates infra-red radiation which is sensed by the two cells. The vane is positioned between the diode and

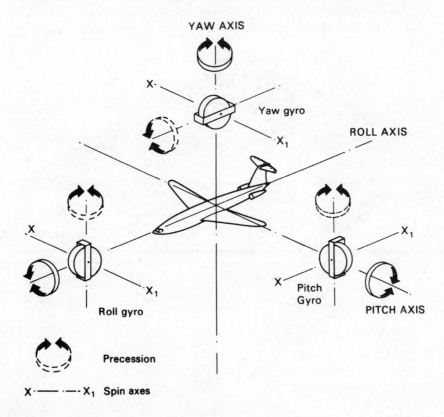

Fig. 3.11 Attitude sensing by rate gyroscopes

the cells and it differentially obscures the radiation when the gimbal ring is displaced. The outputs from the photo-electric cells are combined and amplified and then supplied to a moving-coil type of torqe motor which drives the gyroscope and pick-off element to the balance position.

Rate sensing about three axes

From the description given earlier of the operating principle of the rate gyroscope, we have observed that sensing of a turn is a direct result of precession caused by movement about a vertical input axis or, what is the same thing, movement of the gyroscope in the yawing plane. It should, therefore, be apparent that if two additonal rate gyroscopes can be positioned in an aircraft such that one can respond to movement in the pitching plane, and the other to movement in the rolling plane, then the resulting precession and spring balancing force in each case will be a measure of 'turn rates' in these two planes. We thus have the basis of a combind system for sensing the rates at which attitude changes occur in relation to all three axes of an aircraft, the disposition of the gyroscopes being arranged as shown in fig. 3.11.

Fig. 3.12 illustrates an example of the method of rate sensing about three

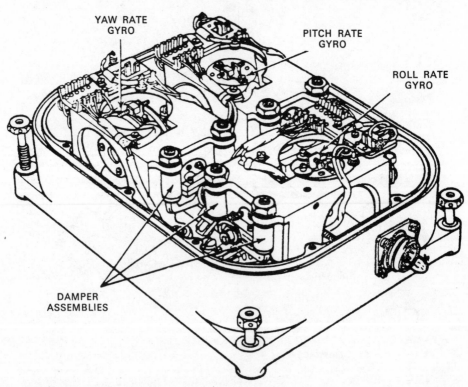

Fig. 3.12 Three-axis rate transmitter

axes. In this case, the unit which is referred to as a three-axis rate transmitter, is used in conjunction with a vertical-axis gyroscope reference unit (see page 107). The rate gyroscopes, which operate synchro transmission type detector elements, are spring-restrained, and are damped by individual dashpot assemblies.

Single-axis rate sensing

For certain types of small aircraft, automatic control systems are available for the purpose of providing simple wing-levelling or roll control, and yaw damping, via the ailerons only. In such systems, sensing is by means of a single rate gyroscope.

As noted earlier, the sensing attitude changes about the roll and yaw axes of an aircraft can be effected by the relative positioning of the input and output axes of two rate gyroscopes. However, since the spin axes of both gyroscopes are in the same horizontal direction (see fig. 3.11), then if we take either one of the gyroscopes and mount it so that its gimbal ring and precession axis is tilted at a preset angle (30° is a typical value) from the horizontal, it alone will sense both roll and yaw attitude changes. Examples of this sensing method are to be found in instruments known as turn co-ordinators, and as turn and bank stabiliser/trackers, the latter forming an optional feature in certain of the Edo-Aire Mitchell 'Century' series of control system for the provision of turn rate commands, and VOR radial and ILS localiser beam tracking.

Combined use of displacement and rate gyroscopes

A number of automatic flight control systems currently in service make use of error information, based not only on the magnitude of displacements of an aircraft and its flight control surfaces but also on the rate of change of these displacements. In these systems, a vertical-axis gyroscope unit detects displacements as a primary attitude change sensor, and applies appropriate corrective control, but as there is always a tendency for a displacement sensing device to cause 'overshoot' the displacement corrections are damped by rate signals from rate gyroscopes. When the displacement error is no longer changing, the rate signals fall to zero and the error existing at that instant is acted upon by control forces that are proportional only to the magnitude of the error.

Thus, by combining the signals from the attitude sensing elements coupled to each type of gyroscope, the possibility of large deviations from reference conditions is greatly reduced and smoother control application and stability of operation is obtained. Furthermore, very small displacement errors and signals which would otherwise not cause corrective action, if left to a vertical-axis gyroscope alone, are detected more quickly by rate gyroscopes and can be built up into stronger corrective signals.

Levelling and compensation systems

As we learned earlier in this chapter, a free gyroscope must be 'tied' to the earth by gravity sensing, before it can be utilised as a practical aircraft attitude sensing element; this applies in particular to horizontal-axis and vertical-axis gyroscopes. It is necessary, therefore, to provide systems which will level erecting gyroscopes to their appropriate reference datums, and compensate for any tendency to depart from them.

The design of systems varies, but in all cases they operate by applying torques which result in gyroscopeic precission.

An erection system which is commonly adopted is shown schematically in fig. 3.13. It consists of two electrolytic switches of the variable resistance type; one positioned so as to detect movement of the whole gimbal system about the

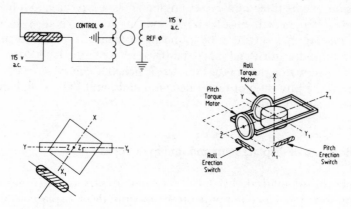

Fig. 3.13 Torque motor and levelling switch system

roll axis, and the other to detect movement of the inner gimbal ring about the pitch axis. Both switches are mounted on the inner gimbal ring which encases the gyro motor. The *roll* erection switch is connected to a torque motor mounted parallel to the *pitch axis* such that the stator is fixed to the outer gimbal ring and its rotor is fixed to the inner gimbal ring. The *pitch* erection switch which is mounted parallel to the *roll* axis is connected to a similar torque motor having its rotor connected to the outer gimbal ring, and its stator fixed to the frame of the unit. The stators are two-phase wound; one phase, known as the reference phase is continuously energised from an a.c. supply (115 volts or 26 volts in some cases) while the other phase (the control phase) is double wound with one winding for each direction of rotation. The rotors are of the squirrel-cage type with no windings.

118

Each switch consists of a sealed glass tube, or envelope, partially filled with an electrolytic solution,and containing three electrodes: one connected to the a.c. supply and each of the other two connected to the respective sections of the control phase windings of the appropriate torque motors.

When the gryo rotor axis is stabilised in the vertical position, both switches are horizontal and as the end electrodes are immersed in equal amounts of electrolyte, the current flowing in the two sections of the control phase winding and electromagnetic effect in the rotor will be equally opposed and so no torques are applied.

Assume that the gimbal system is tilted, say to the right, about the roll axis, then the tilting of the roll erection switch will cause a change in the amount of surface area of electrolyte in contact with the electrodes. This in turn causes an unbalance in the electrical resistance, e.g. the resistance will be lower at the 'low' end electrode than at the 'high' end electrode. As a result, more current will flow in that half of the torque motor stator control phase winding connected to the 'low' end electrode, and the electromagnetic effect induced in the squirrel-cage rotor will be increased. The tendency for the rotor to rotate is resisted by the gyro and so a reactive torque is applied to the inner gimbal ring, causing the whole gimbal system to precess about its roll axis and so take up its stabilised vertical position once more.

If the gyro rotor axis is tilted either forward or rearward about the pitch axis of the gimbal system, then by action similar to that just described, the pitch torque motor will apply a torque to the outer gimbal ring in order to precess the gyro back to the vertical position.

Electrolytic switches, although quite satisfactory for the purpose of maintaining gyroscope axes at their respective reference datums, are at a disadvantage when exposed to the forces developed under accelerating, decelerating and turning conditions. For example, accelerating or decelerating forces will cause the electrolyte of the pitch erection switch to be displaced and the torque produced by the pitch torque motor will precess the gyro rotor axis forward or rearward as the case may be. In other words, the gyro is made to take up a false vertical position. Similarly, during a turn the roll erection switch electrolyte will be displaced by centrifugal force, and the rotor axis will be precessed to a false vertical position left or right about the roll axis. It is therefore necessary to compensate for these effects, otherwise the synchros on the respective axes of the gimbal system will transmit false attitude command signals to the automatic contol system.

The method generally adopted is one which employs additional electrolytic switches positioned on the pitch and roll axes of the gyro, and connected to the torque motors in such a way that under the influence of forces they isolate the control phase windings from the pitch and roll erection switches. The operating principle may be understood from fig. 3.14, which illustrates the circuit arrangement appropriate to pitch erection switch isolation or 'cut-out'.

119

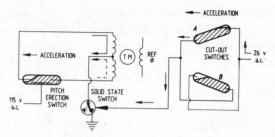

Fig. 3.14 Erection cut-out switch operation

The cut-out switches are arranged as a pair set at an angle to each other so that there is differentiation between acceleration and deceleration forces. If we consider the effects of an acceleration in the direction shown, the electrolyte in the pitch erection switch will be displaced in the opposite direction and the unbalanced current condition produced in the torque motor control phase winding will tend to precess the gyro away from the vertical position. At the same time however, the acceleration force displaces the electrolyte in the cut-out switch 'A', and as will be noted, it completes a circuit to a solid-state switch which is then operated to interrupt the control phase winding circuit to ground, thereby preventing torque motor operation. Switch 'B' performs a similar function which is only effective under the influence of a decelerating force.

Roll erection switch 'cut-out' is accomplished by an arrangement identical to that shown, except that the cut-out switches are angled with respect to each other about the roll axis to differentiate between the centrifugal forces produced when turning either left or right.

Sideslip sensing and turn co-ordination

As discussed earlier (see page 39), the displacement of the ailerons for initiating a turn, causes a difference between the lift force of each wing and a related difference in drag, with the result that the aircraft will yaw in a direction that will oppose the rolling moment required for turning. The yaw, the extent of which depends on the roll angle and on the airspeed, also produces sideslip in a direction opposite to that of the yaw (see page 21). Another effect produced by turning is loss of lift resulting in a nose-down displacement of the aircraft. Turning is therefore a rather complex man-oeuvre requiring counteraction of the effects of several forces, and the application of simultaneous counteracting displacements of all control surfaces in order to achieve a co-ordinated turn.

The primary gyroscopic-type attitude sensing elements of an automatic flight control system, are somewhat limited in their capability of directly establishing the requisite control signals for turn co-ordination. For exam-

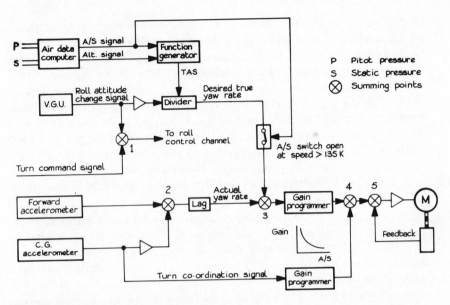

Fig. 3.15 Turn co-ordination

ple, under sideslip conditions the movement of the aircraft causes bodily displacements of the stabilised axes of the elements, so that aircraft movement is no longer relative to the axes. It is therefore necessary to provide 'back-up' methods of detecting yaw and sideslip effects, and of producing co-ordination signals for integration with those of the main control channels. Various methods of achieving this are adopted and some representative examples are described in the following paragraphs; some methods of counteracting nose-down displacements will be described under 'Lift compensation' on page 144

Figure 3.15 illustrates a method of achieving turn co-ordination and is one in which the required corrective control signal is established as a result of any difference between a desired true yaw rate signal, and an aircraft yaw rate signal derived from two accelerometer type sensors. One sensor is mounted at the c.g. position of the aircraft, while the other is mounted at some forward position in the fuselage; their signal outputs are summed at junction 2.

When a turn command is applied to the system, the signal produced is supplied to the roll control channel via summing junction 1, and after processing, the roll servomotor displaces the ailerons in the appropriate direction and the turn is initiated. The change in attitude about the roll axis is sensed by the vertical-axis gyroscope unit, and so its synchro detector element will develop a roll attitude change signal which is summed with the turn command signal at junction 1. The resultant signal therefore limits aileron displacements to ensure that the aircraft is flown at the roll angle required for the turn.

Since an opposing yawing motion occurs, it is necessary for the rudder to

121

be displaced in a direction required to keep the aircraft in the turn; thus, a signal must be supplied to the yaw control channel and the rudder actuator. In the system illustrated, this is achieved by feeding the roll attitude change signal from the vertical-axis gyroscope unit to a circuit network which divides the signal by a true airspeed signal calculated by a function generator, the latter being supplied with airspeed and altitude signals from an air data computer. The output signal from the divider circuit therefore establishes what is termed the desired true yaw rate of the aircraft at the particular roll angle and airspeed, and it is supplied to the yaw control channel from summing junction 3, for processing and operation of the rudder actuator.

Ideally, the desired true yaw rate signal only should be sufficient for achieving turn co-ordination, but variations in an aircraft's aerodynamic and control characteristics require additional monitoring of yawing motion and the derivation of a signal corresponding to the actual yaw rate of the aircraft. The yawing motion exerts a force on the mass within the forward accelerometer unit, causing it to be displaced in the appropriate direction, and thereby induces a signal which is applied to summing junction 2. Similarly, a signal will be induced by the accelerometer unit at the c.g. position as a result of sideslip force causing displacement of its mass, and since this signal is also applied to summing junction 2, then the sum of the signals from both accelerometer units corresponds to actual yaw rate and is applied to summing junction 3. If, at this moment there is a difference between actual yaw rate and the desired true yaw rate, the remaining signal is gain programmed (see also page 153) as a function of indicated airspeed and fed to the yaw control channel and rudder actuator which repositions the rudder to provide further damping of the yawing motion, and co-ordination of the turn. It will be noted from the diagram that gain is reduced as airspeed increases, since smaller displacements of the rudder are then required.

The actual yaw rate and the true yaw rate signals are essentially of a short-term nature, and so if it is necessary to continually co-ordinate an extended turn, a signal capable of being sustained for longer periods is required. Reference to fig. 3.15 shows that this co-ordination signal is derived by 'tapping off' the output from the accelerometer unit at the c.g. position, and applying it so summing junction 4 via a lag circuit element and a second gain programmer. The signal to the rudder actuator therefore produces a steady state displacement of the rudder to oppose sideslip and to maintain co-ordination.

In order to ensure compatibility of an automatic flight control system with the flight handling characteristics of a type of aircraft in which it is installed, it is sometimes required that at airspeeds above or below certain values, the input of computed yaw rate signals should either be isolated completely, or their gain reduced. For example, the aerodynamic and flight control characteristics of an aircraft may be such that during turns above a specified airspeed, co-ordination is an inherent characteristic, and any further application of a computed yaw rate signal could induce an undesirable condition of spiral divergence (see page 25). A method of overcoming this, is to pass signals through an airspeed-monitored switch or switches in some cases. In the system shown in fig. 3.15 a switch is inserted in the desired true yaw rate signal line, and when the airspeed sensed by the air data computer exceeds a specific value (135 knots in this case) the switch is opened. Thus, yaw rate control is then related solely to the actual yaw rate of the aircraft as sensed by the accelerometer units.

Fig. 3.16 shows another example of sideslip monitor known as a dynamic vertical sensor. It comprises a pendulum-actuated synchro transmitter

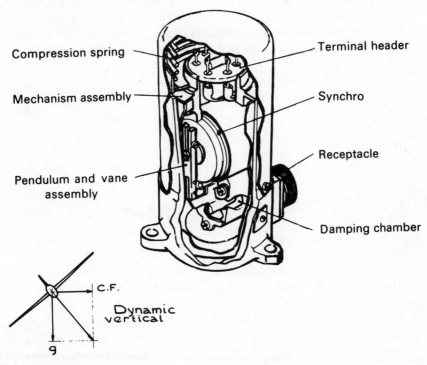

Fig. 3.16 Dynamic vertical sensor

the axis of which is aligned with the fore-and-aft axis of the aircraft, and so restricts displacement of the pendulum to the athwartships axis direction only. Oil damping is provided to prevent the pendulum from being affected by transient oscillations and vibration. In a co-ordinated turn, the pendulum is aligned with the resultant of centrifugal and gravitational forces, i.e. the dynamic vertical, and no output signal is produced in the synchro stator. If however, the pendulum is displaced as a result of a slip or skid, the synchro rotor will also be displaced to induce a proportional signal in the stator. The signal is then amplified and supplied to the rudder servo control channel, the

123

output of which will displace the rudder causing it to co-ordinate the turn.

Another example of producing turn co-ordination signals is shown in fig. 3.17. In this case, initial rudder displacement is provided by a command signal which is derived by cross-feeding the roll angle signal from a vertical gyroscope unit to a turn co-ordination high-pass filter. The filtered signal is then a yaw function of rate of change of roll attitude, and producing proportional rudder displacement on a short-term basis. Long term rudder displacement is attained by applying the signals from a yaw rate gyro to a yaw damper low-pass filter which passes only the steady-state yaw rate signals present during a sustained turn. The summated turn co-ordination signal is modified within the servo amplifier as a function of airspeed such that the amplifier gain is programmed to compensate for the effectiveness of the rudder as airspeed is varied. Thus for example, low rudder displacement is required when airspeed is increased and therefore, the gain is reduced.

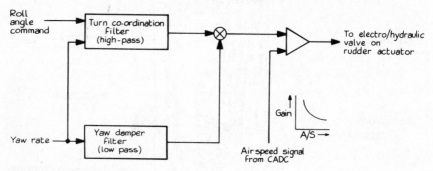

Fig. 3.17 Turn co-ordination

Inertial attitude references

In aircraft utilising inertial (IN) or inertial reference (IR) systems, it is no longer necessary for the associated automatic control and flight director systems to be dependent on their own individual gyroscopic sensing elements. The reason for this is, quite simply, that an IN or IR system depends for its operation on inertia sensing elements which must always be stabilised horizontally with respect to the aircraft's axes, and since gyroscopes are used for this purpose, then together with certain position transmitters they can also establish the attitude references and steering commands required for automaic flight control.

The method of integrating all three systems is schematically illustrated in fig. 3.18. The inertia sensing elements (not shown in the diagram) are accelerometers producing signal outputs which, after processing by the IN computer, provide data essential for en-route navigation and guidance of an aircraft.

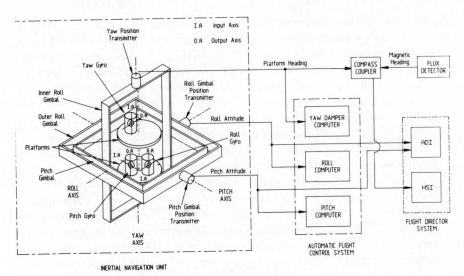

Fig. 3.18 Attitude references from an inertial platform

The gyroscopes used in this example of IN system are of the rate integrating type (i.e. one that provides an output displacement proportional to the integral of the input rate) and as will be noted there is one for each axis and they are mounted on two platforms within a gimbal system. Their input and output axes are arranged so that they sense attitude changes in an identical manner to the three-axis rate transmitter already described (see page 116). The gimbal system of each gyroscope is mechanically coupled to a pick-off element, and each of these is electrically connected via an amplifier to individual torque motors. The motors are mounted on the gimbal rings of the IN unit such that they are disposed about the three principal axes.

Whenever there is a change in attitude of the aircraft about either of its axes, the gimbal system and platforms of the IN unit are tilted. This is sensed by the appropriate rate gyroscope which precesses about its output axis so that its pick-off will develop an output signal proportional to the number of degrees of displacement, enabling the torque motor to drive its associated gimbal ring of the IN unit to a position at which the platforms are again level.

Let us consider as an example a displacement of the aircraft occurring about the roll axis. Since the IN unit gimbal system and casing are 'tied' to the aircraft, the platforms will also be displaced. This displacement will, however, be sensed by the roll rate gyroscope whose pick-off transmits a signal via an amplifier to a torque motor on the inner gimbal ring. The torque motor therefore drives the inner gimbal ring about its roll axis to restore the platforms to the level position. At the same time, a signal is produced by a resolver synchro, the rotor of which is positioned by movement of the inner gimbal ring. The output signal from the synchro is applied to a torque motor on the outer gimbal ring, so as to drive this ring about the roll axis on which it is supported within the unit casing. The outer gimbal ring also rotates the pitch gimbal ring about the roll axis. The reason for having this second gimbal ring is to prevent 'gimbal lock' which would otherwise occur between the inner gimbal ring and pitch gimbal ring (see also page 103).

In order to transmit the degree of displacement to the automatic flight control and flight director systems, synchros are mounted on the IN unit gimbal rings to detect their positions; there is one synchro for each principal axis. Thus, for the roll displacement we have considered, as soon as the torque motors start driving the inner and outer roll gimbal rings to the 'platform level' position, the rotor of a control synchro is rotated within its stator by the outer roll gimbal ring. The signal produced in the stator corresponds to the angular difference between the outer roll gimbal ring and the aircraft's position about the roll axis. In other words, it is a roll attitude error signal and is supplied to the roll control channel of the automatic flight control system computer as a command to restore the aircraft to its normal attitude. As will be noted from fig. 3.18, the signal is also supplied to the flight director system attitude director indicator which then displays the changes taking place in aircraft attitude.

Levelling of the platforms and production of output signals to an automatic flight control and flight director system, as a result of aircraft displacements about the pitch axis, are implemented in a similar manner. There is, however, a difference in the case of displacements about the yaw axis. The yaw rate gyroscope. in detecting the change in azimuth, causes its pick-off to develop an output signal which is supplied to a torque motor on the yaw axis of the inner gimbal ring. Unlike the pitch and roll torque motors, the azimuth motor cannot rotate the gimbal ring system, and so instead, it rotates the levelled platform on which it is mounted, in the opposite direction to aircraft displacement, thereby maintaining it in the same position relative to the gimbal system. The platform rotates the rotor of an azimuth control synchro to produce a platform heading signal that is supplied as a command to the yaw damper channel of the automatic flight control computer, and also to the flight director system horizontal situation indicator for display of actual heading changes.

Location of attitude sensing elements

The locations of attitude sensing elements, and in particular those which are remote from the flight crew compartment of an aircraft, have to be carefully chosen otherwise the inherent flexibility of the aircraft structure will be interpreted by sensing elements as attitude changes, and thereby result in a condition of unstable coupling between the aircraft and its automatic flight control system. Locations must, therefore, be in areas where flexural frequency sensing is at a minimum.

TEST QUESTIONS

1 Define the two fundamental properties of a gyroscope and state the factors on which they depend.

2 What corrections must be applied to a basic gyroscope in order to ensure its suitability as an attitude sensor?

3 What is meant by the term 'earth rate'?

4 If a gyroscope positioned at a latitude λ has an apparent drift of $15°\sin \lambda$, its input axis would be aligned with the:

    (a) earth's axis.

    (b) local vertical component of the earth's rate.

    (c) local N – S component of the earth's rate.

5 What is meant by 'transport wander', and how does it relate to horizontal-axis and vertical-axis gyroscopes?

6 Under what conditions would a gyroscope by subject to gimbal lock?

7 The effect of an oscillation or 'wobbling' of a gyroscope's spin axis is known as:

    (a) tumbling.

    (b) gimbal error.

    (c) nutation.

8 Explain the operating principles of a rate gyroscope, and also how the principle can be applied to the sensing of aircraft attitude changes about all three axes.

9 How can a single rate gyroscope be adapted to sense both roll and yaw attitude changes?

10 For what purpose are displacement gyroscope and rate gyroscope elements employed in combination with each other?

11 Why is it necessary to provide additional detecting elements to ensure automatic turn co-ordination?

12 Describe the operation of a typical method of achieving turn co-ordination.

13 How are electrolytic switches and torque motors used for the levelling of a vertical-axis gyroscope, positioned in relation to the axes of the gimbal system?

14 Describe how a levelling switch and a torque motor operate when the gyroscope is tilted about the pitch axis.

15 What effects can acceleration forces have on a levelling system, and how are they compensated?

16 How is the stabilising system of an inertial platform used for providing attitude references to an automatic control system?

4
Command Signal Detection

The primary attitude sensing elements employed in automatic flight control systems form the most vital part of the servomechanism loop since they detect attitude changes in terms of errors which demand monitoring and correction. Both these functions, however, cannot be performed by the elements alone, and in this respect they are not unlike the primary flight instruments in that they demand some action on the part of the pilot in his role as the error monitoring and correcting element in the control loop. In other words, it is necessary to provide error signal sensors which by suitable coupling to the attitude sensors will automatically detect the phase and magnitude of the errors, and transmit this intelligence to the output section of the servomechanism. Signal sensors, or transducers as they are often called, are normally of the inductive type, although in some basic types of autopilot the principle of variable capacitance is adopted: some typical examples are considered in this chapter.

Inductive elements

The fundamental operating principle of inductive elements is based on that of the conventional transformer, i.e. for a particular ratio between the number of windings of a primary coil and a secondary coil, and for a certain fixed value of voltage input to the primary coil, some higher or lower fixed value of voltage output can be obtained from the secondary coil. In addition, however, the elements must have the ability to change the phases of their output in order to establish the direction of the correcting control signals. In applying this principle to error sensing, it is necessary for the secondary coil output to be of a variable nature, and in order to derive this the basic iron core structure is arranged in two parts, one part being fixed while the position of the other part is variable. Some examples of the methods commonly adopted are the 'E' and 'I' method; the moving vane method; and the method of synchronous transmission.

E and I bar sensors

An example of this type of sensor is illustrated in fig. 4.1. The centre limb of the fixed E-shaped core is wound with a primary coil supplied with alternating current at the required level, while the two outer limbs are wound with secondary coils connected in series opposition. The I bar is pivoted at its centre, and is rotated by the attitude sensing element, in this case of the gyroscopic type, so that the bar varies the air gaps between it and the outer limbs of the E-shaped core. When the I bar is in its neutral position, the air gaps are equal, an equal magnetic flux flows in each limb of the E-shaped core, thereby inducing equal and opposite voltages in the secondary coils; the output from the coils is therefore zero.

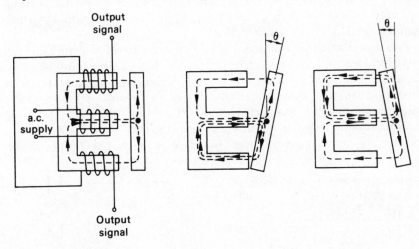

Fig. 4.1 E and I bar sensor

When the attitude sensing element detects a change in attitude (either as a result of disturbance of the aircraft or by injection of a required attitude change command signal) the I bar is deflected through a small angle such that the air gaps will no longer be equal, and the reluctance of the magnetic circuit will change. The flux in one outer limb of the E core will increase, while the flux in the other decreases; thus, there will be corresponding changes in the voltages induced in the secondary coils, and an output signal voltage will be produced. The greater the I bar deflection, the greater will be the signal voltages, and since the secondary coils are wound in opposition the voltage will be either in-phase or out-of-phase with respect to the input voltage to the primary coil, depending on the direction in which the I bar is deflected. The phase and magnitude of the signal are directly proportional to the direction and magnitude of the detected attitude change; thus, by amplifying the signal and feeding it to a servomotor, an appropriate flight control surface can be moved either to correct a disturbance or to manoeuvre the aircraft in response to an attitude change command. To ensure that the servomotor provides the required amount of control surface displacement, or runs at a rate proportional to that of a disturbance as the case may be, a feedback signal is applied to the control loop to oppose the error voltage signal; (some typical methods adopted for the generation of feedback are described in chapters 5 and 7).

In some applications of this type of sensor, the I bar is deflected linearly to produce output voltage signals in the same manner as that described.

Moving vane method

This is adopted in some types of flight control system in which the inductive transducers are actuated by the vertical gyroscope of a steering horizon indicator, an example being one of the flight director/autopilot systems manufactured by Edo-Aire Mitchell.

Two transducers are employed, and they each consist of a moving vane and a fixed coil assembly as shown schematically in fig. 4.2. One transducer has its vane mounted on the inner gimbal ring of the gyroscope, and therefore senses pitch attitude changes, while the vane of the second is mounted on the outer gimbal ring, and senses changes in roll attitude.

A square-wave alternating voltage is applied to coils 1 and 3 of each fixed coil assembly, the voltages being 180° out-of-phase. In the level flight attitude

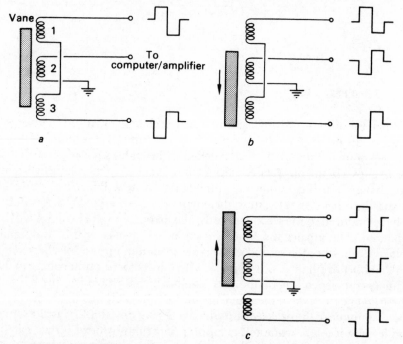

Fig. 4.2 Moving-vane pick-off element

(diagram *a*) the vanes of both transducers are centred over the number 2 coils, and since in this position there is equal electromagnetic coupling between coils 1 and 3, no voltage is induced in coil 2 and no command signal will be applied to the computer/amplifier.

When a change in aircraft attitude occurs about one or other of the vertical gyroscope axes, there will be relative movement between the vane and coil assembly of the relevant transducer. Thus, assuming that movement causes the vane to be centred between coils 2 and 3 (diagram *b*) the inductance will be increased and a square-wave voltage will be induced in coil 2, and which is in phase with the input to coil 3. A command signal will therefore, be applied to the computer/amplifier. Movement of the vane towards coil 1 (diagram *c*) results in a similar response except that the voltage induced in coil 2 is in phase with the inputs to coil 1.

Synchronous transmission systems

In many automatic flight control systems, the detection of error signals is accomplished by self-synchronous inductive transducers which are usually classified under the generic term *synchro*. They are divided into four main groups according to their function: (i) torque synchros, (ii) control synchros, (iii) differential synchros and (iv) resolver synchros.

Torque synchros

These are the simplest form of synchro and are used for the transmission of angular position information by means of induced signals, and for the reproduction of this information by the position of a shaft at an output or receiver element. A typical application of torque synchros is in flight instrument systems.

A torque synchro system is comprised of two electrically similar units interconnected as shown in fig. 4.3, and by convention one is designated the transmitter (TX) and the other the receiver (TR). Each unit consists of a rotor carrying a winding, and concentrically mounted in a stator carrying three windings the axes of which are 120° apart. The principal physical differences between the TX and the TR are that the rotor of the TX is mechanically coupled to an input shaft, while the TR rotor is free to rotate. The rotor windings are connected to a source of single-phase alternating current supply, and the corresponding stator connections are joined together by transmission lines. A similarity between these connection arrangements and a conventional transformer may also be noted; the rotors corresponding to primary windings and the stators to secondary windings.

When the rotors are aligned with their respective stators in the position indicated they are said to be at 'electrical zero'; this refers to the reference angle standardised for synchros at which a given set of stator voltages will be

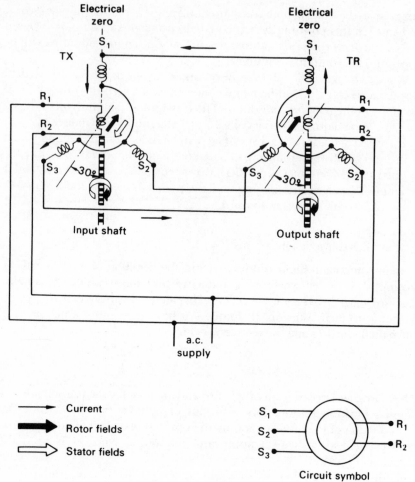

Fig. 4.3 Torque synchro system

produced, and by this convention enables replacement synchros to be matched to each other. Other positions are measured in degrees increasing in an anti-clockwise direction when viewed from the output shaft end of the unit. With power applied to the rotors the alternating flux set up will, by transformer action, induce certain voltages in the stator coils, the voltage values being governed, as in any transformer, by the ratio of the number of turns of the rotor (primary) and stator (secondary) coils.

When the rotors are at 'null', the induced voltages will be equal and opposite; therefore, no current flows in the stator coils and so there are no magnetic fields produced to cause rotation of the rotor of TR. However, when the rotor of TX is turned, say, through an angle of 30° an imbalance occurs between the voltages induced in the stator coils, causing current to flow in the stator coils and transmission lines. The currents are greatest in the circuit where voltage imbalance is greatest, and their effect is to produce resultant magnetic fields which exert torques to turn the rotor of TR to the same position as that of TX. As the TR rotor continues to turn, the misalignment, voltage imbalance and currents decrease until the 30° position is reached and no further torque is exerted on the rotor.

Control synchros

Control synchros differ from torque synchros in that their function is to produce an error voltage signal in the receiving element, as opposed to the production of a rotor torque. Since this error signal is an indication of misalignment between an input and an output, control synchros are more widely used as attitude error detectors which, as we learned earlier, form part of closed-loop servo control systems.

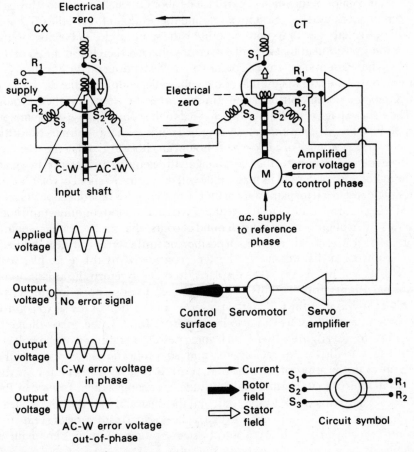

Fig. 4.4 Control synchro system

133

The interconnection of the two elements of a control synchro system as applied to a gyroscopic attitude sensing element, is shown in fig 4.4. By convention, the transmitter is designated at CX, and the receiver designated as a control transformer CT. The CX is similar to a torque transmitter, and from the diagram it will be noted that the alternating current supply is connected to the CX rotor only. The CT rotor is not energised since it acts merely as an inductive winding for detecting the phase and magnitude of error signal voltages which are supplied to an amplifier. The amplified signals are then fed to a two-phase motor which is mechanically coupled to the CT rotor. Another difference to be noted is that a control synchro system is at electrical zero when the rotor of CT is at 90° with respect to the CX rotor.

In practical applications, the transmitters are located about the appropriate axes of the attitude sensing element, for example, the pitch and roll axes of a vertical-axis gyroscope reference unit, the rotors being secured to the gimbal rings. Thus, assuming that a disturbance about the pitch axis takes place, the stator of the pitch CX will rotate about the stabilised rotor through a certain angle and the resultant angle and the resultant flux in the CT stator will be displaced from its datum point by the same angle, and relative to the CT rotor position at that instant. An error voltage is therefore induced in the rotor, the phase and magnitude of the voltage depending on the direction CX rotor, the phase and magnitude of the voltage depending on the direction of CX rotor rotation and on the degree of misalignment between it and the CT rotor. The error voltage is then amplified and fed to the control phase of the motor, the other phase being continuously supplied with alternating current. Since the control phase voltage of a two-phase motor can either lead or lag the reference phase voltage, the phase of the error voltage will determine the direction in which the motor will rotate, and its magnitude will determine its speed of rotation. As the motor rotates, it turns the rotor of the CT in the appropriate direction, thereby reducing its displacement relative to the CX rotor. Rotation continues until both rotors are in alignment (bearing in mind of course that the electrial zero points are at 90° from each other), at which position no further error voltage is induced.

Following a disturbance of the type considered in this example, it is necessary for the elevator to be displaced in order to return the aircraft to its normal flight attitude. This is accomplished by also applying the error voltage induced in the CT, to the power output section of the servo control channel loop. Thus, as can also be seen from fig. 4.4, the error voltage is applied to a servo amplifier which increases the magnitude of the voltage sufficient to drive the servomotor and so proportionately displace the elevators in the appropriate direction, until there is no further error. As the aircraft returns to its normal flight attitude, the change is again sensed by the vertical-axis gyroscope reference unit and the pitch CX, but the error voltage induced is now opposite in phase to that of the original displacement. Thus, the control synchro and pitch servo control systems are operated in the same manner as that described but in the opposite direction.

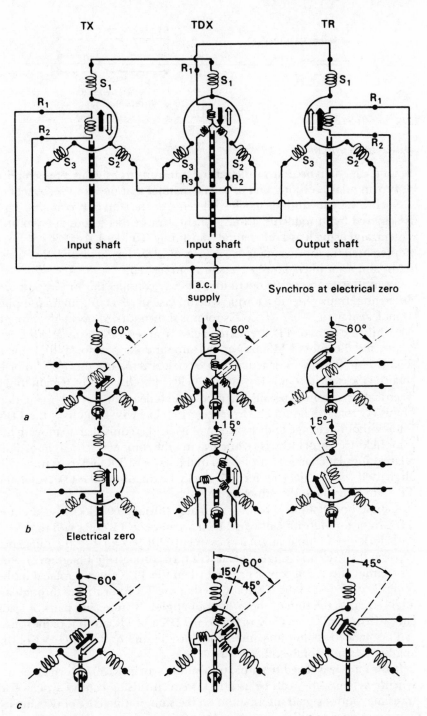

Fig. 4.5 Differential synchro in torque synchro system

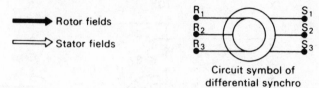

➡ Rotor fields

⇨ Stator fields

Circuit symbol of
differential synchro

Fig. 4.5 (*contd.*)

Differential synchros

In some cases, it is necessary to detect and transmit error signals representative of two angular positions, and in such a manner that the receiver element of a synchro system will indicate the difference or the sum of two angles. This is achieved by introducing a third synchro into either a torque or control system, and using it as a differential transmitter. Unlike TX or CX synchros, a differential transmitter (designated TDX or CDX) has an identically wound stator and rotor interconnected as shown in fig. 4.5.

As an illustration of the operation, we may consider the application of a differential transmitter to a torque synchro system at varying angular inputs as indicated in fig. 4.5. At *a* the TX rotor is shown rotated clockwise through 60° while the rotor of TDX remains at electrical zero; all the magnetic fields rotate, and the rotor of TR takes up the same angular position as the rotor of TX. If now the TX rotor remains at electrical zero, and the TDX rotor is rotated clockwise through 15°, say, the fields of both synchros remain in the electrical zero position because their position is determind by the orientation of the TX rotor (diagram *b*). However, a 15° clockwise rotation of the TDX rotor without a change in the position of its field is equivalent to moving the rotor field 15° anti-clockwise while leaving the rotor at electrical zero. This relative angular change is duplicated in the stator of TR and so its rotor will align itself with the field, i.e. for a 15° clockwise rotation of the TDX rotor, the TR rotor will rotate 15° anti-clockwise.

Assume now that the TX rotor is rotated through 60° clockwise, and the TDX rotor through 15° clockwise, then because the TR rotor will rotate 15° anti-clockwise its final angular movement will be equal to the difference between the two input angles, i.e. it will turn through 45° (diagram *c*). The differential effect is of course reversed when the TDX rotor is rotated in the opposite direction to the TX rotor, so that the TR rotor rotates through an angle equal to the sum of the two input angles. By reversing pairs of leads either between TX and TDX, or between TDX and TR, any one of the rotors can be made to assume a position equal to the sum or the difference of the angular positions of the other rotors.

In the same way that differential transmitter synchros can be used in torque synchro systems, they can be used in systems utiliising control synchros to transmit control signal information on the sum or difference of two angles. The basic arrangement is shown in fig 4.6.

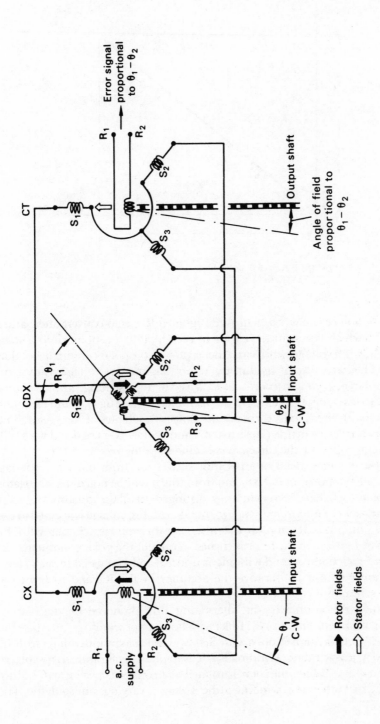

Fig. 4.6 Differential synchro in control synchro system

137

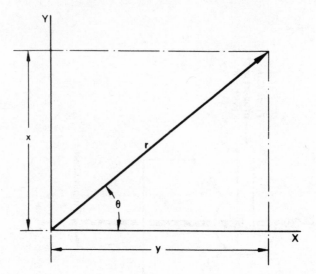

Fig. 4.7 Cartesian coordinates of a point

Resolver synchros

The function of resolver synchros (designated RS) is to convert alternating voltages, which represent the cartesian coordinates of a point, into a shaft position, and a voltage, which together represent the polar coordinates of that point. They may also be used in the reverse manner for voltage conversion from polar to cartesian coordinates. A vector representing an alternating voltage can be defined in terms of the vector length (see fig. 4.7) and the angle it makes with the X axis; these are the polar coordinates of the vector. The vector r can also be defined in terms of x and y where $x = r \cos \theta$ and $y = r \sin \theta$; these expressions are the cartesian coordinates of the vector.

A typical arrangement of an RS for conversion from polar to cartesian coordinates is shown in fig. 4.8, and from this it will be noted that the stator and rotor each have two windings arranged in phase quadrature, thus providing an eight-terminal synchro. An alternating voltage is applied to the rotor winding $R_1 - R_2$, and the magnitude of this voltage, together with the angle through which the rotor is turned, represent the polar coordinates. In this application, the second winding is unused, and as is usual in such cases, it is short-circuited to improve the accuracy of the RS and to limit the spurious response.

In the position shown, the alternating flux produced by the current through rotor winding $R_1 - R_2$, links with both stator windings, but since the rotor winding is aligned only with $S_1 - S_2$, then maximum voltage will be induced in this winding. Winding $S_3 - S_4$ is in phase quadrature so no voltage is induced in it. When the rotor is rotated at a constant speed it will induce voltages in both stator windings, the voltages varying sinusoidally. The

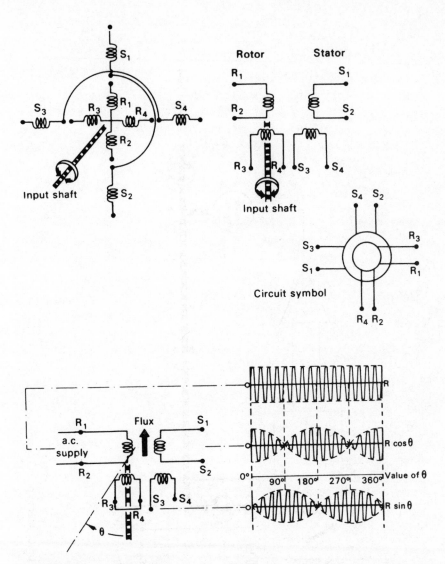

Fig. 4.8 Resolver synchro

voltage across that stator winding which is aligned with the rotor at electrical zero will be a maximum at that position and will fall to zero after rotor displacement of 90°; this voltage is therefore a measure of the cosine of the displacement. The voltage is in phase with the voltage applied to $R_1 - R_2$ during the first 90° of displacement, and in anti-phase from 90° to 270°, finally rising from zero at 270° to maximum in-phase at 360°. Any angular displacement can therefore be identified by the amplitude and phase of the induced stator voltages. At electrical zero, stator winding $S_3 - S_4$ will have zero

139

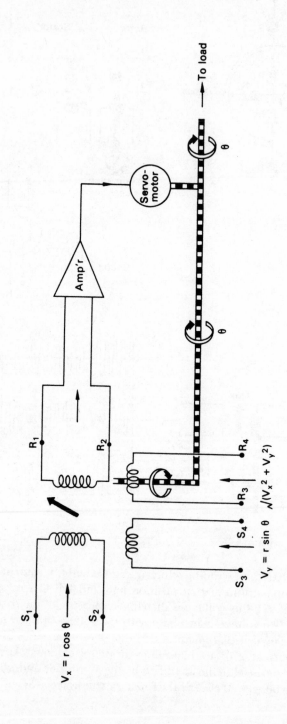

Fig. 4.9 Conversion of cartesian coordinates to polar coordinates

voltage induced in it, but at 90° displacement of rotor winding R_1 - R_2, maximum in-phase voltage will be induced and will vary sinusoidally throughout 360°; thus, the S_3 - S_4 voltage is directly proportional to the sine of the rotor displacement. The phase depends on the angle of displacement, any angle being identified by the amplitude and phase of the voltages induced in stator winding S_3 - S_4. The sum of the outputs from both stators, i.e. $r \cos \theta$ plus $r \sin \theta$, therefore defines in cartesian coordinates the input voltage and rotor rotation.

Fig. 4.9 illustrates an arrangement whereby cartesian coordinates may be converted to polar coordinates. An alternating voltage $V_x = r \cos \theta$ is applied to the cosine stator winding S_1—S_2, while a voltage $V_y = r \sin \theta$ is applied to the sine stator winding S_3 - S_4. An alternating flux representing cartesian coordinates is therefore produced inside the complete stator. One of the rotor windings, in this case R_1 - R_2, is connected to an amplifier and in the position shown it will have maximum voltage induced in it; this voltage will be applied to the amplifier. The output from the amplifier is applied to a servomotor which is mechanically coupled to a load and to the rotor. When the rotor is turned through 90° the induced voltage in winding R_1 - R_2, reduces to zero and the servomotor will stop. The rotor winding R_3 - R_4 will now be aligned with the stator flux, and a voltage will be induced in it which is proportional to the amplitude of the alternating flux as represented by the vector r, i.e. a voltage proportional to $\sqrt{(V_x^2 + V_y^2)}$. This voltage together with the angular position of the rotor therefore represents an output in terms of the polar coordinates.

A typical example of RS application to a control channel of an automatic flight control system is shown in fig. 4.10. In this case, the control system is one employing rate gyroscopes and a vertical-axis gyroscope, for attitude sensing, and the resolver performs the function of converting cartesian coordinates to polar coordinates in order to establish a true pitch rate (movement of an aircraft about a true horizontal axis) for pitch stabilisation. When the aircraft turns, the outputs from the pitch and roll rate gyroscopes contain a rate-of-change-of-heading component, and the output from the yaw rate gyroscope contains a rate-of-change-of-elevation component. The effect of the component in the pitch rate signal is to produce a continuous pitch-down signal; the elevation rate component is nulled by the yaw channel circuit. If, therefore, the pitch and yaw rate signals can be resolved with respect to the roll rate then the true pitch rate of the aircraft during turns can be determined.

The roll attitude signal is fed to the stator of a CT synchro and this establishes an error signal representing the roll angle, in the rotor. After amplification, the signal is applied to the control winding of a motor, the shaft of which is mechanically coupled to the CT rotor and to the RS rotor. The motor therefore rotates the CT rotor to reduce the error signal to zero (generally termed datum chasing) and also rotates the RS rotor to a position

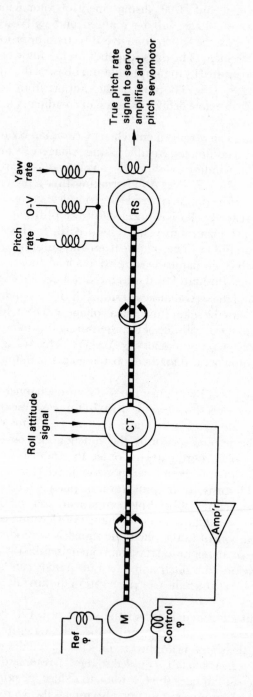

Fig. 4.10 Resolver synchro application

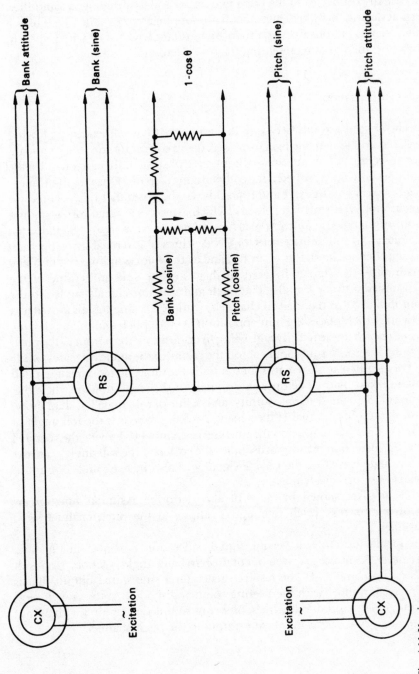

Fig. 4.11 Versine generator

which mechanically represents the roll angle at that instant. The RS stator is electrically connected to the pitch rate signal and yaw rate signal amplifier, so that during turns, two rate signals are supplied to the stator which have a sine/cosine relationship, and produce a resultant error signal with respect to the rotor, the signal representing the true pitch rate.

Lift compensation

As already pointed out (see page 121) an aircraft has the tendency of being diplaced nose-down during a turn. In order to correct for this, the command signal sections of an automatic flight control stystem therefore require the addition of what is termed a lift compensation circuit. One circuit arrangement is shown in fig. 4.11 and from this will be noted that it is essentially a synchronous transmission network, which generates a signal corresponding to the trigonometric function of an angle known as the versine. Signals from the pitch and roll attitude detector CX synchros of a vertical gyroscope unit are supplied to the stators of an RS, and as the rotor windings are in phase quadrature, the signals induced in them are the sine and cosine of the transmitted attitude signals. The pitch and roll sine signals are fed to the appropriate corrective control channels, while the cosine signals are fed to a network which places them in opposition. At zero pitch and roll angles, the cosine of each angle is unity and, being in opposition, the output to the pitch channel is zero. At some angle of roll the cosine of the angle decreases, while that of the pitch angle remains substantially the same, no movement in pitch having taken place. The opposing signals in this condition are, therefore, cosine of pitch angle equal to unity, and cosine of roll angle less than unity; thus, the resulting signal is the versine $1-\cos \theta$, where θ is the roll angle in degrees. This signal is fed to the pitch servo channel to provide the required nose-up correction during turns. Since the cosine of the roll angle decreases as the angle increases, the versine signal will also increase and so result in greater nose-up correction.

The resolver shown in fig. 4.10 also performs a similar function by supplying its true pitch rate signal output to the pitch channel servo amplifier.

A further example of versine signal generation is shown in fig. 4.12. Whenever the motor is driven out of the zero bank angle position, as a result of steering commands, the resolver generates a sine signal output that is summed at point 1 with the steering command signals. At the same time, a cosine signal is produced which, on being summed at point 3 with an a.c. reference signal, forms the versine output to the pitch channel.

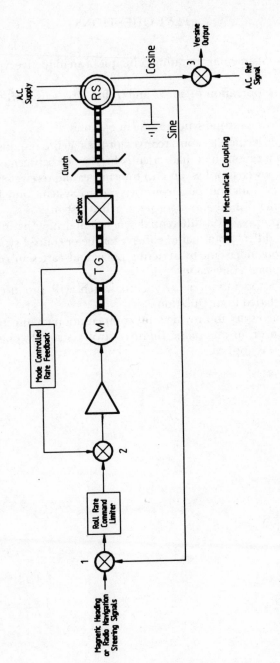

Fig. 4.12 Versine signal generation

TEST QUESTIONS

What is the fundamental operating principle of an inductive type error signal sensor?

2 Explain the operation of an 'E' and 'I' bar type sensor when an attitude change occurs.

3 Describe how a torque synchro system operates.

4 What would be the effect on a receiver torque synchro response in the event that cross-connections had inadvertently been made between (a) transmitter and receiver power supplies, and (b) transmitter and receiver stators?

5 What is the function of a control synchro system, and how does its operation differ from that of a torque synchro system?

6 State the purpose of a differential synchro and how its internal circuit arrangement differs from that of either a torque or control synchro.

7 What do you understand by the terms 'polar' and 'cartesian' co-ordinates in relation to voltage conversion?

8 Explain the operation of a synchro which will produce the voltage conversion referred to in Question 7.

9 Why is it necessary to provide a lift compensation circuit in a command signal section of an automatic flight control system? Explain how such compensation is applied.

5
Command Signal Processing

The signals produced by error signal sensors, in whatever form the sensors may take, cannot be applied directly to their associated servomotors for the principal reasons that further computation of signals is necessary particularly when outer loop control is adopted (see chapter 6), and in terms of power capability they are not strong enough to cope with the aerodynamic loads acting on the control surfaces. Therefore, in any one flight control system it is necessary to incorporate within the corresponding servo control loops a signal processing system having some, or all, of the following functions:

(i) Differentiating, e.g. deriving simulated rate information from a vertical-axis gyroscope controlled signal sensor.

(ii) Demodulating, i.e. converting a.c. error signals into d.c. control signals which have the same phase relationship.

(iii) Integrating to obtain simulated attitude information or to correct any sustained attitude errors.

(iv) Amplifying to increase sensor signals to a level high enough to operate the servomotors.

(v) Limiting to ensure that certain parameter changes are kept within prescribed limits.

(vi) Gain adjustments that may be pre-set and/or automatically programmed to adapt system response to suit the handling qualities or flight path of an aircraft.

(vii) Programming to produce a precise manoeuvre, e.g. when selecting a particular outer loop control mode (see chapter 6).

(viii) Applying feedback signals to ensure that corrective control is proportional to command signal inputs.

147

The methods adopted for performing the foregoing functions are varied and, in common with the other elements which make up any one complete control system, such methods are governed by system design and how it relates to the handling characteristics of various types of aircraft. Within the confines of this chapter, therefore, it is not possible to go into any great detail of the individual control channel configurations. There is, however, a basic similarity between the requirements for, and the applications of, signal processing elements, and the fundamentals of purpose and operation may be understood with the aid of the block diagram of fig. 5.1. Although the diagram is based on a roll control channel of a particular type of flight control system, it may nevertheless be considered generally representative.

When a turn has been commanded either through the medium of the compass system, the turn controller, or by the VOR or Localiser navigation receivers, a corresponding roll attitude error signal is determined by summing the values of the commanded roll attitude signal and the signal corresponding to the exisiting attitude; the latter signal is sensed by the roll sensing element of the vertical reference unit. Summation takes place in this case at point 'A' and the error signal produced is fed into the servo-control loop at point 'B'. Also at this point, a signal from a roll rate gyroscope sensing element is fed in to establish a turn rate for the command, and to prevent over-controlling. This is an example of the use of displacement gyroscope and rate gyroscope in combination (see page 117). Since the commanded roll attitude requires the ailerons to be displaced from their existing position, a position comparison process is also necessary to compute the error signal for servomotor operation. This is effected at the summing point 'C' to which is supplied what may be termed an 'existing position' feedback signal. The purpose of this signal, which is supplied from a position synchro type transducer, is to correct for non-linearities between the servomotor and the aileron system. The resulting difference signal is then applied to a discriminator, or pre-amplifier module, which removes quadrature and harmonic voltages and also increases the gain of the servo-control loop, thereby improving its response to signals commanding only small changes in aileron position. At the output side of the discriminator, and at summing point 'D', a rate feedback signal from the servomotor tachogenerator, is injected to back-off the command signal and so provide damping and servo-loop stability. The combined signal is therefore the one required to drive the servomotor to the commanded position, but in order to do this the signal must pass through a further stage of amplification and, as in all types of flight control systems, this is accomplished by means of a servo-amplifier.

In the system considered, the servomotor is of the two-phase induction type, and the control signal is supplied to its variable-phase winding. The direction of motor rotation is governed by the phase angle between the current flowing in the variable-phase winding, and that in the fixed-phase winding, the motor rotating clockwise or anti-clockwise depending on

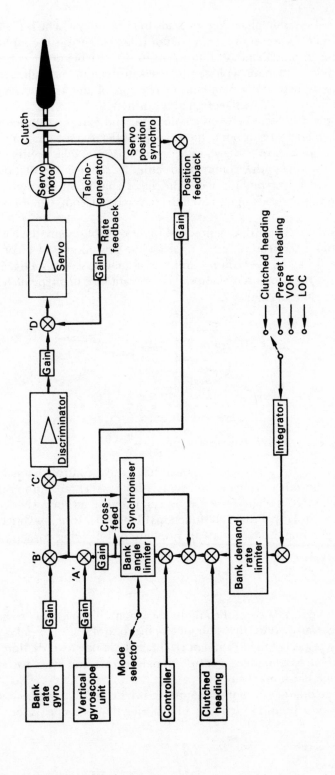

Fig. 5.1 Signal processing (BAC 1-11 2000 series A(?))

149

whether the variable-phase lags or leads the fixed-phase which is supplied from the main power source. A capacitor is inserted across the input to the servomotor to provide phase adjustment to the variable-phase current and this will always maintain a phase angle (whether lagging or leading) relative to the fixed-phase, thus maintaining rotation of the servomotor in the direction commanded by the original input signal.

When the difference between commanded and existing attitude is zero, there is then no further input to the servo-amplifier, the servomotor ceases to rotate, and the control surfaces (ailerons in this case) take up the position required to satisfy the commanded attitude change. Oscillations and 'hunting' of the servomotor about the zero signal point are prevented by supplying rate feedback signals from the servomotor tachogenerator (see page 157).

In an aircraft that utilises a powered flight control system, the command signal from a servo-amplifier is used for the positioning of a control or transfer valve in a power control unit, and as may be seen from fig. 5.2, this obviates the need for a servomotor. The operation of this type of system is further described in chapter 7.

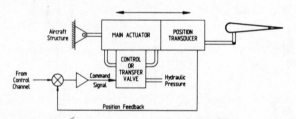

Fig. 5.2 Electro-hydraulic powered control

Referring to fig. 5.1 it will be noted that a servo-control channel is also dependent on other elements, the signals from which are utilised for the improvement of system response to commanded attitude changes and ultimate control capability. The functions of these elements, and brief details of their operating fundamentals are given in the following paragraphs.

Limiting

Under automatically controlled flight conditions, it is necessary to monitor what is generally termed the 'authority' of the control system (see also p. 278) notably in respect of the roll and pitch channels; in other words, limits must be placed on commanded control signals to prevent excessive attitude changes and harsh manoeuvring.

In the example of roll control channel shown in fig. 5.1, it will be noted that there are two limiting elements in the signal processing chain: a roll

150

command rate limiter, and a roll command limiter. The rate limiter limits the rate of change of command signals to some selected value, e.g. 5 degrees/second, so as to 'soften' aileron displacements and prevent harsh rolling of the aircraft. Signal processing through the limiter network is such that it imposes a specific time constant on the roll command signal. The roll command limiter controls the roll angle authority of the control system, the limit which the circuit is actually capable of being dependent on the control mode selected. Limits are accurately pre-set, and when the control channel is operating in the appropriate mode they are controlled by a d.c. bias signal applied to limiting diodes within the limiter module.

The roll command rate limiter consists of a limiting demodulator, a simple d.c. integrator, and a 400 Hz modulator stage with overall unity feedback. As already mentioned, it imposes lag on the roll command signal with a specific time constant; in this example the constant is about 10 seconds.

The output from the limiter module is summed with signals from the appropriate outer loop elements, and fed into the servo-control signal chain at summing points 'A' and 'B'. In addition, the limiter output is crossfed to the rudder control channel to provide co-ordination of the turn resulting from the displacement of the ailerons (see also page 122).

Synchronising

The necessity for synchronising has already been explained in chapter 2, (page 95) and as was also noted, the manner in which it is effected is dependent on the type of control system and the signal processing circuit arrangements adopted.

In the case of certain basic types of system, it is usual for the control panel pitch or roll controls, as appropriate, to be operated, thereby injecting a command signal into the appropriate amplifier channel, such that it will oppose any standing signal from an attitude signal transducer and reduce it to zero before engaging the control system. In the majority of systems however, it is effected by specifically designed synchronising circuits which automatically sense standing signals and oppose, or 'wash out' any resulting error signals.

An example of a circuit as applied to a roll control channel is shown in fig. 5.3 and is one which utilises the characteristics of both an operating amplifier in the integrating function, and of servomechanism feedback. Assuming that prior to engagement of the automatic control system, the aircraft is at some angle of roll there will be a corresponding roll attitude signal output from the roll sensing transducer of the vertical-axis gyroscope unit, and this is supplied to summing point 2. All other command inputs normally supplied to summing junction 1 are at zero, since the control system is not at this stage coupled to any mode. The roll attitude signal is therefore, an error signal

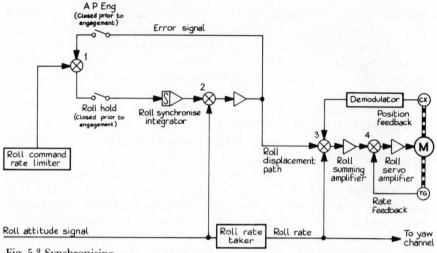

Fig. 5.3 Synchronising

which flows out from summing junction 2 to summing junction 3 via an amplifier and the roll displacement path, and also back to summing junction 1. Since the AP ENG and ROLL HOLD switches are both closed prior to engagement of the control system, then the error signal is also applied to the input of the integrating amplifier so as to drive it until its output to summing junction 2 is equal to the roll attitude signal, thereby zeroing the output from junction 2.

During the time that the foregoing synchronising process is taking place, an error signal is also produced at the output of summing junction 3 as a result of summing the signal along the roll displacement path, with a roll rate signal developed from the roll attitude signal after passing it through a 'rate taker' circuit; the purpose of the rate signal is to provide a short-term damping of servomotor operation. The resulting error signal passes to the aileron servomotor, via the summing and servo amplifiers, and so it is driven in the appropriate direction; the ailerons are not displaced of course, since with the control system not engaged the servomotor clutch is de-energised. At the same time that the motor operates, it drives a position feedback synchro (CX), the output of which is demodulated and fed to summing junction 3 to oppose the error signal which, as a result of the synchronising process, becomes less than the feedback signal, leaving the latter as the sole means of driving the servomotor until the feedback signal itself is reduced to zero.

The servomotor also drives a tachogenerator which supplies a rate feedback signal to summing junction 4, the purpose of this signal being to stabilise servomotor operation and to prevent any tendency for it to overshoot its nulled position. Thus, in the synchronised condition, the net signals at summing junctions 2 through 4 are zero, and since the servomotor is stopped at a position synchronised with the datum attitude detected by the vertical-axis gyroscope unit, it can be engaged with the aileron control system without snatching.

On engagement, the AP ENG and ROLL HOLD switches are opened and so the integrator is isolated from the circuit. Since the aircraft is still at some angle of roll, the appropriate roll attitude signal is now predominant, and from summing junction 3 is able to drive the synchronised servomotor which thereby displaces the ailerons to restore a wings-level attitude.

Demodulation

In the processing of command signals, it is necessary at certain stages of appropriate control channels to convert those signals having an alternating waveform into signals of unidirectional waveform; futhermore, the changes of phase polarity must also be detected in order to obtain comparable waveform characteristics. Such a conversion process is known as demodulation and the circuit element performing the conversion is called a demodulator. A typical example of its application is shown in fig. 5.3. In this case, the a.c. signal from the position feedback synchro is supplied as an input to the demodulator. A reference a.c. signal is also supplied to the demodulator so that the phase sense of the feedback signal may be detected. Both signals are passed through a transformer, full-wave diode, and resistance network, and as a result of comparison between input and reference signals, a d.c. output of the required polarity and amplitude is supplied to summing junction 3.

Gain and gain programming

The rates at which different types of aircraft respond to displacements of their flight control surfaces vary between types and their basic handling characteristics. In particular they vary with altitude, speed, aircraft load and configuration, and rate of manoeuvre. Thus, it is necessary to incorporate 'gearing' elements within flight control systems which will adapt them to aircraft and thereby reduce the effects which variations in flight parameters can have on handling characteristics. Similarly, in applying particular types of automatic flight control system to individual aircraft control systems, it is necessary to provide facilities for altering the response of an automatic system to any given level of input signal, thereby obtaining a signal ratio best suited to the operation of the systems when working in combination. Such a ratio is known as 'gain' and may be considered as having a function analogous to the changing of gear ratios in a mechanical gearing system (see page 33).

Figure 5.4 shows a closed-loop control system in simple form. The signal path from error to response is known as the system forward path, and the amplification from error to response, measured as amplification ratio, is the

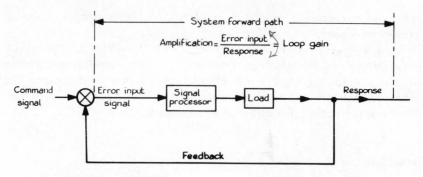

Fig. 5.4 Simple closed loop system

loop gain. Within limits, increased gain improves performance in two ways: (i) residual error in steady state is reduced and so improves long-term accuracy, (ii) initial response to a given command is more rapid. The limit on these improvements arises from the need for adequate dynamic stability of the system. If, for example, loop gain is increased to some excessive value then dynamic instability would be produced so that response is grossly oscillatory and never settles to a steady state. Even before instability is reached, excessive loop gain reduces dynamic stability such that it would take too long for response to settle at a steady state, and furthermore, it would initially overshoot and then 'hunt' about the steady-state value.

Satisfactory closed-loop performance depends on determining a loop gain which compromises between long-term accuracy plus initial response, and acceptable settling time plus limited overshoot. These factors, in turn, require sufficient inherent damping in the load.

Certain adjustments of command and feedback signals can be pre-set within amplifier and/or computer units in order to produce gain factors which establish a basic 'match' between an automatic control system and aircraft characteristics. Adjustments are based on the variation of electrical resistance at appropriate sections of signal circuits, and as in several types of control system, this is accomplished by means of potentiometers located on a calibration panel that forms an integral part of an amplifier or computer unit.

In addition to the foregoing adjustments, it is also necessary, particularly when a control system is operating in any of the outer loop control modes, for gain factors to be altered automatically to offset variations in handling characteristics resulting from changing flight conditions. This process is called 'gain programming or scheduling', and is part of a technique referred to as adaptive control. Some examples of programming the gain of servo control loops in response to airspeed changes have already been illustrated (see pages 122 and 124).

Another example of gain programming relates to an approach to an

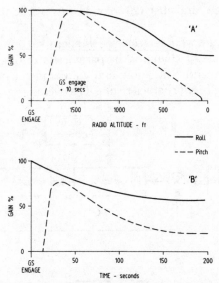

Fig. 5.5 Gain programme – ILS coupled approach

airport runway when the automatic control system is coupled to the instrument landing system in the localiser (LOC) and glide slope (GS) modes (see also page 180). The purpose of gain programming in this case is to reduce the gain of beam deviation signals and thereby allow for convergence of the LOC and GS beams.

The results of a programme based on a representative aircraft/automatic control system combination are shown graphically in fig. 5.5. The programme is accomplished by using signals from a low range radio altimeter which are supplied to a gain programmer control section in a vertical path module of the pitch control channel. After the GS mode is engaged plus 10 seconds, the GS deviation beam signal is modulated and amplified, and supplied as a pitch down command signal. Initially, the gain of the beam deviation amplifier is zero, but it then increases to, and is held at, 100% until the aircraft descends to 1,500 ft radio altitude. The altitude signal then produced by the radio altimeter develops a bias voltage which is applied to the GS beam deviation amplifier so that its gain is reduced as the aircraft descends (graph 'A'). The gain programmer control section of the vertical path module also supplies a gain control signal to a lateral path module in the roll control channel in order that the gain of the LOC beam deviation amplifier may also be reduced. In this case, the reduction is gradual from 100% to 57%.

In the event that there is an invalid signal from the radio altimeter, a time programme control is developed (see graph 'B'). In respect of the GS, this programme starts 10 seconds after GS has been engaged, and results in an initial gain of 80%, decreasing to approximately 20% over a period of time of 120 seconds. The LOC beam deviation amplifier gain programme is initiated directly at GS engage, and after 120 seconds time period the gain is reduced to 57%.

Figure 5.6 illustrates what is termed a self-adaptive control system and it is one which is capable of changing its parameters throughout an internal process of measurement, evaluation, and gain adjustments, without direct sensing of changing flight characteristics. The overall response of the system

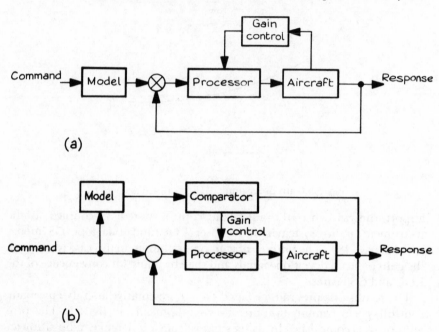

Fig. 5.6 Self-adaptive control system

is optimised, irrespective of flight conditions, by means of an electrical analogue system referred to as a 'model reference'. The model defines the optimum dynamic behaviour of the aircraft, based on selected response characteristics subject to any constraints that the airframe may impose, and the control system parameters are adjusted to match the response of the aircraft to that of the model.

One form of model reference system is shown schematically at (a). Command signals are fed through the model to the system, and the actual response tends towards that defined by the model as loop gain is increased; the error signal is amplified and fed to the control servo system. The system overall is referred to as a high loop gain system since in order to optimise response relative to the model, maximum gain is required. Fig. 5.6(b) illustrates an alternative form of model-reference system, in which command signals are fed to both the flight control system and the model. The output from the model is compared with actual response, and the external error so obtained is used to adjust the loop gain, in either sense, to minimise any discrepancy.

Feedback

When a control command signal is supplied to a servo control loop, then in accordance with closed-loop servomechanism principles, the operation of the associated servomotor or power contol unit must be so controlled that correction proportional to the command signal input will be applied. This requirement is satisfied, as we have already seen from several examples, by means of *position feedback* signals produced by sensors or transducers directly controlled by a servomotor or power control unit. In some cases, transducers may be controlled by the relevant flight control surfaces.

There is also a second requirement, and that is for the amount of applied control to be limited to prevent overshooting a commanded position, and also 'hunting' about that position. This is satisfied by applying *rate feedback* signals produced by a tachogenerator.

In some types of automatic control systems, the feedback signals are a part of the output from the servo amplifier itself, and after passing through an integration network they are algebraically summed with the amplifier input.

Integration

In addition to the establishment of a synchronised condition, there are other operating conditions of an automatic control system which require the 'washing out' of error signals resulting from sustained or recurring displacements from stabilised references; for example, under crosswind conditions while operating in the localiser or VOR mode (see pages 180 and 185). Since the resulting errors are time-related, integrators such as the operating amplifier referred to on page 151 are commonly applied to the signal processing circuits of the appropriate control channels. The time constant (in seconds) of an integrating circuit varies depending on the particular control channel to which it is applied, and on the associated outer loop control mode selected.

Reversing links

These are provided in some control systems for connection across the output of a servo amplifier to permit phase reversal when, on account of the servomotor mounting or capstan installed in individual aircraft, it is necessary for the direction of servomotor rotation to be reversed to provide the required control surface displacement.

TEST QUESTIONS

1 In connection with command signal processing, the function of adapting control system response to an aircraft's handling qualities, is known as:
   (a) limiting.
   (b) integrating.
   (c) gain programming.

2 In order to derive a d.c. control signal having the same phase relationship as an a.c. error signal, it is necessary for signals to be:
   (a) differentiated.
   (b) demodulated.
   (c) modulated.

3 What methods are employed to prevent an automatic control system from applying excessive attitude changes or harsh manoeuvring of any aircraft?

4 State the function of a synchronising circuit and briefly explain its operation.

5 What is meant by 'the gain of a control system'?

6 What do you understand by the term 'gain programming'?

7 Why is a gain programme necessary when operating in the 'GS' and 'LOC' modes?

8 From which source is a signal required to initiate the gain programme during an ILS-coupled approach?

9 For what purpose would a gain programme based on changes in airspeed be used?

10 Why is it necessary for a demodulator to be supplied with an a.c. reference signal?

11 In what type of flight control system are servomotors not required?

12 Why is feedback necessary in command signal processing channels?

13 State the two types of feedback signals normally required, and how they are produced.

14 Is it possible for feedback signals to be produced without the use of transducers?

6
Outer Loop Control

In addition to performing the primary function of stabilisation an automatic flight control system can also be developed to perform the tasks of modifying the stabilised attitude of an aircraft by computing the necessary manoeuvres from inputs of such raw data as airspeed, altitude, magnetic heading, interception of radio beams from ground-based aids, etc. Such data inputs constitute outer loop control (see fig. 6.1), the number of inputs serving as an indication of the progressive development of automatic flight from the basic single-axis wing-levelling type of autopilot to the highly sophisticated flight guidance systems now used in many present-day transport aircraft. The provision of raw data inputs relevant to a particular flight path is referred to as 'coupling' or as a 'mode of operation', the selection of each mode being made by the pilot via appropriate control panel switching devices. Other terms commonly used in connection with operating modes are: 'hold', 'lock' and 'capture'; for example, an aircraft flying automatically at a selected altitude is said to be in the 'altitude hold' or 'height lock' mode. The term 'capture' relates principally to modes associated with the selection and interception of beams from ground-based radio navigation aids; for example, 'glide slope capture'.

In some cases, mode switching is automatic; thus, to switch from intercepting a beam or a heading to tracking the beam on reaching it, a beam sensor is installed. This device senses beam deviation and switches modes automatically when the aircraft flies into the beam. Glide slope capture can also take place automatically, in this case the pitch control channel is switched from 'altitude hold' mode to glide slope track when the aircraft flies into the glide slope beam.

The raw data is supplied from sensors which convert the data into appropriate electrical signals that can be mixed in with inner control loop signal data to produce the changes to the aircraft's flight path. The traditional raw data instrument displays are used by the pilot for monitoring, and programming management. Outer loop control modes which may be incorporated in a control system are listed in the table on page 161. The number of modes actually adopted depends, of course, on the aircraft/control system combination; for example, in a single-engined light aircraft having a basic wing-

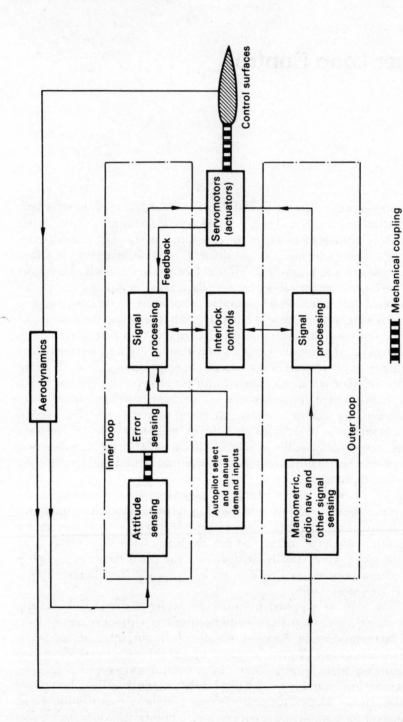

Fig. 6.1 Inner loop stabilisation and outer loop control

levelling control system, only altitude and heading modes might comprise the outer loop control, whereas in a more complex type of transport aircraft using a flight guidance system, and having automatic landing capability, the outer loop could comprise all the modes listed in the table.

Pitch axis	*Roll axis*
Manometric or air data:	Heading select and hold
Altitude select and hold	
Vertical speed	Bank hold
Airspeed select and hold	
Mach hold	Radio navigation:
	VOR
Pitch hold	Back beam
Pitch trim	Area navigation:
	Doppler
Turbulence penetration	Inertial
Vertical navigation	

Instrument Landing System

Glide slope	Localiser

Autoland

Approach	Runway align
Flare	Roll out

Control Wheel Steering
Touch Control Steering

Manometric or air data

Raw data inputs which come under this heading are those associated with altitude, airspeed, vertical speed, and speed in terms of Mach number, each providing outer loop control about the pitch axis of an aircraft. Sensing may be carried out either by independent sensor units, or by a central air data computer. The sensors operate on the same fundamental principles as the basic pitot-static flight instruments, the measuring elements being coupled to appropriate types of electrical pick-off elements in lieu of indicating pointer mechanisms.

Altitude hold

As we learned from chapter 4, any changes of aircraft attitude about its pitch axis while in straight and level flight, will be detected by the pitch attitude sensing element of the automatic control system, and the changes will be accordingly corrected. However, in the event that the changes are associated with a pure vertical displacement of the aircraft, detection and corrections might still be effected, but straight and level flight could possibly be resumed at some altitude above or below that at which flight is required. In other words, an attitude sensing element alone cannot detect an altitude change, and neither can it maintain a required altitude. In order to meet this requirement, and also to provide for automatic 'levelling off' at any desired altitude, an altitude hold, or lock sensor, is employed. Sensors vary in construction, particularly in connection with the type of pick-off element adopted for a specific flight control system. The fundamentals of the operating requirement may, however, be understood by considering the example illustrated in fig. 6.2.

The sensor consists of a pressure transducer comprising an evacuated capsule assembly, and E and I type of inductive pick-off element (see page 129) an amplifier, and a two-phase induction type of chaser motor. The capsule assembly is subjected to changes of static pressure supplied to the case of the sensor unit from the aircraft's static pressure system, and is mechanically linked to the I bar of the pick-off element. A change of altitude produces

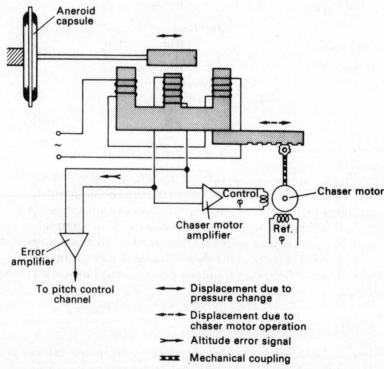

Fig. 6.2 Altitude-hold sensor

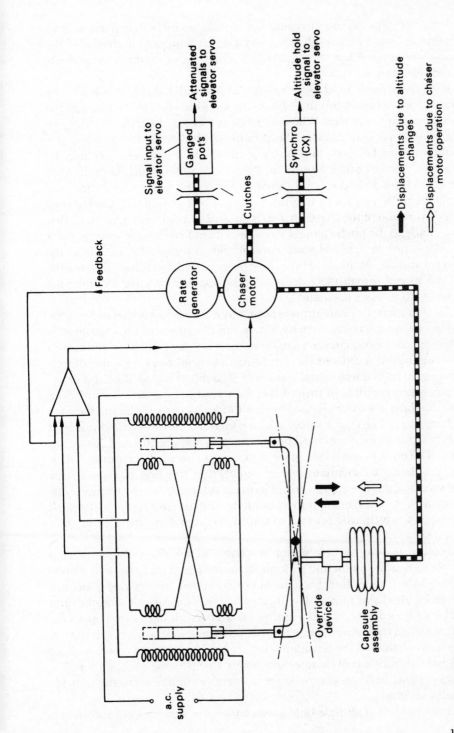

Fig. 6.3 Altitude-hold sensor

a change of static pressure to cause the capsule assembly to expand or close up; this, in turn, displaces the I bar and a signal is induced in the coil of the centre limb of the E bar, the signal being a measure of the direction and rate of altitude change.

With the altitude hold mode unselected, the induced signal is fed to the chaser motor which drives the E bar in the same direction as the I bar, and so reduces the signal to zero. When the mode is selected, the pick-off will be in the zero signal condition at the prevailing altitude of the aircraft; this condition thus becomes the datum from which altitude changes may be detected. When a change does occur, the capsule assembly displaces the I bar which induces a proportional signal in the centre limb coil winding, the signal being analogous to an altitude error. The signal, which cannot now cause operation of the chaser motor, is applied to a separate error amplifier, and finally to the pitch channel servo amplifier. The elevator servomotor is thus operated to apply elevator control and so restore the aircraft to the selected altitude. At the same time, the change in static pressure will cause the capsule assembly to displace the I bar in the opposite direction to reduce the error signal to zero once again.

Another example of an altitude hold sensor which forms part of a central air data computer, is shown in fig. 6.3. In this case, the pressure transducer is connected to the cores in such a manner that they move differentially within the windings of a differential transformer element, to provide an altitude error signal from a zero signal condition. The signal is amplified and drives a chaser motor which, in turn, drives the transducer capsule assembly in a direction opposite to that caused by an altitude change, so reducing the error signal to zero. The chaser motor is also connected to two solenoid-operated clutches, one engaging ganged potentiometers, and the other a CX synchro rotor. The potentiometers are in the signal line to the pitch servomotor, their function being to attenuate control signals as a function of sensed static pressure, and thereby adjust control loop gains for optimum operation. The function of the CX synchro is to transmit the altitude error signal to the pitch servomotor which will operate to return the aircraft to the altitude it is required to hold.

Another feature of this sensor is chaser motor damping to prevent oscillations as the motor and pick-off attain the zero signal position. This is accomplished by feeding back an opposing signal from a rate generator driven by the chaser motor. The linkage between the capsule assembly and the pick-off element contains a spring-loaded override device that opens the linkage when a pressure change is applied. This action also occurs if there is a pressure change on the capsule assembly when the electrical power is off, or when the altitude rate of change exceeds the dynamic range of the sensor. The linkage closes and the sensor becomes operative immediately the override conditions cease.

A unique type of altitude-hold sensor adopted in some types of autopilot is

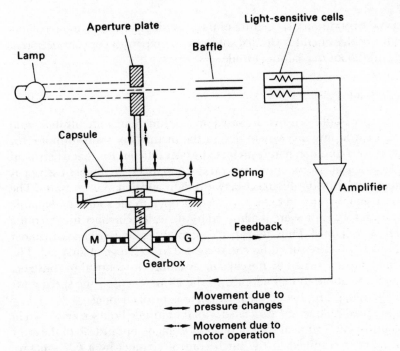

Fig. 6.4 Altitude-hold sensor

shown in fig. 6.4. In this case, the aneroid capsule actuates a detecting element, consisting of an aperture plate mounted on the capsule, an incandescent lamp, and two light-sensitive cells connected in a resistance bridge circuit. At a constant altitude, the aperture is centred with respect to the lamp, and the cells respond to equal amounts of light so that the bridge is in balance.

When the capsule expands or contracts as a result of an altitude change, the aperture plate is displaced, thereby deflecting the light beam from one or other of the cells causing an unbalanced condition in the bridge circuit. The resultant altitude error signal is amplified and is fed to the motor of a tachogenerator which then drives the complete assembly so as to centralise the aperture and thereby rebalance the bridge circuit. Overshoot of the balanced condition is prevented by a feedback signal from the generator which runs at a speed proportional to that of the motor. Thus, the sensor is continuously maintained in the balanced condition to provide the necessary flight level datum from which the altitude hold mode may be selected. This action is continuous until the hold mode is selected, at which point the altitude error signal voltage is switched from the tachogenerator motor to a summing network in the pitch control amplifier.

Any deviations from a selected altitude will result, therefore, in a signal being applied to the pitch servomotor to return the aircraft to that altitude.

165

Under these conditions, cancelling of the altitude error signal and rebalancing of the bridge circuit is effected solely by the expansion or contraction of the capsule about the datum altitude.

Airspeed hold

Since airspeed-hold sensors are used in conjunction with altitude-hold sensors, then in any one system design the methods of transmitting error signals are of a common nature; in fact, the only difference is that whereas an altitude sensor measures only static pressure changes, an airspeed sensor is required to measure the difference between static and dynamic pressures. The capsule assembly, instead of being sealed, is open to the source of dynamic pressure, and static pressure is admitted to the sealed chamber in which the assembly is contained. Thus, the capsule assembly expands or closes up under the influence of a pressure differential created by a change of airspeed. The pick-off element actuated by the capsule assembly, is identical in construction, and operation, to that adopted in the altitude sensor, the speed error signal also being supplied to the pitch servo control channel.

The airspeed-hold sensor associated with the altitude-hold sensor shown in fig. 6.3 utilises an identical type of pick-off element, but instead of the error signal being transmitted to the pitch control channel by a CX synchro, transmission is by means of ganged potentiometers driven by the chaser motor. The capsule assembly is housed in the same chamber as the altitude capsule assembly.

Mach hold

In high-performance aircraft, the airspeed is measured in terms of Mach number, in addition to the conventional unit of speed, knots. There is, therefore, a requirement for both modes under automatically controlled flight conditions, the airspeed hold mode being most commonly used during the low-altitude cruise phase of flight, and Mach hold during the high-altitude phase. Since Mach number varies with airspeed and altitude, the signal outputs from the independent sensors can be integrated to provide the required Mach signal output. This is accomplished by incorporating all sensors in a unit called a central air data computer.

Central air data computers

It is clear from the foregoing that the transmission of the raw data associated with airspeed, altitude, and Mach number is, primarily, the transmission of pressure from two sources; a static source and a dynamic source. In some types of aircraft, both sources are combined in a pitot-static probe, which is located in the airflow at an experimentally determined point. In the large majority of aircraft, however, the sources are independent; dynamic pressure is detected by a pitot pressure probe in the airflow, while static pressure is detected by a vent located at a point of undisturbed airflow, for example, at the side of a fuselage.

The pressures are transmitted to the primary flight instruments, i.e. airspeed indicator, altimeter, and vertical speed indicator, via pipelines the length and quantity of which will vary according to the size of aircraft, and the number of stations within an aircraft at which indications of the relevant parameters are required. In order, therefore, to minimise the 'pressure plumbing' arrangements, the idea of supplying the pressures to a central location from which they could be transmitted to any number of stations, and in the form of synchronous signal data links, was developed and resulted in the design of units designated as central air data computers (CADC).

In common with the other units and systems, a CADC can vary in design and it is, therefore, beyond the scope of this book to go into specific operating details of the various computers in current use. However, the principal features of CADC design concept may be understood from fig. 6.5, which, although based on an electro-mechanical analogue type, does serve to convey the fundamental principles involved generally.

The computer consists of two pressure transducers, one for the measurement of airspeed and the other for measuring altitude. Each transducer is coupled to an inductive pick-off element the signals from which operate motors, gear trains and shafts; the rotation of the shafts being proportional to dynamic pressure and static pressure. As is the case with any airspeed and altitude indicating system, it is also necessary to correct the dynamic and the static pressure inputs to CADC, for non-linear characteristics, i.e. the airspeed square-law, and the inverse pressure/altitude characteristics. Furthermore, corrections for errors arising from variations in airflow, which might possibly arise at a static vent location, must also be considered.

Corrections are, in this example, accomplished by coupling accurately profiled cams to the appropriate output shafts driven by the motors of the pressure transducer pick-off elements. The cams are provided with 'followers' which actuate gear trains, and further output shafts coupled to the rotors of CX synchros, the stators of which are connected to CT synchros in an airspeed indicator, an altimeter, and in the relevant hold mode circuits of the automatic flight control system. Thus, the rotation of the shafts and the synchro signals are converted into the required linear outputs.

For the derivation of Mach number outputs, a somewhat different mechanical and synchronous data link arrangement is required because, as noted earlier, Mach number varies with airspeed and altitude. In terms dynamic and static pressures, Mach number is equivalent to the ratio $(P—S)/S$; it is therefore necessary to convert the mechanical outputs from both the airspeed and altitude pressure transducers into an electical signal corresponding to this ratio. In the example of CADC considered, this is effected by coupling

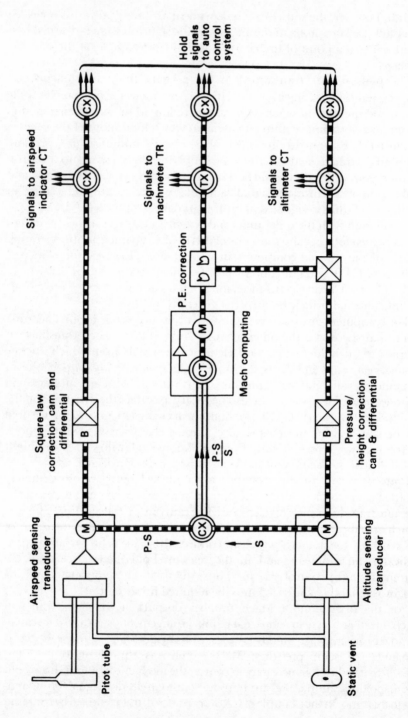

Fig. 6.5 Schematic arrangement of a central air data computer

the transducer output shafts, via cams, to a CX synchro, the dynamic output shaft being coupled to the stator, while the static output shaft is coupled to the rotor. The synchro therefore serves a dividing mechanism to produce an angular output corresponding to the foregoing ratio.

The output is transmitted to the stator of a synchro control transformer (CT) contained within the Mach computing section which has no mechanical link with the other sections of the computer. The output from the CT is then fed to an amplifier which energises the control phase of a servomotor causing it to drive the CT rotor to a position where it nulls the pressure ratio signal from the divider synchro CX. The motor also drives two cams, one to modify the motor output to ensure that the CT rotor is positioned in accordance with the required pressure ratio, and the second to correct the Mach number output for pressure error. The corrected output signal is fed to a torque synchro receiver TR contained within a separate Mach/airspeed indicator, and forming a synchronous data link with a TX, the rotor of which is positioned by the Mach computing section output shaft. Mach-hold mode signals are provided by a CX having its rotor coupled to the same shaft as that of the TX.

In any type of aircraft there are difficulties in measuring true static pressure because of variations in the pattern of the airflow at the location of the pitot-static pressure probe, or the static vent when used. The airflow pattern varies according to the position of the pressure head, static vent, Mach numbers and altitutde; under certain conditions, therefore, inaccuracies could be present. For conventional pitot-static flight instruments correction data are given in tabular or graphical form, the appropriate values being applied directly to indicated readings. In the case of a CADC, however, corrections are continuously and automatically applied, and in the example illustrated, this is done by means of cams profiled from values calculated to suit the conditions of a particular aircraft. The correction is applied as a function of Mach number, to the altitude and Mach number computing sections, the cams being connected to differential gear assemblies located between the pressure transducer and CX synchro of the altitude section, and between the CT and TX synchros of the Mach number section. Thus, the cams apply the pressure corrections, by modifying the angular positions of the output shafts, and the CX and TX synchro rotors, and consequently the output signals from the stators of these synchros.

Vertical speed selection and hold

In climbing out after take-off, it is necessary for a particular rate of climb or vertical speed, to be maintained and in order for this to be effected by an automatic control system, a vertical speed reference signal must first be established before engagement of the system. This rate signal is originated by

169

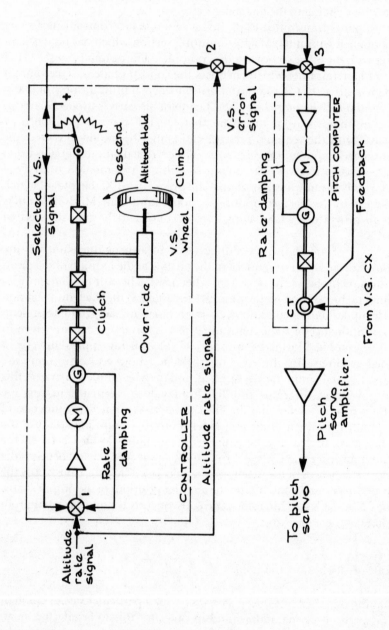

Fig. 6.6 Vertical speed selection and hold

a tachogenerator driven by the altitude sensor of a central air data computer, and is supplied to the pitch channel of the control system through a vertical speed mode select circuit which forms part of a pilot's control unit (see fig. 2.16). Circuits may vary between control systems, but the fundamentals of mode selection and operation may be understood from fig. 6.6.

The rate signal is applied to summing point 1, and after amplification it drives a vertical speed motor and generator, a gear train and an electrically-operated clutch assembly. Since the signal must be synchronised before engagement of the pitch control channel, the clutch at this stage is energised and so through a further gear train and override mechanism, the clutch drives the vertical speed wheel of the controller in the 'climb' direction and to the position corresponding to the prevailing vertical speed of the aircraft (speed indications are provided on the wheel). The rate signal is also supplied to summing point 2 and the pitch computer, via summing point 3 but as the pitch servomotor is not engaged no pitch control is applied.

The vertical speed motor also drives a potentiometer wiper which feeds back a signal to summing point 1 and cancels the rate signal from the central air data computer when the vertical speed wheel is positioned at the requried speed. The potentiometer signal is also supplied to summing point 2, and also cancels the rate signal at this point; thus the vertical speed section of the pilot's controller is in overall synchronism with the prevaling vertical speed of the aircraft. The purpose of the override mechanism is two-fold; it permits the pilot to overpower motorised operation of the wheel and potentiometer wiper, and provides a certain amount of 'feel'.

The pitch attitude reference during the climb is obtained from the sensing element of a vertical gyroscope unit, and the corresponding signal is supplied to a CT synchro in the pitch computer. The synchro is at 'null' when the sensed pitched attitude corresponds to that existing at engagement of the pitch channel. To ensure synchronisation before engagement, the output from the CT synchro is fed back to the pitch computer amplifier to drive the motor and synchro rotor and maintain the latter at 'null'.

Automatic control of the aircraft at the reference or 'en-route' rate of climb is obtained by selecting the 'VS' mode on the pilot's controller and, of course, by engaging the automatic control system itself. In the system on which fig. 6.6 is based, the VS mode engagement is effected when a 'servo engaged' switch is moved to the engaged position and when all necessary pitch control channel interlocks have been satisfied. In this situation, the clutch in the vertical speed section controller is now de-energised and so the vertical speed wheel and the potentiometer remain at their sychronised positions. If the aircraft's vertical speed should subsequently deviate from the reference speed at engagement, then an error signal will be produced at summing point 2 and after amplification, it drives the motor in the pitch computer. Since the motor is mechanically coupled to the CT synchro rotor, the latter is driven from its 'null' position to produce an error signal output principally as a result of the

171

vertical gyro having detected the pitch attitude change corresponding to the vertical speed change. This signal is then fed to the pitch servo amplifier and servomotor to displace the pitch control surfaces in the direction appropriate to that required for restoring the aircraft attitude and vertical speed, to that prevailing at the time of engagement of the control system.

Since the vertical speed wheel serves as the primary means of selecting pitch attitude changes, then in order to level off the aircraft at the altitude it is required to hold, the wheel is rotated in a 'descend' direction to reposition the potentiometer wiper. This establishes an error signal at summing point 2 which after processing by the pitch computer, causes the pitch control surfaces to be displaced in the appropriate direction. The wheel has a centre detent position corresponding to zero vertical speed and when at this position, a microswitch is operated to activate the altitude hold mode.

Heading hold

As the name suggests, in this mode of operation the automatic flight control system holds the aircraft on a pre-selected magnetic heading. Since turning of an aircraft is carried out by displacement of the ailerons, the heading hold mode relates to control about the roll axis, and the heading error signals are applied to the roll control channel of the flight control system. The error signals may be derived in a variety of ways depending on the source of magnetic heading data provided in a particular type of aircraft, and on how such source may be utilised in automatic flight control system operation.

In the case of some types of basic control systems utilising a directional gryo for the supply of heading data within the turn control loop, it is usual to provide a heading selector which may be a separate unit or incorporated in the pilot's control panel (see fig. 6.7). In this example, the selector contains a

Heading selector

Fig. 6.7 Heading selector

heading dial which can be rotated by means of a setting knob so that it may be referenced to any heading indicated by the directional gyro. The dial is mechanically coupled to a CT synchro which develops a heading error signal voltage as a function of dial position. The heading set knob is linked to a switch, and when the knob is pushed in the switch connects the error signal voltage to a summing amplifier in the roll control channel of the autopilot. Thus, the aircraft will turn on to the selected heading, and when this is reached the error signal is 'nulled' and the aircraft is held on the selected heading.

In the majority of aircraft, it is usual for heading data to be supplied from either a basic form of remote-indicating compass system, or from a flight director system (see chapter 9).

In both the foregoing systems, heading data are obtained by direct sensing of the earth's magnetic field as opposed to directional gyro indications which must always be referenced to those of a magnetic compass. Sensing is effected by a flux detector unit located at some remote point in the aircraft, e.g. a wing tip, the detector forming the transmitter (CX) of a synchronous control system (see also page 133). In this application, the complete detector turns with the aircraft so that a resultant field is produced which is aligned with the earth's magnetic field. The signals induced in the transmitter coils are fed to the stator of a slaving CT synchro, the function of which is to monitor the azimuth position of a directional gyroscope via a slaving amplifier and torque motor. The gyroscope may be contained within a panel-mounted indicator, but more generally it is designed as a separate and remotely-located unit. The fundamental arrangement of such a system is illustrated in fig. 6.8.

On a constant heading, the synchro system is in the 'null' condition, the heading being indicated by a heading card referenced against a lubber mark. During a turn, the flux detector senses the changing heading, and the field in the slaving CT synchro will rotate and thereby induce a heading error voltage in the synchro rotor. The signal is then amplified by the slaving amplifier and fed to the torque motor which precesses the directional gyroscope in azimuth and, at the same time, causes the rotor of a servo CX synchro to rotate. The signals induced in the stator of the CX are applied to that of a servo CT synchro in the indicator and, because turning of the aircraft causes mis-alignment to exist between the rotors of both synchros, a servo-loop error voltage is induced in the CT synchro rotor. This voltage is then applied to a servo amplifier, and after amplication, it is applied to the reference winding of a servomotor which is mechanically coupled to the CT synchro rotor and to the heading card of the indicator. Thus, the rotor and heading card are rotated, the card indicating the direction of the heading change taking place.

On cessation of the turn, the rotor reaches a 'null' position, and as there is no further input to the servo amplifier, the servomotor stops rotating. Oscillation of the servo system is prevented by velocity feedback damping signals from a tachogenerator which is also driven by the servomotor. The

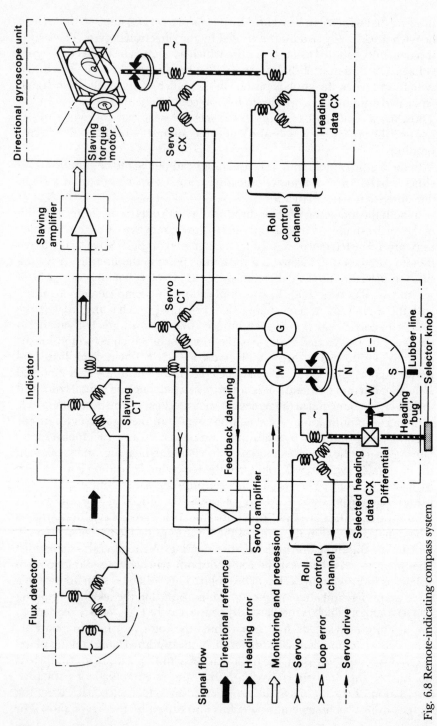

Fig. 6.8 Remote-indicating compass system

slaving CT synchro rotor is also coupled to the servomotor, the purpose of this being to drive the rotor in synchronism with the rotating field in the stator. Thus, during turns, the directional gyroscope is continuously slaved to the changes in magnetic heading, and by means of the servo synchro loop, the complete system is monitored such that when a turn ceases, the system is in a 'null' condition, and the indicator displays the corresponding heading.

In order to apply the foregoing principle of remote-heading indication to an automatic flight control system as a heading-hold mode of operation, and as a means of automatically turning an aircraft on to a selected heading, it is necessary to provide additional data synchros in the compass system. In the example shown in fig. 6.8, the data synchro for heading hold is contained within the directional gyroscope unit, its rotor position being controlled by the gyroscope in the same way as the servo CX synchro. The data synchro stator is connected to the roll control channel of the flight control system via the mode selector circuit; the stator output therefore, provides the heading hold reference.

The signals for turning the aircraft onto any desired heading are derived from a data CX synchro contained within the indicator. The synchro rotor is mechanically coupled to a selector knob via a differential gear which also drives a heading 'bug' with respect to the heading card. When the knob is rotated to select a heading, the synchro rotor induces an error signal proportional to the difference between the aircraft's heading and the selected heading, the signal being supplied to the roll control channel as a turn command. As the aircraft turns, the compass system will respond in the manner already described, until the aircraft is on the selected heading and the data synchro error signal is balanced out. The heading-hold mode is then selected so that the flight control system is monitoried by the data CX synchro in the directional gyroscope unit.

Since the 'heading select' facility of the compass system provides automatic turn control it is comparable in function to the turn control provided on a pilot's control panel (see page 88). It is necessary, therefore to incorporate an interlock circuit between the two to prevent their signals from opposing each other. Thus, before the heading selector knob is rotated, the turn control knob on the control panel must be at its centre 'detent' position. When the turn control knob is rotated from 'detent', the compass signal circuit to the roll control channel is interrupted, but because the copass system continuously senses the heading changes produced, the appropriate signals will be re-applied when the control knob is returned to 'detent'.

Turbulence penetration

Flight in turbulent air conditions can impose varying degrees of load on the structure of an aircraft, and although designed to withstand such loads, it is necessary for the pilot to adjust power and speed, and to operate the flight control system in a manner compatible with the flight conditions prevailing.

If an aircraft penetrates turbulent air conditions while under automatically-controlled flight, the control system will sense the turbulence as disturbances to aircraft attitude, but in applying corrective control it is possible for additional structural loads to be imposed. The reason for this is that the rate of control system response tends to get out of phase with the rate at which disturbances occur, with the result that control response tends to become 'stiffer'. In turbulent conditions, therefore, it is normal to disengage the automatic flight control system. In some current systems, however, turbulence penetration may be selected as a mode of operation such that the gain of both pitch and roll channels is reduced thereby 'softening' flight control system response to turbulence.

Instrument landing system

An Instrument Landing System (ILS) is a short-range navigational aid which provides azimuth and vertical guidance during the approach to an airport runway. The system comprises ground-based transmitting elements and also receiving elements carried on board an aircraft. The ground-based elements are: (i) a *localiser* which transmits runway azimuth approach information; (ii) a *glide path*, or glide slope, transmitter which provides vertical approach information; and (iii) *marker beacons* which transmit information on the distance to the runway threshold. The airborne elements are: (i) a *localiser signal receiving antenna* (usually this is the same antenna as the one used for the VOR installation since both the localiser element and the VOR operate in the same frequency band); (ii) a *glide path signal receiving antenna*; (iii) an *ILS receiver unit*; (iv) an *indicator* which shows whether the aircraft is on the correct approach path; (v) *marker beacon antenna and receiver*; and (vi) *marker lights* on the main instrument panel.

Localiser element

The transmitter is located at the far end of the runway and it transmits on a given frequency in the band 108.0 and 112.0 megahertz. To direct an approaching aircraft onto the extended centre line of the runway, the transmitter radiates azimuth guidance signals to the left and to the right of the centreline as shown in fig. 6.9. The signal transmitted to the left has a 90 Hz signal superimposed on it, while a 150 Hz signal is superimposed on the signal transmitted to the right. The two transmissions overlap along the runway centreline, and when an aircraft is approaching on the centreline extension, the ILS receiver receives both signals at equal strengths. This condition is indicated on the indicating element, usually by a vertical bar

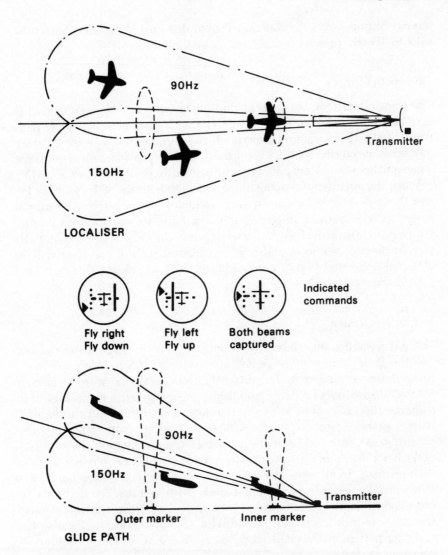

Fig. 6.9 ILS guidance signals and commands

which takes up a central position over the dial of the indicating element.

If the aircraft deviates to the left of the centreline, the strength of the 90 HZ signal will be greater than that of the 150Hz signal. Both signals pass through a comparator circuit within the receiver which then produces an output causing the vertical bar of the indicating element to be deflected to the right, thereby directing the pilot to 'fly right' in order to intercept the centreline again. Similarly, if the aircraft deviates to the right of the centreline, the 150 Hz signal is stronger than the 90 Hz signal, and so after comparison, the

177

receiver output causes the vertical bar to be deflected to the left to direct the pilot to 'fly left' in order to intercept the centreline.

Glide path element

The transmitter is located near the threshold of the runway and it transmits on a given frequency in the band 329.3 to 335.0 megahertz. The glide path transmitter radiates a signal pattern which is similar to that of the localiser but, as will be noted from fig. 6.9, the transmissions provide vertical guidance above and below a descent path established at an angle of between 2.5° and 3°.

When the aircraft approaches along this path both the 90 Hz and 150 Hz signals are received at the same strength, and this is indicated by a horizontal bar or, as is more usual in present-day flight director systems, by a pointer which takes up a central position over a scale in the indicating element. If the aircraft deviates below or above the established path, the pointer will be deflected respectively up or down and this will provide the pilot with the corresponding flight directions.

Indicating element

When ILS was first introduced, the deviations of an aircraft from the localiser and the glide path, were presented on a separate ILS indicator having a presentation as shown in fig. 6.10. However, with the introduction of integrated instrument systems, and flight director systems, it was logical to combine the indications with the relevant instruments, and this is now current practice (see chapter 9). Although there are many types of these systems in use, each varying in the method of data presentation, the examples of the latter shown in fig. 6.10, may be considered generally representative of such methods. In all cases, the localiser bar, or lateral deviation bar as it is more usually referred to, and the glide path pointer are deflected by independent meter movements to which the respective receiver channel signals are supplied. Scales are provided for reference against the localiser bar and glide path pointer, and thereby indicate by a series of dots the amount of deviation in degrees from the respective beam centrelines. For example, a two-dot deflection of the localiser bar corresponds to an aircraft deviation of 2.5°, and a full-scale deflection of the glide path pointer corresponds to a deviation of 0.5°. The dots are also indicative of the value (in micro-amps) of the signal currents producing meter deflections. Warning flags are provided and are visible when power is off, whenever signals are below the required strength, and whenever any malfunction or failure of the system occurs.

Marker beacons

Marker beacon transmitters are located at points along the runway approach

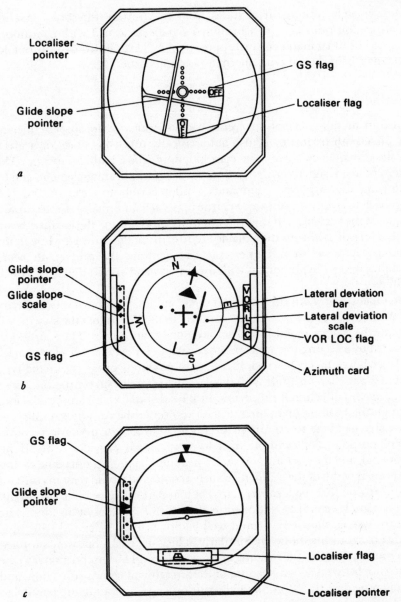

Fig. 6.10 *a* ILS indicator *b* Horizontal situation indicator *c* Attitude director indicator

path (see fig. 6.9), and their signals are beamed vertically into the descent path on a frequency of 75 megahertz. The signals are coded, and when an aircraft flies over a beacon, they are received and can be heard over the aircraft's intercommunication system; they also illuminate appropriately coloured lights on the cockpit instrument panel. The outer marker is situated

179

approximately four nautical miles from the runway threshold, and for identification purposes, its transmitted signals are coded with continuous dashes. The inner marker is sited approximately 3,500 feet from the threshold, its signals being coded with alternate dots and dashes.

ILS coupling

When an aircraft's navigation receiver has been tuned to a localiser frequency, the glide path frequency is also automatically tuned in, since for a given localiser frequency there is a corresponding glide path frequency. The receiver output signals are fed to the appropriate indicating element, and by following the displayed commands a pilot is able to carry out an ILS approach to an airport runway. Such an approach is normally effected in two stages; in the first stage, the aircraft intercepts and captures the localiser beam so that it is aligned with the extended centre line of the runway, while in the second stage, the aircraft intercepts and captures the glide path beam enabling it to fly in alignment with the runway and also in the correct pitch attitude.

In order to carry out the approach under automatic control it is necessary for the flight control system to be 'coupled' to the ILS so that the system will capture the beams smoothly and at the desired beam angles. The coupling is initiated by selecting the appropriate switches on the mode selector panel.

As we have already learned, ILS signals are purely of the command type and they vary in amplitude with displacement from beam centres but, since they have no directional properties, in the sense that they cannot take into account the heading of an aircraft with respect to the runway, coupling of these signals alone to an automatic flight control system would serve no useful purpose. For example, if a localiser signal provides a 'fly right' command, and the aircraft is on such a heading that it does not come within the normal width of the beam, then such a command would remain constant for the reason that the localiser signal at that part of the beam is a constant. If this signal were to be supplied to the control channel of an automatic control system, the aircraft could well be flown in a circle, and with little chance of capturing the beam. Similarly, if heading data alone were supplied to a control channel, the heading error signals would be proportional to the difference between actual heading of the aircraft and runway direction, and would provide a 'fly left' command resulting in the aircraft flying parallel to the localiser beam.

In the practical case, therefore, it is necessary to feed the signals from both sources to the roll control channel of an automatic control system, the beam intercept and tracking commands being the resultant of both signals. The effects are shown in fig. 6.11. At point 'A', it is assumed that the aircraft is under automatic control in the heading mode of operation, and that the ILS localiser frequency has been tuned in. The deviation pointer of the

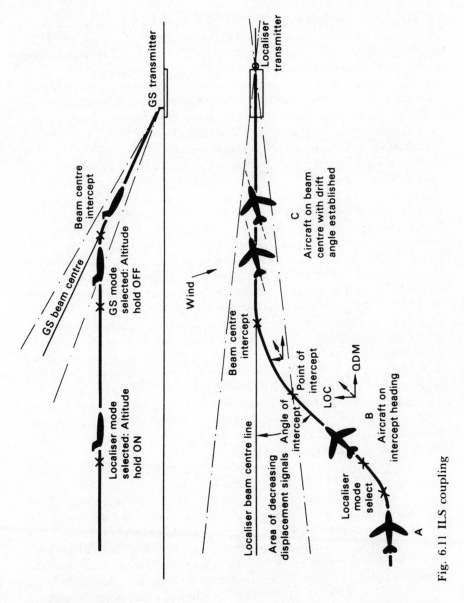

Fig. 6.11 ILS coupling

appropriate indicator will, therefore, display a 'fly left' command. In order to satisfy the command, the aircraft must, of course, change its heading and since it is being flown in the heading mode, the change can be made via the heading selector of the appropriate indicator. The heading selected is the magnetic direction, or QDM as it is called, of the runway. Thus, a heading error signal is established and is applied to the roll control channel which then initiates turning of the aircraft on to an intercept heading. The localiser

(LOC) mode is then selected so that the roll control channel can now respond to the resultant of the beam signal and the heading error signal. When the heading is such that the signals are in balance, the aircraft is then controlled so that it will fly straight and level on the intercept heading (point 'B') and at an angle governed by the ratio between the beam and heading signals. By pre-adjustment of the signal circuits, the angle of intercept can be set at a constant value as required for a particular automatic flight control system; some typical values are 35°, 45° and 65°. As the aircraft enters the normal width of the beam (in which the signal is proportional to deviation) the signal is correspondingly reduced, and the now predominant QDM signal causes the aircraft to turn towards the centre of the beam until both beam and QDM signals are again in balance. This control action is continuous until the aircraft is on the beam centre line and tracking it, when both the beam and QDM signals are reduced to zero.

During an automatic approach, allowance must be made for the effects of crosswinds otherwise the aircraft would take up a position downwind of the localiser beam centre and would fly a 'stand-off' track parallel to the beam, and at a particular drift or 'crab' angle. This distance from the beam centre and the crab angle would depend on the strength of the crosswind, and because the aircraft takes up a position where the beam and QDM signals balance each other, 'stand-off' and crab angle would be maintained. The method of compensating for crosswind effects varies depending on the type of automatic control system. In some cases, it is necessary to pre-calculate the drift angle appropriate to the wind conditions, and to adjust the compass indicator such that its indications and heading error signal output are offset from the QDM by the amount of drift angle. The relevant signal circuits are so arranged that the aircraft is turned in response to the localiser beam signal, and when this and the heading error signal are reduced to zero, the aircraft is then flown along the beam centre line with its heading off-set by the drift angle (point 'C' in fig. 6.11).

In a number of systems, it is more usual to supply part of the beam signal to an integrator circuit with a long time-constant. The circuit is activated when the aircraft is near the beam centre line, i.e. when the beam signal falls to a low value, and remains in action until the signal has fallen to zero. Since the presence of a crosswind slows the speed of interception of the beam centre line, the integrator signal is built up in porportion to the amount of crosswind. The build up continues until the beam centre line is reached, at which point the aircraft's heading is controlled by the integrator signal and the pre-selected heading signal. signal and the pre-selected heading signal.

As noted earlier, when the navigation receiver is tuned to the localiser frequency, the glide path frequency is also tuned in; thus, when the aircraft is correctly established on the localiser beam, the glide path signals can be used to effect the final phase of the approach. The glide path can be intercepted and captured while the aircraft is being flown in the altitude-hold mode, and from above or below the glide path. Ultimately, the aircraft must, therefore, fly through the glide path and its proximity will be evidenced by 'fly down' or 'fly up' commands of the associated indicator. At the point of beam interception, the glide path mode is selected on the mode selector panel, and the beam signals are then supplied to the pitch control channel of the flight control system. Thereafter, changes of position of the aircraft from the glide path produces control channel response to restore the required pitch attitude.

At the same time that the glide-path mode is selected, the altitude-hold mode is automatically disconnected. A pitch control channel incorporates a circuit network which phase advances the glide path error signals so that they are damped to give progressively tighter control as the aircraft flies down the glide path, and thereby allowing for the converging nature of the beam (see also page 155. In flight control systems which use a vertical-axis gyroscope as the attitude sensing element, the pitch error signal produced would tend to 'back off' the beam error signal and cause the aircraft to fly above the beam. This is also prevented by passing the signals through an integrator circuit.

VOR system

A VOR (VHF omni-directional radio range) system not unlike the ILS is a short-range navigational aid comprising ground-based transmitting stations, or beacons, and receiving elements carried on board an aircraft. It differs in function however, in that in provides en-route information on the bearing of an aircraft from the points at which the stations are geographically located. The stations are spaced at intervals of 50 to 80 nautical miles within what is termed the 'airways system'.

A VOR station transmits a very high frequency (VHF) carrier wave operating in the 108 to 118 MHz band, and on which are superimposed two low frequency modulating signals. One of these signals, known as the reference signal, is radiated in all directions (hence the term omni-directional) with a fixed phase, while the other is a rotating beam signal and varies in phase to produce an infinite number of 'radials'. Thus, at any particular point relative to the station (which is lined up on magnetic north) a specific phase relationship exists between the two signals, and this is indicated in fig. 6.12. Each station is identified by a Morse code signal which is received by the navigation receiver in the aircraft when the corresponding station transmitting frequency has been selected. The display of bearing information is presented on an indicator mounted on the aircraft's main instrument panel. The type of indicator depends on the equipment specified for a particular type of aircraft; for example, it may be an omni-bearing indicator, a radio magnetic indicator, or it may be a horizontal situation display indicator which forms part of a flight director system (see chapter 9). In general, however, the dipslay is comprised of three main indicating elements: (i) a

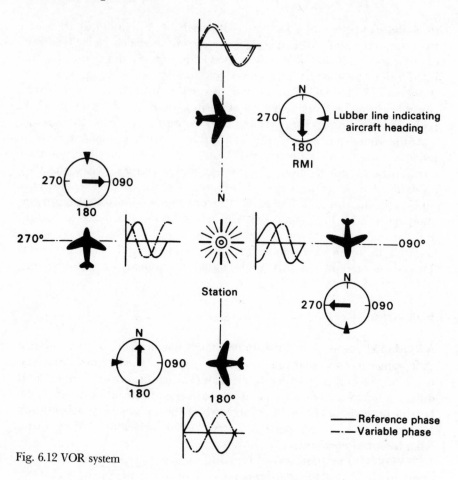

Fig. 6.12 VOR system

bearing scale or an index, which is positioned by a selector knob to indicate the radial on which the aircraft is to be flown; (ii) a deviation pointer indicating whether the aircraft is flying on the radial; and (iii) a TO-FROM indicator to indicate whether the aircraft is flying towards a station or away from it. A warning flag is also provided to indicate 'system off', receiving of low-strength signals, or no signals at all.

Figure 6.13 illustrates an omni-bearing indicator, and this serves as a useful example in understanding the fundamentals of VOR operation as a navigational aid. After a station has been identified from its Morse signal and tuned-in, the omni-bearing selector knob is rotated to set the required bearing on the bearing scale, and also to position the rotor of a resolver synchro. The navigation receiver which continuously compares the phases of the transmitted signals, and compares them in turn with the phase shift produced in the resolver synchro, supplies an output signal to a meter movement controlling the vertical pointer of the indicator. When the pointer lies in the centre of the

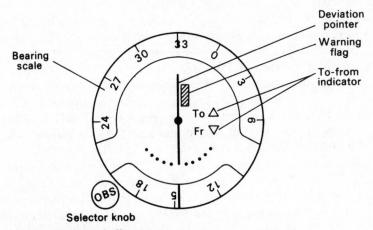

Fig. 6.13 Omni-bearing indicator

indicator it indicates that the phasing of the required bearing radial signals has been matched and that further rotation of the selector knob is unnecessary. The reading shown on the bearing scale at that instant indicates the heading on to which the aircraft must be turned in order to fly along the corresponding radial to the station.

At the same time, the TO-FROM indicator indicates TO usually by means of an arrow-shaped pointer. Any departure from the radial as a result of, say crosswind drift, the deviation pointer will be deflected to one or other side, and so command a turn in the direction of the deflection in order to intercept the radial once again. Thus, the command function is identical to that of the localiser pointer of an ILS indicator and, since localiser and VOR operate in the same frequency band, omni-bearing indicators and the indicators of flight director systems, are in fact designed such that their deviation pointers serve the dual command function.

As the aircraft approaches overhead the station, so the deviation pointer mechanism becomes more sensitive as a result of the convergence of the radials, and its indications, together with those of the TO-FROM indicator, become erratic. In this part of the approach, overhead the station and in departing from it, the aircraft is said to be in the 'cone of confusion'. The extent of the cone varies with altitude and groundspeed, typically from a few seconds at low altitude, to as much as two minutes at high altitude. Outbound flight from the station is indicated by the TO-FROM indicator changing to FROM and, provided an accurate heading is maintained, the deviation pointer continues to give corrective command information for the interception of the outbound radial.

VOR coupling

Operation in the VOR coupled mode is similar in many respects to that of the localiser mode, in that it also involves the capture of radio signal beams radiated in azimuth in association with steering commands from magnetic heading data; such data, however, being related to a pre-selected VOR station radial instead of a runway QDM. When the navigation receiver has been tuned to the station frequency and the required radial has been selected on the course indicator, coupling to the roll control channel is initiated by selecting the LOC/VOR mode. As a result of the convergence of the radials, and of the cone of confusion over a VOR station, the signal from a selected radial is unreliable and could, therefore, cause the automatic flight control system to carry out unwanted manoeuvres. To prevent this, it is usual to 'cut off' the VOR signal at the entrance to the cone of confusion, so that the roll control channel responds only to heading data signals. Cut off takes place automatically by means of an over-station sensor (OSS) circuit, and is maintained for a pre-set time period, after which, and with the aircraft departing from the cone of confusion, the VOR signal corresponding to the outbound radial is switched in.

Inertial navigation system

The requirement for the navigation of an aircraft is, quite simply, the one of determining its position in relation to its point of departure, and points en-route, in order to reach a known destination. The basic data necessary for this purpose are principally time, speed, distance between points, longitude and latitude, magnetic heading, wind speed and direction, and bearings relative to known points on the earth's surface and to celestial points. The provision of such data is made by a variety of navigational aids, most of which are dependent on an external reference of one form or another.

Although such aids can provide reasonably accurate answers to the problems associated with the navigational task, the remaining errors involved make them only relatively useful. In the continuing development of navigational aids, particularly in relation to the stringent requirements laid down for the strategic roles of military aircraft, for missiles, and for spacecraft, it became essential to provide aids having much greater accuracy. These also needed to be independent of references derived from ground-based navigational beacons in particular. The attendant research ultimately resulted in the application of a theory which, as is so often the case, is based on old established laws; in this instance the theory of inertia applied to what subsequently became known as an Inertial Navigation System (INS), the basic elements of which are shown schematically in fig. 6.14. The navigational problems which can be solved by INS are shown in fig. 6.15.

Inertial theory is based on Newton's second law, i.e. that force is equal to time rate of change of momentum, without approximation or correction for any effect. In plainer terms, it can be stated that velocity is the rate of change

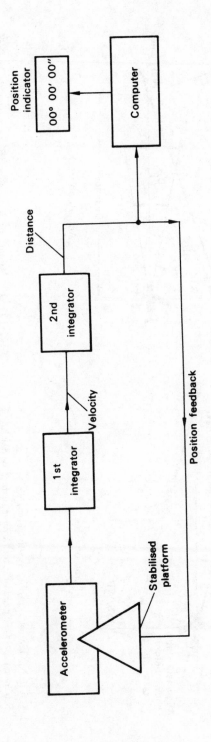

Fig. 6.14 Basic elements of an inertial navigation system

187

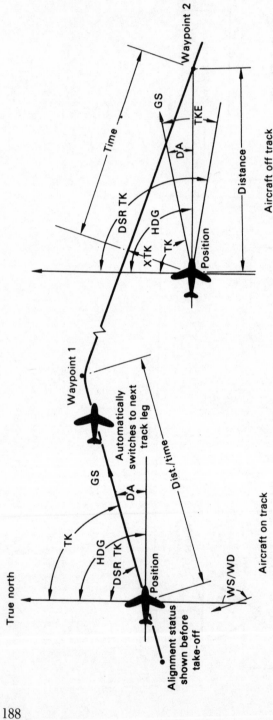

Fig. 6.15 Navigational problems solved by INS

GS (*Ground speed*): Speed of aircraft over surface of earth.
DA (*Drift angle*): Angle in degrees that aircraft track is to right or left of aircraft heading.
TKE (*Track angle error*): Angle in degrees that aircraft track is to left or right of desired track.
XTK (*Cross track*): Distance left or right from desired track to present position, measured perpendicular to track desired.

TK (*Track*): Actual path of aircraft over earth's surface. Measured clockwise from true north through 360°.
DSR TK (*Desired track*): A great circle path on surface of earth connecting two waypoints.
HDG (*Heading*): Angle between true north and longitudinal axis of aircraft.

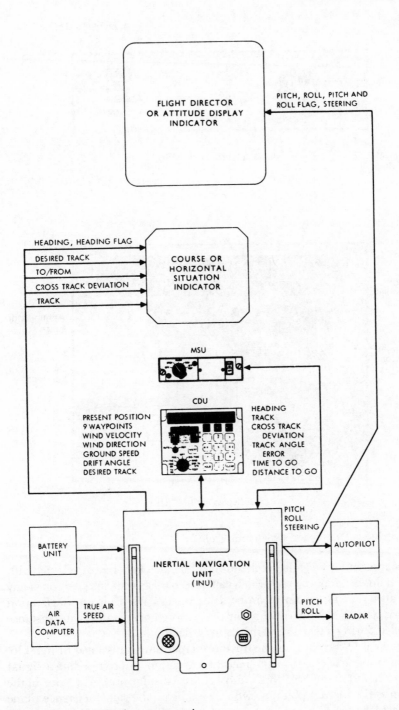

Fig. 6.16 Inertial navigation system units.

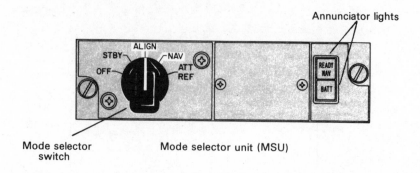

Mode selector unit (MSU)

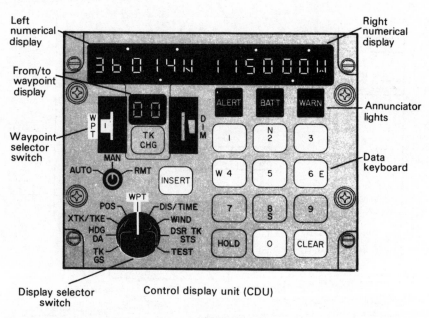

Control display unit (CDU)

Fig. 6.16 Inertial navigation system units (*contd.*)

of distance with time, and acceleration is the rate of change of velocity with time. If this deduction is reversed, it can be seen that a vehicle's position at any time after starting to move can be determined solely from its acceleration history, and by double integration of measured accelerations the distance travelled during a given time may also be determined.

A typical INS comprises the three principal units illustrated in fig. 6.16, they are a mode selector unit, an inertial navigation unit comprising a digital computer and inertial platform, and a control display unit. The 'core' of the system is the inertial platform which establishes the stable reference plane from which measurements can be computed. The inputs needed to keep the system in touch with the outside world come from accelerometer-actuated pick-off elements, the signals being fed to the computer in proportion to acceleration forces. Since the functions of navigational geometry lie in a horizontal plane, two accelerometers are mounted on the platform; one oriented north-south, the other oriented east-west. Thus, the computer is able to record the acceleration history of an aircraft, and therefore determine its position in relation to its starting point. Angles that fall between the north-south or east-west relationship are calculated by the computer solving algebraic vector problems. A third accelerometer measures acceleration in the vertical direction.

To make the measurements refer only to translational accelerations, the accelerometers must at all times be maintained in accurate alignment with their respective directions, i.e. the platform must be maintained in correct azimuth alignment. This is accomplished by mounting the platform in a gimbal ring system and controlling the position of the rings by three rate-integrating gyroscopes and torque motors. In addition, the platform must be maintained accurately horizontal in relation to the earth's surface in order to prevent the accelerometers from sensing misleading gravity accelerations. Errors resulting from earth rate and transport rate (see pages 100 and 102) and from Coriolis effect, are also automatically corrected by computed signals applied to the torque motors. The arrangement of the platform and gimbal system, and method of stabilising, have already been described in Chapter 3 (see page 124).

Figure 6.17 shows the schematic arrangement of the accelerometers and their interconnection with the latitude and longitude counters of the display

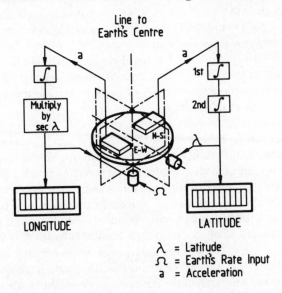

λ = Latitude
Ω = Earth's Rate Input
a = Acceleration

Fig. 6.17 Schematic arrangement of accelerometers

unit. To allow for changes in latitude, the output of the north-south accelerometer is doubly integrated so that the angular acceleration of the aircraft above the earth's centre can be followed. A slightly more complex correction must be applied to allow for changes in longitude because such changes are also dependent upon latitude. The output velocity signal of the east-west accelerometer integrator is therefore multiplied by the secant of the latitude and then passed to the platform monitoring torque motor.

The inertial platform has one further characteristic and that is of being tuned so that at all times it accurately seeks a local vertical reference coincident with the earth's centre. This is achieved by applying the principle of what is known as the Schuler pendulum in such a way that by utilising error compensations from the computer together with a mathematical model in the computer, the platform is made to behave like a pendulum whose arm is equal in length to the earth's radius, and whose centre of rotation is coincident with the earth's centre. The result is that any build-up of errors in the accelerometers and gyroscopes is limited and minimised, and the platform stays parallel to the earth's surface regardless of which latitude and longitude it is put into operation.

The digital computer continuously solves the associated navigation equations, from the signal data fed into it by the control display unit, and by a central air data computer. The signals from the latter relate to true airspeed, which information is used for determining wind speed and direction and thereby the drift angle, and to altitude information for damping an integrating loop in altitude computation. Output signals are used for displaying computed data, and also for manoeuvring the aircraft towards the selected waypoint, via the roll channel of the automatic flight control system.

The control display unit utilises a digital readout which presents the pilot with all the data necessary for monitoring flight progress. Information for display is inserted by means of a 'keyboard'; it can also be obtained by turning the knob of a data selector switch to desired settings. A digital readout also provides information on the changes of track of the aircraft as it proceeds from one waypoint to the next.

Prior to departure, and before any movement of the aircraft takes place, the system is operated in a 'standby' and an 'align' mode, during which the inertial platform is automatically aligned to the aircraft's axes. The latitude and longitude of the aircraft at its departure position are also inserted at the control display unit, and this information is integrated into a mathematical model within the computer and, by a procedure known a gyrocompassing, the system is also aligned to its north reference point. The co-ordinates of the en-route waypoints and of the destination are also subsequently entered in the control display unit. When the alignment sequence is completed, an annunciator light illuminates to indicate that the system is 'ready to navigate' and that following selection of the navigate mode on the mode selector unit, the aircraft may commence its flight.

During flight, and approximately two minutes before a waypoint is reached, a light on the control panel comes on, and then begins to flash on and off thirty seconds before the waypoint is crossed, thereby signalling for the aircraft to be turned. With the automatic flight control system engaged, the INS supplies command signals to the roll control channel so that the aircraft will automatically roll into a turn towards the waypoint and will level out on the new heading from the waypoint. This is repeated at each en-route waypoint until the final destination is reached.

In several types of current generation aircraft, the inertial systems are of somewhat sophisticated design in that conventional forms of gyroscope are replaced by units to which laser beam techniques are applied. They still operate in conjunction with accelerometers and a display unit, but with the advantage of eliminating rotating parts and gimbal systems. Such gyros are referred to as ring laser gyros and are arranged as shown in the simplified diagram of fig. 6.18.

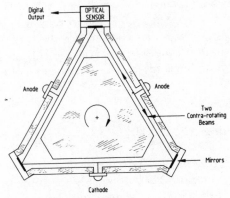

Fig. 6.18 Ring laser gyro principle

The first thing to note is that it is quite unlike a conventional gyroscope in that there is no rotor and gimbal system; rotating parts are in fact unnecessary. The basis of it is a triangular block of specially fabricated glass (known as cervit glass) that it is extremely hard and does not expand or contract with heating and cooling. By means of computerised ultrasonic diamond drilling techniques a cavity is formed within the whole block. A mirror is fitted at each corner of the block, and a cathode and two anodes are located as shown.

The cavity is filled with a lasing medium (typically helium-neon) and when excited by an electrical potential across the cathode and anodes two light beams are emitted and, by design, are made to travel in opposite directions. Since they are 'bounced off' by the mirrors, they then follow closed paths around the cavity. Both beams combine in a prismatic type of optical sensor at one corner of the block.

In applying the technique to the inertial system mentioned earlier, three laser gyro assemblies are required, and they are mounted mutually at right angles to each other so that when they are 'strapped down' to an aircraft's structure they relate directly to movements about its pitch, roll and yaw axes.

With the aircraft in straight and level flight, all three gryros are in a static condition, and in this condition, the resonant frequencies of the beams are equal.

If the aircraft's attitude is now changed about, say the pitch axis, the corresponding gyro will also be rotated about this axis. This sets up a difference between the resonant frequencies of the two beams or, putting it another way, one beam takes slightly longer than the other to complete a circuit around the triangular block.

When the two beams combine in the optical sensor an interference pattern results, and the movements of this pattern are counted by the sensor which then produces a digital output that is proportional to the angular rate at which the gyro has been rotated.

Similarly, the other two gyros would produce output signals proportional to the angular rates at which they rotate about their respective axes. After computerised integration processes, the rates provide an inertial position reference equivalent to that achieved when gyroscopes of the more conventional type are used.

Control wheel steering

A control wheel steering mode (CWS) is provided in some automatic flight control systems, its purpose being to enable the pilot to manoeuvre his aircraft in pitch or roll, through the automatic control system by exerting normal manoeuvring forces on the control wheel. In adopting this mode, it is not necessary for pitch and turn controls to be provided on a system control panel.

When the control wheel is released, the automatic control system holds the aircraft at the newly-established attitude. The pitch and roll forces applied by the pilot are sensed by force transducers which generate output voltage signals proportional to the forces; the signals are supplied to the pitch and roll channels of the automatic flight control system. The locations of transducers depend on the type of aircraft and control system, but typically they are either in the hub of each pilot's control wheel, or in the control system below each pilot's control column.

In some cases, limits may be imposed, e.g. if a roll angle is less than 5°, wing levelling will automatically occur, and the control system will hold the aircraft on a heading established one second after the wings are level. Prior to, and during, capture phases of radio navigation modes of operation, the pilot can use CWS for supervisory override of the automatic flight control system.

Thus, with the aid of the CWS mode, the pilot always has a control capability of the aircraft, and the aircraft does not have to follow a pre-programmed flight path when particular conditions dictate a different manoeuvre.

In one example of CWS sensor unit used in a current type of flight guidance system, piezo crystal elements are employed which have the property of varying their electrical resistance whenever they are subjected to varying pressures. The piezo-resistive elements as they are generally known, are connected to the form of an electrical bridge, and are embedded in the upper and lower portions of a specially designed spring contained within the sensor unit casing which is itself secured within the hub of the control wheel on the pilot's control column.

One bridge circuit responds to roll command forces applied through rotation of the control wheel, while the second circuit responds to pitch command forces applied by fore and aft movement of the control column. Pairs of elements of each bridge circuit are located on opposing sides of their appropriate portions of the spring, and they are supplied with a d.c. excitation voltage of 9 V from the flight guidance system computer. The output signals from the bridge circuit are fed as appropriate to the roll and pitch channel circuits of the computer, only when the CWS mode of operation is selected, and when forces are manually exerted on the control wheel. With no forces applied each bridge circuit is in a balanced condition and so no signal outputs are produced.

When, for example, the control wheel is rotated, the force exerted causes the roll spring to bend thereby compressing the pair of piezo-resistive elements on the inner side of the spring causing their resistance to decrease. The pair of elements on the outer side are stretched and as a result their resistance is increased. The bridge circuit is therefore unbalanced and a change in polarity and voltage occurs, corresponding to the direction of control wheel movement and amount of force applied. After processing by the computer the signal is supplied to the aileron actuator which displaces the ailerons in the direction required; typically, positive and negative output signals result in roll displacements to the right and left respectively.

The pitch spring and its associated piezo-resistive elements respond to forces in the same manner to produce output signals for the operation of the elevator actuator. In this case, positive and negative signals result in nose up and nose down displacements respectively.

In another example of automatic control system, the sensing of control wheel steering forces is accomplished by devices known as dynamometric rods. These are connected directly into the appropriate flight control circuits of the aircraft, and consist essentially of a cylinder containing a spring-controlled synchro. One end of the cylinder is connected to the controls via a fixed rod while the other end is connected via a rod in such a way that relative movement between this rod and the cylinder is obtained when the controls are operated by the pilot. The rod is also connected to the spring so that as

195

appropriate movement takes place, the spring is subjected to either compression or tension forces. Rod movement also causes rotation of the synchro rotor which produces output signals proportional to the forces applied.

Force transducers may also be of the E and I bar type (see page 129) housed inside a spring unit mechanically coupled at each end into the elevator and aileron control systems. When either the control column or control wheel is displaced, then depending on the direction of displacement the spring is compressed or extended. This results in relative linear displacement of the E and I bars, and an output voltage to the control channels that is proportional to the force applied.

Touch control steering

Touch control steering (TCS) also permits a pilot to manoeuvre his aircraft in pitch or roll, but unlike CWS the appropriate automatic control channels and servomotors are disengaged while the pilot flies the aircraft to the desired attitude. Disengagement is established by operation of a switch on the pilot's control wheel. At the same time that the switch is operated, a feedback signal path is provided into the integrating circuits of the appropriate control channel to ensure synchronisation with the new attitude required, and also nulling out of the servo loop output.

When the TCS switch is released, the feedback path is interrupted, and the relevant integrator retains the attitude signal existing at that time. The servomotor is re-engaged to hold the new attitude. If the aircraft deviates from the synchronised attitude, an error signal is produced at the integrator output and is used to drive the servomotor and aircraft back to the synchronised attitude.

TEST QUESTIONS

1 What outer loop control inputs constitute manometric data, and to which control axis are they related?

2 Why is it necessary to provide an altitude hold mode?

3 How is it ensured that an altitude hold unit is always at a datum altitude?

4 Explain how in the altitude hold mode, a typical unit detects and corrects any departure from the datum altitude.

5 State the sequence in which an altitude alerting system operates when an aircraft descends to a pre-selected altitude.

6 What sources of air pressure are required for the operation of airspeed and Mach hold sensor units?

7 What is the purpose of a central air data computer?

8 In terms of a pressure ratio, Mach number is equivalent to:
  (a) P - S/P
  (b) S/P - S
  (c) P - S/S

9 Describe how a Mach number output signal from a central air data computer is derived.

10 Heading hold signals for an automatic flight control system are supplied to the:
  (a) yaw channel
  (b) roll channel
  (c) pitch and roll channels

11 How are the heading signals transmitted from a compass system to the appropriate channel of an automatic flight control system?

12 How is it ensured that corresponding magnetic heading change signals are supplied after the pilot has injected a turn command signal through his control panel?

13 What is the purpose of the turbulence penetration mode, and what effect does it have on a control system when selected?

14 Azimuth information during an ILS approach is provided by signals from:
  (a) the glide slope transmitter
  (b) marker beacons
  (c) the localiser transmitter

15 Explain how deviations of an aircraft from the signal paths transmitted by the ILS are indicated, and by means of a simple diagram show a typical situation.

16 How is it ensured that during an automatic approach an aircraft intercepts the ILS localiser beam at the correct angle and point on the beam centre?

17 What is meant by 'beam stand-off' and how is compensation made for it?

18 Briefly explain the operation of a VOR system.

19 How is the VOR mode selected and to which channel of an automatic control system are the signals supplied?

20 What is the purpose of an over-station sensor?

21 In connection with the provision of navigational data, in what way does an INS differ from other systems?

22 Define the following: TKE, XTR and DSR TK and by means of a diagram show how they are related to the position of an aircraft.

23 How are accelerometers utilised in an INS and what method is adopted to ensure that they are maintained in accurate alignment?

24 What part does the Schuler pendulum principle play in the operation of an INS?

25 Briefly describe the construction of a ring laser gyro.

26 How does a ring laser gyro detect movements of an aircraft about an axis?

27 What is the purpose of the control wheel steering mode?
28 Describe a typical control wheel steering transducer and how it transmits signals to the appropriate control channel.
29 How does touch control steering differ from control wheel steering?

7
Conversion of Command Signals to Powered Control

The power output element of any automatic flight control system consists of servomotors, or servo-actuators as they are sometimes called, connected in the aircraft's primary flight control system circuits; the number of servomotors employed is governed by the number of control loops required. In addition to the actuation of primary flight controls, servomotors may also be used, in some cases, for the actuation of the secondary flight controls provided for trimming purposes and for yaw damping (see pages 206 and 214). In the case of aircraft utilising hydraulic power-operated controls, automatic control system servomotors are not required, since command signals can be applied direct to the actuators of the relevant power control units.

In general, servomotors operate on either electro-pneumatic, electro-mechanical, or electro-hydraulic principles, the choice, and constructional features adopted in applying such principles being dependent on the type of automatic control system, and on the methods adopted for actuation of the primary flight control surfaces. Servomotors may be connected either in series or in parallel with the normal flight control system of an aircraft. A series-connected servomotor is one which moves the flight control surfaces without moving the pilot's controls, while a parallel-connected servomotor moves both the control surfaces and the pilot's controls.

Electro-pneumatic servomotor

An example of a servomotor designed for use in one particular type of three-axis autopilot system is shown schematically in fig. 7.1. It consists of an electro-magnetic valve assembly, comprised of dual poppet valves which are connected via pressure ports and orifices to two cylinders containing pistons sealed against pressure loss by rolling diaphragms (also called 'roll-frams'). The valves are controlled by electrical command signals from the autopilot signal processing element, and the pressure for actuation of the pistons is supplied either from an engine-driven pump or from a tapping at a turbine engine compressor stage. The operating pressure is determined by the control force characteristics of the aircraft in which the particular autopilot is

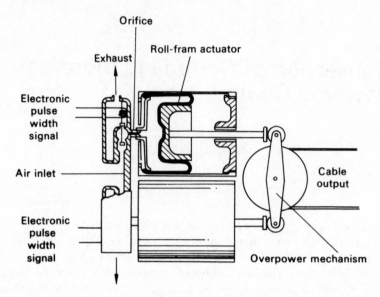

Fig. 7.1 Electro-pneumatic servomotor

installed; a typical pressure range is from 7.5 to 30 lb/in². The piston rods are designed to drive an output linkage assembly which is connected to the appropriate flight control system circuit through a cable drum. The control input to the solenoid of each poppet valve is, in this example, a 22 Hz pulse-width modulated, square-wave signal, the particular frequency being chosen for minimum pressure disturbance and maximum valve life. The input pulses alternately open and close the valves.

With no command input, each valve is open for an equal period of time, and so there is equal pressure in both cylinders and no output torque is transmitted to the control system. When a control command signal is introduced, the open-time period of one valve is increased, while the open-time of the other valve is decreased. Thus, a differential pressure is developed in the two cylinders causing one piston rod to be extended and the other to be retracted, thereby causing rotation of the output linkage and deflection of the control surface(s) to which it is connected. A fixed orifice is installed at the inlet to each cylinder, the size of the orifice being selected to establish the response rate, or control gain, for the particular aircraft type.

As is conventional for the power output element of any automatic control system, the output linkage assembly of the servomotor shown can operate in any of three conditions: namely dis-engaged, engaged, and override. In the dis-engaged condition, the links and piston rods are retracted, allowing free rotation of the output shaft and cable drum, which is connected into the control system, to equal or to exceed the stop-to-stop travel of the appropriate control surface. When the servomotor is pressurised on engagement of the autopilot, the piston rods and links move into contact with the output shaft arm and limit rotation of the arm such that the nominal control range of the autopilot does not exceed 50% of the range of the aircraft's flight control system. To provide full control capability for overriding the automatic control system, the linkage assembly is articulated, but is normally held rigid by springs. Application of override force by the pilot allows deflection of the springs, and provides extension of the servomotor's nominal control range to that of the flight control system.

Electro-mechanical servomotors

Depending on the type of automatic control system, these servomotors may utilise either direct current or alternating current for operation. An example of a direct current operated servomotor is shown in fig. 7.2. It consists of a motor which is coupled to the flight control system via an electro-magnetic clutch, a gear train, and a sprocket and chain. The servomotor also carries a solid-state servo amplifier which amplifies the error signal transmitted by the attitude sensing transducer. Feedback is provided by a potentiometer, the wiper of which is driven by the motor.

Fig. 7.2 Direct-current operated servomotor

Alternating current-operated servomotors may be either of the two-phase induction motor type, or of the type using the principle of hysteresis as applied to the gyroscopes of certain attitude sensing elements (see page 111). A two-phase induction motor type of servomotor (fig. 7.3) has its reference phase constantly supplied with 115 volts alternating current at a frequency of 400 Hz. The control phase is supplied by the output of the associated servo amplifier, the voltage varying from zero to 240 volts. The motor drives an output pulley via a gear train, and an electromagnetic clutch, the pulley providing the coupling between the servomotor and cable of the aircraft's flight control system. A CX synchro, and a device known as a tachogenerator, are also geared to the motor, their respective functions being to provide position and rate feedback signals.

A servomotor utilising a hysteresis motor is shown in fig. 7.4. It operates on

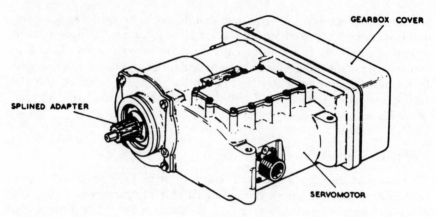

GEARBOX COVER

SPLINED ADAPTER

SERVOMOTOR

Fig. 7.3 Two-phase induction type servomotor

the same fundamental principle as the gyroscope motor described on page 111, but whereas in the latter the stator is directly connected to a three-phase supply of 115 volts at 400 Hz to produce a unidirectional rotating field, the three-phase stator in the example of servomotor illustrated, is fed from a single-phase supply, and field rotation in either direction is obtained by splitting the phases by means of capacitors. The single-phase supply is connected to, or disconnected from, the stator by means of silicon controlled rectifiers (SCRs). Activation, or 'firing', of one or other SCR is achieved by connecting the firing circuit to those circuits supplying the command signals which determine the direction in which the stator field, and hence the servomotor, must rotate in order to apply corrective control. Coupling between the motor and the aircraft's flight control system is by means of a gear train and an electromagnetic clutch, and feedback signals are supplied by a tachogenerator coupled to the motor gear train.

Servomotor mountings

Servomotors, as we have already noted, are mechanically connected into the cable runs of an aircraft's primary flight control system. The method of connection is governed by such factors as the type of automatic system, and the type of primary flight control system with which it is to be used. In those systems which may be considered as more basic in concept, servomotors are designed to have a direct method of connection, i.e. their output shafts are fitted with either a cable drum or sprocket around which control cable or chain may be directly fitted. In the application of a number of systems, however, there is another factor which has to be taken into consideration; this relates to the disturbing effect which the removal and replacement of servomotors, under certain aspects of system maintenance, might have on the settings and adjustments made to a primary flight control system. In order,

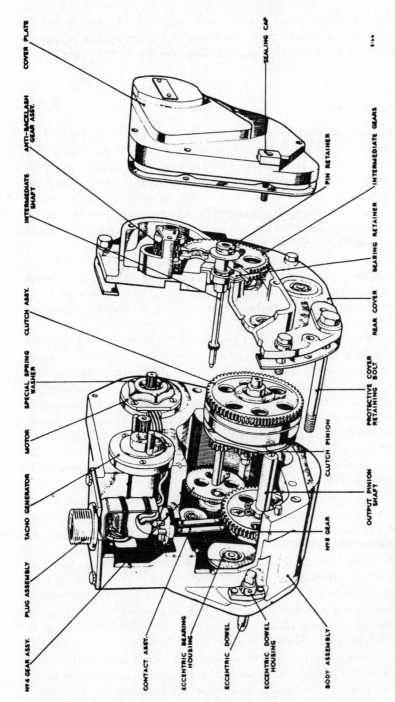

Fig. 7.4 Servomotor utilising a hysteresis motor

therefore, to minimise this effect a large majority of systems utilise servomotors which are designed for attachment to, and removal from, special mountings connected into the primary control system on a more permanent basis.

Power control units

In primary flight control systems of the hydraulic power-operated type, displacements of the control surfaces are effected through the medium of power control units; it is therefore possible to directly apply automatic control command signals to these units and thereby eliminate the need for independent servomotors, as in the conventional forms of automatic control systems. This control concept is adopted in several types of high-performance aircraft for elevator, aileron and rudder control, the latter serving the role of yaw damping in particular.

An example of a power control unit used in an aileron control system is schematically illustrated in fig. 7.5. The principal components of the control unit directly associated with automatic control are (i) solenoid actuator, (ii) engage mechanism, (iii) select valve, (iv) spool valve, (v) transfer valve, and (vi) LVDT position transducer.

When the aileron channel is not engaged with the power control unit, the solenoid actuator is de-energised, and so the select valve and engage mechanism are isolated from the hydraulic system fluid supply. The transfer valve and spool valve are inoperative since they are isolated from the main actuator by the select valve. The cam spring of the engage mechanism is extended to release the cam so enabling the pilot to move the control wheel, and through the medium of the external and internal input cranks, the main control valve piston is positioned to admit hydraulic fluid to one or other side of the main actuator piston. Since the actuator piston is secured to the aircraft structure, the pressure of the fluid causes the entire power control unit to move in the appropriate direction. The unit itself, being connected to the aileron cable drum, will therefore displace the ailerons and also the wing spoilers in this case. In other words, the system functions as a basic power-operated system (see also page 35).

As will be noted from fig. 7.5, the body of the main control valve will also move with respect to its piston which is mechanically linked to the pilot's control column; thus, the valve is repositioned to shut off the hydraulic fluid supply when the required aileron displacement is attained.

When the roll control channel is engaged, the solenoid actuator is energised to allow the hydraulic fluid under pressure to the engage mechanism so that as its spring is compressed the cam is rotated and locks the input cranks to the power control unit. This action also prevents the main control valve piston from moving with respect to its housing. At the same time, hydraulic pressure is admitted to the select valve, causing its piston to open the lines between the spool valve and the main actuator, and also the

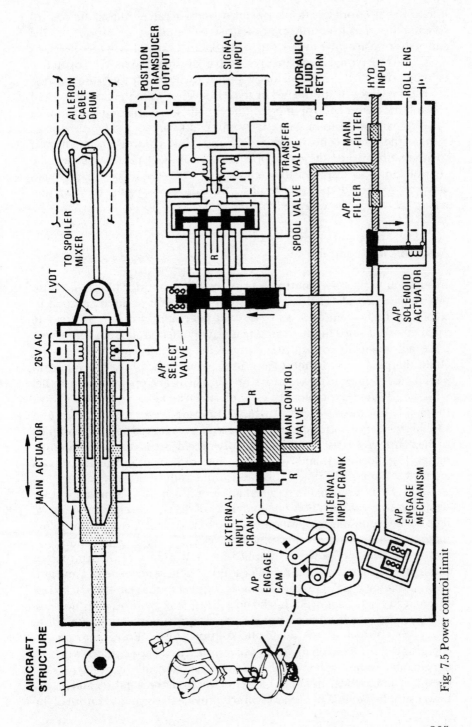

Fig. 7.5 Power control limit

line to the electromagnetically-operated transfer valve. Automatic control command signals from the appropriate servo-amplifier are supplied to the coil of the transfer valve to deflect it to one or other side. This in turn develops a pressure differential across the spool valve, causing it to move to open one or other side of the main actuator piston to hydraulic pressure, via the appropriate line already opened by the select valve. As in the case of manual control, the power control unit will move bodily to displace the ailerons to the commanded position. Since the input cranks are locked by the engage cam, as the power control unit moves, the pilot's control wheel will also rotate; in other words, the system operates as a parallel type. Movement of the control unit also displaces the core of an LVDT transducer in the main actuator, to provide position feedback signals necessary for limiting and taking off control as commands are satisfied.

Automatic trim control

In addition to the servo control of primary flight control surfaces, it is also necessary to provide methods of controlling the trim of an aircraft via its secondary flight control system (see also page 40). However, whereas in manually-controlled flight, trimming is usually effected about the three axes, under automatically controlled conditions it is generally confined to control about the pitch axis. In most cases it is accomplished by a separate trim servomotor coupled to the elevator trim tab system, and operating in parallel with the elevator servomotor. An example of a trim tab servomotor is shown in fig. 7.6. For those aircraft in which trimming is effected by means of a variable incidence horizontal stabiliser, a separate trim servomotor is coupled to the stabiliser. In cases where the stabiliser incidence is varied by hydraulic motors (e.g. Boeing 747 and 767 aircraft) the required automatic trim signals are used to control the flow of hydraulic fluid to the motors.

Figure 7.7 is a schematic representation of a control system adapted for trimming by means of a horizontal stabiliser of the type described on page 42. The trim servo in this application is a three-phase, dual-speed, dual-winding motor which operates in parallel with the elevator power control unit.

The 115 volts a.c. power is supplied to the windings of the trim motor through the contacts of the aircraft 'nose up' and 'nose down' relays, and also a speed change relay. The trim motor is coupled to the stabiliser jackscrew through an electromagnetic clutch and a differential gearbox. The 'nose up' and 'nose down' relays are energised by appropriate command signals from the pitch channel of the automatic control system. Energising and de-energising of the speed change relay is controlled by a flap position switch. In the aircraft trimmed condition shown in the diagram, all three relays are de-energised and so the trim motor is de-clutched from the stabiliser and has no power supplied to it. The elevators which provide the primary control of the

Sprocket for chain
drive to tab

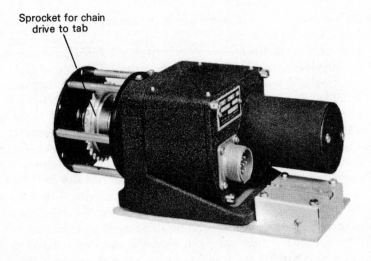

Fig. 7.6 Trim tab servomotor

aircraft's attitude are locked to their hydraulic power control unit (see page 200) when the automatic control system is engaged.

Assuming that a climb command has been initiated, the command signal will be applied to the transfer valve of the power control unit causing it to apply 'up' elevator. At the same time, the pitch control channel will supply a signal to the coil of the 'nose up' relay which, on being energised, completes an engage signal circuit (across the contacts of the de-energised down relay)

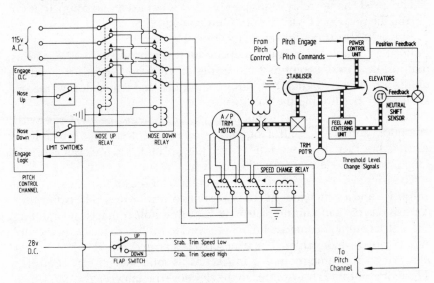

Fig. 7.7 Automatic stabiliser trim system

to the trim motor clutch, and also completes the a.c. supply circuit to one set of trim motor windings.

The operation of the trim motor is governed as a function of stabiliser position versus elevator displacement from the neutral shift position, and this establishes threshold levels at which the stabiliser will start and/or stop trimming. The threshold levels can, in turn, be changed by a trim potentiometer which is mechanically connected to the stabiliser. If the 'up' elevator displacement already assumed exceeds the threshold level at which stabiliser trim will start, then the trim motor will drive the jackscrew in a direction that moves the stabiliser leading edge down. The movement of the stabiliser also moves the elevator feel and centring unit (see also fig. 1.30) and a neutral shift sensor. The sensor supplies a feedback signal to the pitch channel as the stabiliser takes up its new trim position. Since the elevators must also take up a compatible neutral position, as the aircraft responds to the required attitude change the pitch channel supplies a signal to the elevator power control unit transfer valve commanding a downward displacement of the elevators. A feedback signal from the elevator position transducer limits elevator displacement and by summing it with that of the neutral shift sensor the new neutral position of the elevators is determined.

Signals from the pitch trim potentiometer are also fed back into the pitch channel to change the threshold levels of trim motor operation appropriate to the new trim position of the stabiliser. The purpose of the limit switches shown in the trim signal circuits is to disengage the nose up and nose down relays, and thereby the clutch, in the event that the stabiliser is driven beyond its pre-set limits in either the upward or downward directions.

The speed change relay forms part of what is termed a flap compensation circuit, the purpose of which is described on page 212.

Figure 7.8 illustrates the schematic form the stabiliser trim system as used in Boeing 757 and 767 aircraft. In operation it is fundamentally the same as that just described, except that processing of command signals is based on more sophisticated digital computing techniques, and that hydraulic motors are used for positioning the stabiliser.

In certain types of small aircraft flight control systems, e.g. the Century III autopilot, automatic control of pitch trim is based on the principle of sensing the difference in tension between the 'up' and 'down' elevator control cables, when the elevator control is applied.

The trim system (see fig. 7.9) consists of a trim sensor, a trim servo and amplifier, and a switch mounted on the pilot's control wheel. The trim sensor consists of a fixed mounting plate with two adjustable contacts and a sliding bar with a common contact which is attached to pulleys that ride on the 'up' and 'down' elevator cables. The trim servo is a geared, d.c. reversible motor installed on the same mounting bracket as its solid-state circuit amplifier. The motor output is transmitted to the elevator trim tab via a capstan which has a short length of cable, known as a bridle, wrapped round it; the ends of

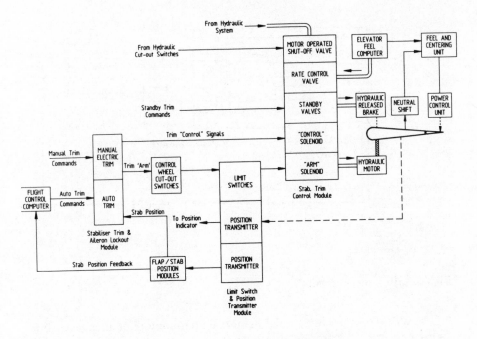

Fig. 7.8 Stabiliser trim system (hydraulic motor operated)

the bridle are fastened mechanically to the trim tab control cables. The amplifier supplies the power for the servomotor, and may be considered as 'dual-circuit', i.e. one circuit for running the servomotor in a clockwise direction, and the other circuit for running it in an anticlockwise direction. The direction and duration of rotation are determined by the trim sensor contacts.

When the autopilot is engaged, power is available to the trim servo system and, with the elevator in a neutral or streamlined position, both elevator cables will have equal tension, and the sliding bar and common contact of the trim sensor will be in neutral so that no trim signal is generated. If say, the elevator is deflected upwards, the force of the airstream acting on it creates a greater tension on the 'up' elevator cable and this causes the sliding bar and contact of the tirm sensor to slide downwards and make contact with the fixed 'up' command contact. The appropriate circuit of the amplifier is therefore activated to cause the servomotor to move the trim tab until it is deflected sufficiently to relieve the tension in the 'up' elevator control cable. At this point, the sliding bar and contact of the trim sensor will have moved back to its neutral position thereby interrupting the circuit to the servo amplifier and motor. Thus, as per conventional trim tab operation, the elevator will be maintained in an upward position by a downward deflection of its trim tab (see also page 41).

209

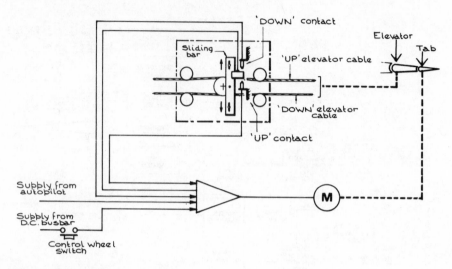

Fig. 7.9 Trim sensor system

The system operates in a similar manner with the autopilot disengaged, but in this case, the pilot supplies the power for servo operation by depressing his control switch.

The elements of another example of an automatic trim system are shown in fig. 7.10. In this case, the output signal from the elevator servomotor is used as the appropriate command signal, its direction being sensed by up-trim and down-trim sensor circuits. These in turn operate relays which apply a signal to the trim servomotor to run it in the appropriate direction. The signal is pulse-width modulated, the pulse duration being a function of airspeed. The holding force, or elevator servomotor torque, resulting from elevator displacement is detected by a trim threshold sensor in terms of a motor current signal proportional to torque. The signal is passed through a time delay circuit which sets a time threshold of three seconds before trim servomotr operation takes place.

Assuming that the holding force is associated with an 'up' elevator displacement, the direction signal is applied to the down-trim sensor, and together with the time threshold sensor signal it is then applied to the relay driver circuit. After the appropriate time delay, the driver circuit output energises the 'down' relay, thus allowing the rate signal from the pulse-width modulator to pass to the 'down' winding circuit of the trim servomotor via the contacts 1 of the relay, and also contacts 1 of the de-energised 'up' relay. The trim tab is therefore displaced downwards at a particular rate thereby relieving the load on the elevator until the trim threshold sensor no longer senses a torque/current signal from the elevator servomotor.

It will also be noted from fig. 7.10, that the pulse rate signal to the trim servomotor also passes through the contacts of a trim transfer relay which is

210

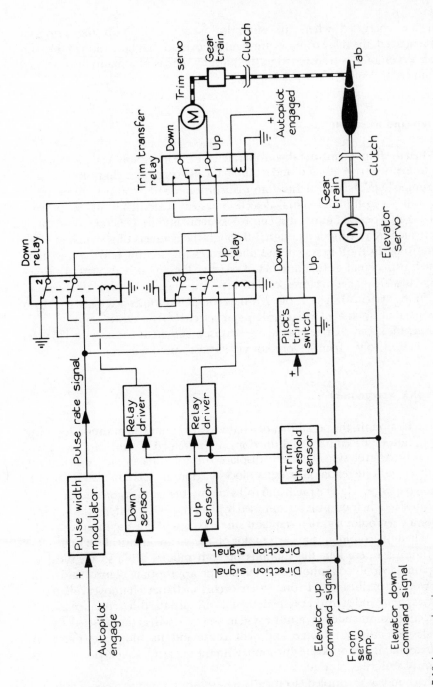

Fig. 7.10 Automatic trim system

always energised when the autopilot is engaged. With the autopilot disengaged, the relay contacts are changed over so that operation of the trim tab servomotor is transferred to the pilot by means of a manually-operated trim control switch.

Flap compensation

When the flaps of an aircraft are operated there is inevitably a change in pitch attitude (see page 49) and under automatically-controlled flight this must be 'trimmed out'. It is usual therefore, to incorporate a flap compensation circuit within the command signal detection system. Circuit arrangements vary between types of automatic control system, but in general, a circuit is activated by passing a d.c. signal through the contacts of a switch or relay controlled by the flap system and, after processing, feeding it to the automatic pitch trim actuator. In a number of systems, the signal is also fed to a timer circuit which is set to correspond to a specific 'flaps in motion' time period.

In the system shown in fig. 7.7, flap compensation is accomplished by a switch that is actuated when the flaps are selected to the 'down' position. This causes the speed-change relay to de-energise and thereby connect the 115 volts a.c. supply to the trim servomotor via its 'fast' speed winding.

Duplex servomotors

In some aircraft, the possibility of a hardover or runaway condition resulting from automatic control malfunctions, is prevented by utilising two independent control systems which displace control surfaces via duplex servomotors and differential gearing; a block diagram of such an arrangement is shown in fig. 7.11. The pitch and roll servomotors are of equal authority and torque, and their outputs are summed by their respective differential gearing; the yaw servomotor is of a standard single type with torque limiting.

When the commands to each motor of a servo are identical, as in the case of normal operation, the motions of both motors are also identical, so providing doubled authority to operate the appropriate control surface. If however, a malfunction in one system occurs such that a hardover roll to port say, is commanded by that system, then it will turn the differential gear in the direction commanded. The other system however, will at the outset, detect the undesired attitude change and will command its motor to rotate the differential in the opposite direction, with the net result that deflection of the control surface is prevented.

Each motor is coupled electrically to a sensor known as a speed monitor, which in turn, is connected to braking units. The purpose of the monitor is to identify a runaway motor, which it does within about two milliseconds,

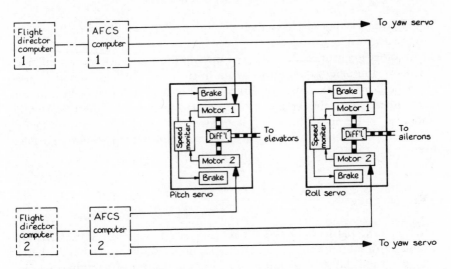

Fig. 7.11 Duplex servomotors

and then to apply a signal to the respective brake thus locking out half of the differential gear and enabling the good motor to drive the control surface through its half of the gearing. Since the servo power is halved, then any hardover risk in the remaining control system is reduced; this is further ensured by the automatic engagement of a torque limiter on the active motor of the servo system.

Feedback

Assuming that an aircraft is subjected to a disturbance producing a pitch-up displacement, an attitude error signal is produced commanding the pitch channel servomotor, or power control unit, to apply down elevator. As the motor or control unit operates, it also drives a position transducer which produces a position feedback signal in opposition to the error signal thereby reducing it and limiting the extent of servomotor or control unit operation, and elevator displacement. The difference between the signals ensures proportionality of corrective control, and when the signals are equal, the error signal is reduced to zero and no further elevator control is applied.

As the aircraft responds to the downward displacement of the elevators, the attitude sensing element now detects this as a nose-down disturbance, and produces a command signal accordingly. The servomotor or control unit now applies control in the opposite direction to apply displacement of the elevators as the aircraft flies into the level flight attitude. As before, a feedback signal is produced to reduce the error signal until there is no further control, at which stage (and assuming that gain adjustments have been accurately made) the elevators will be in their neutral position, and the aircraft is again in the level flight attitude.

In order to ensure stabilisation of the complete feedback loop itself, and thereby eliminate oscillations or 'hunting', a rate feedback signal is also produced by a tachogenerator driven either by a servomotor, or by a motor contained within the servo-amplifier itself. The latter method is normally adopted for the automatic control of power-operated flight control systems. In each case, the signal is summed at the servo-amplifier input (see also page 149).

Yaw damping

All aircraft, particularly those having a swept-wing configuration, are subject to a yawing-rolling oscillation popularly known as 'Dutch Roll' (see page 25) but different aircraft exhibit varying degrees of damping, i.e. the inherent tendency to reduce the magnitude of oscillation and eventual return to straight flight varies. A sudden gust or a short uncoordinated rudder deflection produces a yawing motion, and this, in turn, initiates the Dutch Roll oscillation. The vertical stabiliser and the rudder (if kept in a fixed streamlined position) develop opposing forces that tend to offset the yawing motion, but as a result of the inertias of the aircraft's motions, stabilisation is regained in the form of a damped oscillation. As the aircraft recovers from the Dutch Roll, the magnitude of the oscillations gradually decreases. Thus, the Dutch Roll tendency may be comparatively mild in its effects and may, therefore, be tolerated without recourse to corrective action either manually or automatically.

For some aircraft, however, the natural damping of the Dutch Roll tendency is dependent not only on the size of the vertical stabiliser and rudder, but also on the aircraft's speed, the damping being more responsive at high speeds than at low speeds. It is, therefore, necessary in such cases for corrective action to be taken; such action requires displacement of the rudder in order to further assist the vertical stabiliser in its stabilising function, and is referred to as yaw damping.

It is usual therefore, for these aircraft to utilise a two-axis automatic control system with control about the third axis, i.e. rudder control, being provided by a sub-system called a yaw damper. The system is so designed that it can be operated independently of the automatic control system, so that in the event that the aircraft must be flown manually, Dutch Roll tendencies can still be counteracted. The system may be 'switched in' either by selecting a 'damper' position of the main engage switch on the automatic control system control panel, or by actuating a separately located yaw damper switch.

In those aircraft having upper and lower rudder sections (e.g. Boeing 747) a yaw damper system is provided for each rudder section.

Yaw damper systems

The operating fundamentals of yaw damper systems in general may be understood from fig. 7.12. The principal component of a system is the yaw damper coupler which contains a rate gyroscope powered directly from the aircraft's 115 volts a.c. supply, and the logic switching circuits relevant to filtering, integration, synchronising, demodulation, and servo signal amplification. Servo amplifier output is supplied to the transfer valve of the rudder power control unit; this unit differs from those used for aileron and elevator control (see fig. 7.5) in that it has an additional actuator (the yaw damper actuator) and does not include the automatic control system engage mechanism.

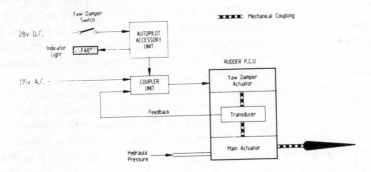

Fig. 7.12 Yaw damper system

The actuator is also mechanically linked with a valve that controls hydraulic pressure to the main actuator, the piston rod of which is extended or retracted to position the rudder left or right respectively. A lever which forms part of the linkage provides for mechanical summing of yaw damper input to the power control unit, and an input from the rudder trim control system. Under manual control, inputs from the rudder pedals also pass through the summing lever to operate the main actuator.

Before the system is switched on, an integration circuit within the coupler unit ensures that the system is in synchronism; the yaw damper fail light is illuminated at this time. When the yaw damper switch is at 'ON', d.c. power is applied to an engage relay in the accessory box, and on being energised, the relay completes a circuit to the actuator solenoid valve in the power control unit to allow hydraulic fluid to flow to the transfer valve; this is indicated by extinguishing of the fail light.

Whenever a yawing motion of the aircraft occurs, the rate gyroscope will be precessed and its sensing element will produce an a.c. output appropriate to the direction and rate of movement. The signal passes through a filtering circuit that discriminates between frequencies associated with flexing of the aircraft's fuselage, and with normal turns, so that only those frequencies related to Dutch Roll are allowed to pass. The signal is then demodulated and amplified, and applied to the transfer valve. The signal also passes through a circuit contained in the airspeed sensing section of an air data computer and is varied as an inverse function of airspeed. The circuit may be of the potentiometric type, or of the switched gain type; the latter being used particularly in digital air data computers.

The transfer valve is operated in the same manner as that described on page 204, but in this case, it directs fluid under pressure to the additional yaw damper actuator. Movement of the actuator piston is transmitted to a control valve in the main actuator which, through its piston rod, then moves the rudder in the required direction. The yaw damper actuator piston also positions the core of the LVDT to produce a position feedback signal to cancel the rate gyroscope input when the actuator piston rod has moved the required amount. The feedback signal is also supplied to a position indicator, the display element of which moves left or right appropriate to the direction of control applied by the yaw damper actuator.

When yaw oscillations have been damped, a constant signal passes from the LVDT to an integrator in the coupler unit; the integrator output then builds up to assist the LVDT in centring the yaw damper actuator, and thereby returning the rudder to its neutral position. The rudder pedals are not displaced during yaw damper operation, i.e. the system is of the series-connected type.

A two-position test switch is provided to simulate the effects of oscillations, and when operated torques are applied to the rate gyroscope causing it to apply left or right rudder as appropriate, to the power control unit. Movements of the position indicator display element provide for monitoring of the position feedback signal from the LVDT.

In order to compensate for differences in aerodynamic damping which in some aircraft can arise between the landing flaps down and flaps up conditions (see also p. 49) the yaw rate gyroscope output signal is also passed through a gain change circuit controlled by a relay that is operated by a flap position switch. The control is such that energising of the relay by-passes a resistance so as to produce a faster rate of response when the flaps are down.

An automatic flight control system may be used in all modes with the yaw damper system engaged; however the associated interlock circuit prevents the use of the control system when the yaw damper is disengaged. When the control system is operating in the localiser mode, the yaw damper is supplied with signals from the aileron control channel through a cross-feed circuit.

Torque limiting

In flight, particularly where high rates of control are to be produced, the movement of the flight control surfaces can result in loads which may impose excessive stresses on the aircraft structure. It is necessary, therefore, under automatically-controlled flight conditions, to safeguard against such stresses, and furthermore to safeguard against a servomotor 'runaway' condition which would cause control sufaces to be displaced to their maximum hardover positions. Such safeguards are implemented by limiting the torque applied to the servomotors, and also by allowing them either to slip, or to be completely disengaged, in the event that preset torque limits are exceeded. The methods adopted usually depend on either mechanical, electrical or electromechanical principles.

A schematic section view of a mechanical torque limiter is shown in fig. 7.13. It forms part of the mounting to which the servomotor is attached, and it utilises a ball and cone principle to provide slippage of clutch plates at a predetermined value of torque. It consists of input, intermediate and output members, the two former members being separated by balls and cones biased by spring 'B'. The clutch plates which form part of the intermediate and

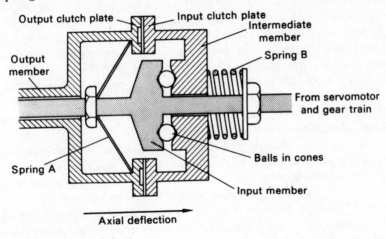

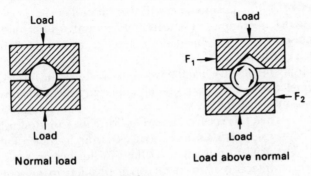

Fig. 7.13 Mechanical torque limiter

217

output members are biased together by means of spring 'A'. Under normal conditions of load, the torque applied to the input member by the servomotor is transmitted to the intermediate member via the balls and cones, and via the clutch plates to the aircraft; a solid coupling is thus formed.

If the load conditions are above normal, the load torque on the output member reacts with the torque of the input member. Shear forces 'F_1' and 'F_2' are thus applied to each set of cones tending to dislodge the balls from their seats, and so displace the cones at right-angles to the direction of the forces. As will be noted from the diagram, this causes the intermediate member to move away from the input member and so causes the clutch plates to slip. When load conditions revert to normal, the reaction of the shear forces decreases and the coupling between all three members again becomes a solid one under the action of spring 'B'.

A typical example of an electrically-operated torque limiting system is one which is applied to a type of servomotor using a two-phase induction motor. In this case a resistor is connected in series with the control phase of the motor to limit the torque by lowering the control phase voltage. Two limit switches are also connected in series with the reference phase of the motor so that, when the preset torque limit is reached, the switches are actuated such that they interrupt the supply to the reference phase. Further rotation of the servomotor is thereby prevented.

An example of an electro-mechanical type of torque limiter is shown schematically in fig. 7.14. The unit operates in conjunction with the electromagnetic clutch of the servomotor, and in the clutch engaged position (diagram *a*) the drive from the motor is transmitted via a spring-loaded cam and roller assembly, and a driving slot which engages with a cam-follower. If the torque at the output shaft exceeds the torque determined by the springs, the input gear turns relative to the output gear and the cam rollers ride up the cam slopes (diagram *b*). This action forces the cam and driving slot to move against the pressure of the springs, and after a specified movement the cam makes contact with the operating pin of a switch whose contacts are opened to interrupt the power supply to the clutch solenoid. In this condition the input drive is disconnected, and the springs are permitted to force the cam back to its normal operating position, i.e. with the cam rollers in the detent of the cam. The switch operating pin returns to its normal position and the switch contacts close, but re-engagement of the clutch is prevented by a relay holding the clutch circuit open.

If the clutch fails to disengage when the switch is operated, the input gear continues to turn relative to the output gear and the cam rollers ride further up the cam slopes until they move over the tops of the cam and drop into recesses (diagram *c*). When this occurs, the springs force the cam upwards to such an extent that the cam driving slot is disengaged from its rollers and on the output shaft. The upward movement of the cam further operates the switch such that its contacts remain in the open position to prevent re-

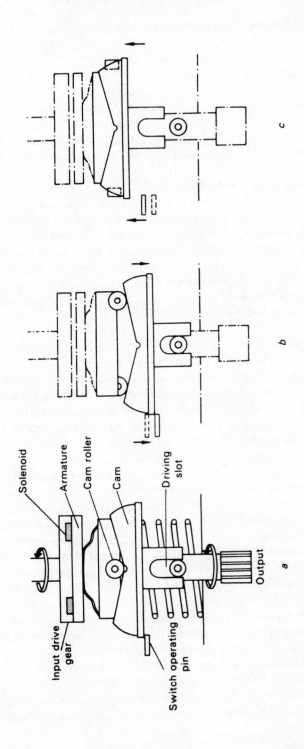

Solenoid

Armature

Cam roller

Cam

Driving slot

Input drive gear

Switch operating pin

Output

a

b

c

Fig. 7.14 Electro-mechanical torque limiter

engagement of the servomotor with the aircraft's flight control system.

Phase advance

Phase advance refers to a method adopted in some automatic flight control systems as a means of providing powered control that will ensure maximum damping of an aircraft's response to the applied control. In order to understand why this is necessary, the response of an aircraft to disturbances should be considered.

Assuming that an aircraft is disturbed in pitch, inertia will momentarily carry it forward in the displaced attitude. The airflow over the aircraft acts on the tail of the aircraft and, because of the longitudinal moment arm and natural damping, a turning force about the centre of gravity is produced causing the aircraft to return to its normal attitude. Displacement of the elevators in the appropriate direction increases the turning force and therefore causes the aircraft to respond more quickly. Thus there are, in effect, two forces available for restoring an aircraft to its normal attitude; the natural damping force, and the additional force created by the use of flight control surfaces.

The damping force is a variable depending on the aircraft type and, in some cases, it is of such a low magnitude that the aircraft in responding to control surface displacement may oscillate about a mean attitude. The effect as appropriate to a disturbance producing a pitch-up displacement is shown in fig. 7.15 a. At point 'A', the displacement is produced and down-elevator is applied to correct the disturbance. The aircraft responds to the elevator displacement (points 'B' to 'C') and during this stage elevator control is progressively taken off, until at point 'C' the normal attitude has been regained with zero control applied. The inertial effect of an aircraft with low natural damping causes it to overshoot the normal attitude, while up-elevator is being applied for correction purposes (points 'C' to 'D'). At point 'D', the aircraft is responding to up-elevator control and is once more approaching the normal attitude.

If the oscillation is to be prevented, then it will be appreciated that during the stage 'B' to 'C' it is not sufficient to take off the applied control, but that opposite control should be applied as the point 'C' is approached, as shown in diagram b. Thus, at point 'A' the control surface is moved to a maximum value to counteract the pitch-up displacement, and from this point to point 'B', control is being taken off and the rate of change of aircraft attitude is decreasing. As the aircraft starts returning to its normal attitude (point 'B') so elevator control is taken off completely, and is applied in the opposite direction to prevent overshoot (points 'B' to 'C').

If the disturbance control and the damping control are referenced to the same time base then, as will be observed from fig. 7.15 c, the damping control

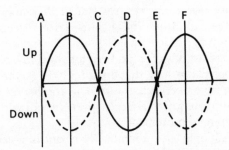

a Aircraft disturbance and control movement

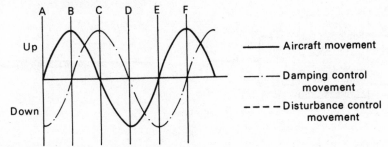

b Aircraft and damping control movement

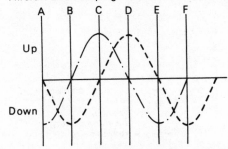

c Disturbance and damping control movement

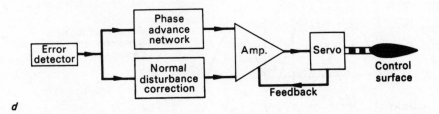

d

Fig. 7.15 Phase advance

is advanced in phase with respect to the disturbance control. The required control for a given disturbance is, therefore, the algebraic sum of both controls, and in any given automatic flight control system they may be applied as components of the signals from the attitude error detecting elements as shown in diagram *d* of fig. 7.15.

For explanatory purposes, the phase advance has been assumed to have a phase angle of 90°. It should be noted, however, that this angle will vary from one aircraft to another, and even from one control surface to another on the same aircraft, e.g. the pitch damping requirement on a given aircraft will be very different from the yaw damping requirement.

The phase-advancing methods adopted in automatic flight control systems vary between systems, but we may consider the example shown in fig. 7.16. In

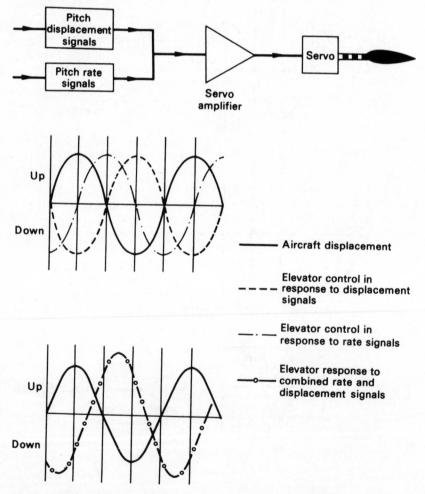

Fig. 7.16 Phase advancing method

this case, two detector signals are fed into the pitch control channel servo amplifiers, one such signal being derived from a pitch rate gyroscope and therefore being proportional to the rate of pitch change, while the other signal is derived from a vertical-axis gyroscope and is proportional to pitch displacement. Both signals are combined to produce an algebraic response in which the aircraft control is phase-advanced with respect to the disturbance.

Trim indicators

In most automatic flight control systems, a trim indicator is provided, its functions being to indicate that signals are being supplied to the servomotors, whether in the engaged or disengaged condition, and also to indicate any out-of-trim conditions of the aircraft under normal operating conditions of the control system. It performs these functions by monitoring the ouputs from the rudder, aileron and elevator servo amplifiers, and by producing deflections of pointers from zero datum marks in response to signals supplied. Two examples of three-channel trim indicators designed for mounting on instrument panels are shown in fig. 7.17. In some control systems, monitoring of the elevator channel only is carried out, the appropriate indicators being incorporated in the flight control panels.

The pointers, which symbolise the flight control surfaces, are actuated by d.c. milliammeters, and are deflected each time servo amplifier signals are supplied to the servomotors. When the signals are balanced out as a result of servo control commands being satisfied, the pointers return to their zero 'trimmed' positions. In the event that a servo amplifier produces a continuous correction signal in order to maintain aircraft attitude, then the appropriate pointer will be continuously deflected as an indication that the aircraft is out-of-trim.

In systems which incorporate aileron and elevator position transmitters, signals from the latter are always present when the automatic control system is powered but disengaged. Thus, whenever the control column and/or the control wheel is moved, the associated trim indicator pointers will also be displaced. As an indication that each servomotor is engaged electrically-operated flags which display the word IN are provided in some types of trim indicator.

The indicator shown in the lower part of fig. 7.17, also incorporates an 'out-of-trim' indicator light which is associated with the elevator channel.

Mach trim system

In aircraft that are subject to the effect known as 'tuck-under' (see page 47) the pitch attitude change arising is compensated as a function of Mach

223

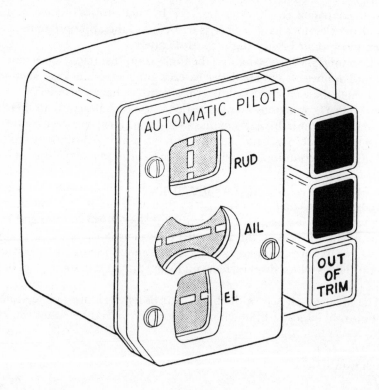

Fig. 7.17 Trim indicators

number by a Mach trim system. As in the case of a yaw damper, it is a sub-system to an automatic control system in that it can be operational whether or not automatic control is engaged. A typical system is shown in block diagram form in fig. 7.18, and in comparing this with fig. 1.30 it will be noted that the actuating section of the system forms part of the horizontal stabiliser trim and elevator control system.

The principal components of the system are a trim coupler unit, an actuator, a test switch and a failure light. The coupler unit is electrically connected to an air data computer from which it receives signals corresponding to airspeed in terms of Mach number. It contains all the logic circuits necessary for the processing of the signals and their amplification before supplying them to the trim actuator.

The actuator consists of a 115 volts 400 Hz single-phase motor which drives a screw type shaft through a gear train. The shaft is connected to the stabiliser via the neutral shift mechanism, while the actuator body is pivoted to the elevator feel and centring unit. A brake mechanism supplied with 28 volts d.c. from the trim coupler unit unlocks the actuator to allow its movement when engaged and operating. Switches are provided to limit actuator motion at its fully extended and retracted positions.

At airspeeds below the value preset for the aircraft type (0.715M in one

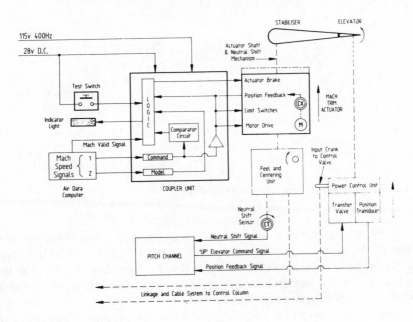

Fig. 7.18 Mach trim system

particular case) the Mach trim actuator is inoperative and its shaft is in the fully extended position. As speed increases and exceeds the set value a signal is supplied from the trim coupler unit to release the brake, and a speed signal from the air data computer is supplied to the motor which then rotates the screwed shaft. Since the shaft is connected to the stabiliser via the neutral shift mechanism the actuator body itself is traversed along the shaft. Movement of the body also rotates the feel and centring unit, and assuming that the automatic control system pitch channel is not engaged, the main control valve of the power control unit will be directly actuated (see also page 204) and displacement of the unit will move the elevators up so that they counteract the 'tuck under' effect. The Mach trim actuator motor drives a CX synchro that provides a position feedback signal to the coupler unit. After demodulation it is supplied to the servo amplifier and when it opposes the command signal no further control is applied by the actuator motor. In addition to a pre-set 'start' value of Mach speed, there is also a corresponding value at which command signals are limited, e.g. the speed value of 0.715M referred to earlier has a corresponding limit value of 0.815M. The elevator correction versus the Mach number values quoted is shown graphically in fig. 7.19. The change in elevator correction commanded at 0.78M is produced by second stage amplification of the signal within the coupler unit.

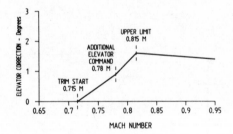

Fig. 7.19 Elevator correction vs Mach number

When the aircraft's speed decreases, the command signal also decreases, and so the position feedback signal now predominates to drive the trim actuator back to the extended position. When this is reached, the circuit to the actuator motor is interrupted, and the elevators will at that time have been returned to their neutral position.

It will also be noted from fig. 7.18 that the air data computer provides two Mach speed signal data outputs to the trim coupler unit. These signals are of equal value and are supplied to a command channel and a 'model' channel. As the command channel is supplying a signal to the trim actuator, the 'model' channel furnishes a signal to a comparator circuit, in which it is compared to the feedback signal from the actuator position synchro. These two signals should be of the same amplitude, but of opposite sign. If the signals are not within tolerance, the circuit to the actuator motor is interrupted and this is indicated by illumination of the fail indicator light.

The system operates in a similar manner when the pitch channel of the automatic control system is engaged, except that the power control unit now moves the elevators up as a result of a command signal being applied to its transfer valve from the pitch channel. This signal is balanced against a feedback signal from the power control unit's position transducer, and also a signal generated by the neutral shift sensor as it responds to movement of the feel and centring unit.

The test switch is provided for checking system operation and control movements by simulating the command signal input when speed is above the preset 'start' level, e.g. 0.715M. Since, under test conditions, the feedback signal from the Mach trim actuator is not equal to the output from the 'model' channel of the coupler unit, the comparator circuit will cause the fail indicator light to illuminate.

TEST QUESTIONS

1 A parallel-connected servomotor is one which:
   (a) moves the appropriate flight control surfaces without moving the pilot's controls.
   (b) is electrically connected in parallel with other servomotors.
   (c) moves both the appropriate flight control surfaces and the pilot's controls.

2 On what principles do servomotors generally operate?

3 In what manner are servomotors connected into aircraft flight control systems?

4 In what type of aircraft's flight control system can the use of conventional servomotors be eliminated?

5 Explain how the system referred to in Question 4 responds to automatic control command signals.

6 Describe the operation of a typical stabiliser trim servo system.

7 Explain how the sensing of control cable tension changes can be applied as a method of adjusting pitch trim.

8 What is the function of a flap compensation circuit when incorporated in an automatic pitch control channel?

9 What is the purpose of a yaw damper system?

10 What methods are adopted in a servomotor system to safeguard against excessive stresses being imposed on an aircraft's structure, and against a 'runaway' condition?

11 What provision is made in a servo control system to ensure maximum damping of an aircraft's response to the control applied?

12 What is the function of a trim indicator, and how is it electrically connected into the control channels of an automatic control system?

13 What effect is produced when the airspeed of certain types of aircraft is increased?

14 Briefly explain the operation of the system that automatically corrects the effect referred to in Question 13.

8
Automatic Control of Helicopters

The pitch and roll control channel arrangement of an automatic flight control system based on that used in the Sikorsky S61 series of helicopter, is illustrated in fig. 8.1. It is designed to assist the pilot in stabilising the helicopter about the appropriate axes, by introducing attitude correction signals as a series input to the hydraulic servo control system of the main rotor. A yaw control channel is also provided and will be described later.

The system differs from those used in fixed-wing aircraft in that when engaged, desired attitude changes are initiated by the pilot manually operating his controls in the conventional manner, and in so doing operating position sensors which establish attitude signals for comparison with actual attitude signals derived from gyroscopic attitude sensing elements; this is shown schematically in fig. 8.2.

Actual pitch and roll attitudes are sensed by synchros mounted on the appropriate gimbal rings of a vertical gyroscope. Desired attitudes in pitch and roll are sensed by stick position sensors which are inductive devices each consisting of a rotor that rotates in a stator through a mechanical coupling to the cyclic stick. The sensors are electrically oriented so that their outputs are nulled when the cyclic stick is at its reference position corresponding to a level flight attitude. Displacements of the stick from this position produce output voltages from the sensors which are proportional to the amount of stick displacement, and are phase related to the direction of displacement as follows:

forward – output voltage out-of-phase with sensor reference voltage
aft – output voltage in-phase with sensor reference voltage
right – output voltage out-of-phase with sensor reference voltage
left – output voltage in-phase with sensor reference voltage

The pilot's controls requried for operation of the system are located in two panels; the control panel and the channel monitor panel. The system is engaged by means of a push-button switch in the pilot's control panel, engagement normally being made before take-off.

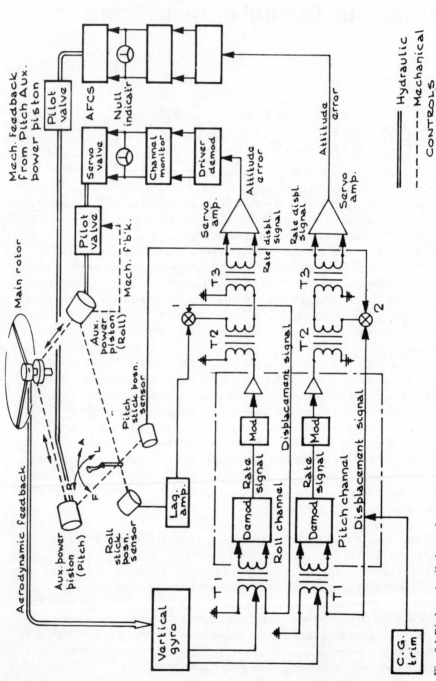

Fig. 8.1 Pitch and roll channel arrangements

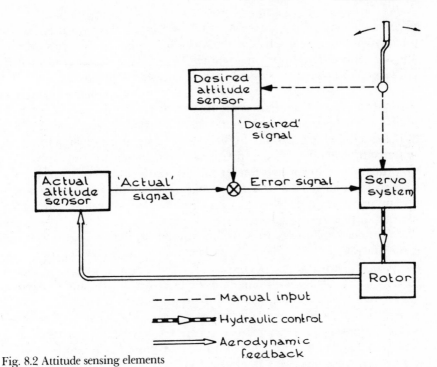

Fig. 8.2 Attitude sensing elements

Pitch control

Let us assume that the helicopter is in forward flight and level attitude and that the pilot moves the cyclic stick forward to initiate a nose-down attitude. As the stick is moved there is a corresponding movement of the pitch position sensor rotor from the null position and a desired attitude signal is therefore developed and fed to summing point 2. Simultaneously, the stick displacement actuates a mechanical linkage to the piston of an auxiliary servo which in turn, controls hydraulic fluid pressure to a primary servo; the latter causing the main rotor to tilt forward and thereby establish the desired nose-down attitude. The voltage output from the stick sensor will as already noted, be out-of-phase with the sensor reference voltage.

The nose-down attitude of the helicopter displaces the vertical gyroscope unit so that its pitch attitude synchro develops a displacement signal voltage which is also supplied to summing point 2 via transformer T1. The displacement signal which corresponds to actual attitude, attempts to apply control to restore the helicopter to a level flight attitude. However, since the signal in the nose-down attitude is in-phase with the excitation voltage supplied to the synchro then it will oppose the stick position sensor signal at summing point 2, and because both signals are supplied to transformers T2 and T3 there will be no output to the servo amplifier. If a nose-up attitude is selected, the signals from the stick position sensor and the vertical gyroscope pitch synchro will be in-phase and out-of-phase respectively, and so would also be in opposition at summing point 2. Thus the automatic control system is always zeroed about the desired attitude selected by the pilot.

It will be noted from fig. 8.1 that the pitch attitude synchro signal also passes through a differentiating network made up of a demodulator which produces a phase-sensitive d.c. signal that corresponds to the rate at which displacement of the helicopter in pitch takes place, and a modulator which converts the signal back to a.c.; the signal is then amplified and supplied to the primary winding of transformer T2. The signal is then combined in the secondary winding of T2 with the signal from summing point 2 so that any output from transforer T3 to the servo amplifier is the algebraic sum of the rate and displacement signals.

If the helicopter moves away from a selected attitude, e.g. a disturbance causes the selected nose-down attitude assumed earlier to be increased, then the vertical gyroscope pitch synchro will produce a displacement signal corresponding to the new attitude. This signal is compared at summing point 2 with the selected attitude, which remains unchanged since the cyclic stick and pitch sensor have not been re-positioned. As a result, a nose-down attitude error signal is now produced at transformers T2 and T3. At the same time, the displacement signal is sampled by the differentiating network which, as already described, produces a rate of displacement signal, and for the foregoing attitude change it will be added to the displacement signal. The output error signal from T3 is therefore a combined one, and after amplification by the servo amplifier, is applied to a flapper type servo valve which will move in such a direction as to allow hydraulic pressure to tilt the main rotor of the helicopter in the aft direction (nose-up condition) through the medium of the auxiliary power piston and the primary servo system. As the helicopter returns to the selected attitude, the rate plus displacement signal, and resulting attitude error signal, are reduced so that corrective control by the rotor servo system is progressively removed. In order to damp out this control and so prevent overshooting the selected attitude, the differentiating or rate network, is so designed that at a certain stage of the helicopter's return to selected attitude, the phase of the rate signal is reversed so that it opposes the displacement signal. When the selected attitude is again reached, the attitude error signal is reduced to zero and all corrective control is removed.

Centre of gravity trim control

Changes in the centre of gravity can, as in the case of fixed-wing aircraft, significantly alter the pitch attitude of an helicopter, and while its automatic control system will attempt to correct the attitude change, it alone cannot

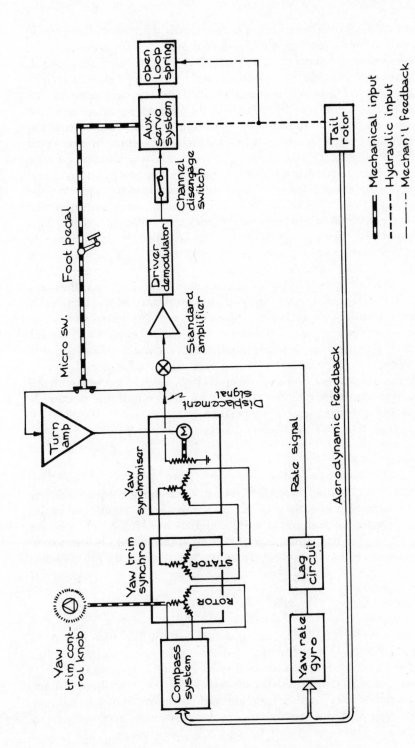

Fig. 8.3 Yaw Control

achieve a fully stabilised condition. The result is the attainment of an attitude which is a compromise between the desired attitude and that which the helicopter would assume if the automatic control system were not engaged. This has two undesirable features; firstly, and because the helicopter is out-of-trim, then obviously it is not at the desired attitude, and secondly, the correction which the control system would have to apply to hold the compromise attitude, would limit the remaining corrective authority of the systems's pitch control channel. Moving the cyclic stick would be an obvious way of correcting the attitude, but the pitch stick sensor would only provide a signal to cause the helicopter to assume a new compromise attitude. The cyclic stick can however, be used for correction provided the signal output relationship between the stick and the pitch sensor can be altered so as to balance actual and desired attitude signals when the stick is in a different position. This is accomplished by a centre of gravity trim control circuit comprised principally of a potentiometer whose output is connected in parallel with the stick sensor output (see fig. 8.1).

The pilot moves the cyclic stick and establishes a signal to cause the main rotor to bring the helicopter to the desired attitude, and at the same time, monitors the position of the flapper valve in the auxiliary servo by means of a null indicator on the control panel. The trim control knob is also rotated to produce a signal that combines (algebraically) with the desired attitude signal from the position sensor until the combined signal balances the actual attitude signal from the vertical gyroscope. The balanced condition with the cyclic stick positioned to maintain the desired attitude, is indicated by the null indicator pointer being at its centre position.

Roll control

The roll control channel operates in the same manner as the pitch control channel except, of course, that desired attitude signals are established by the roll position sensor, and actual attitude signals by a roll synchro in the vertical gyroscope unit. Since the roll attitude is not materially affected by changes in centre of gravity a trim circuit is not required in the roll channel.

Yaw control

Yaw control is also based on the establishment of desired attitude and actual attitude signals, and the circuit arrangement is shown schematically in fig. 8.3. Desired attitude signals are derived as a result of the operation of micro-switches actuated either directly by the pilot's foot pedals or through force link assemblies. After amplification and processing by a yaw synchroniser unit, the signals are compared with actual attitude (displacement) signals supplied from the helicopter's remote-reading compass system through a synchronous transmission loop. Any resulting error signal actuates the hydraulic servo system of the tail rotor to apply corrective turn control in a manner which is basically similar to that of the pitch and roll control channels.

An essential difference relevant to yaw control, is that the signal corresponding to the rate of any displacement is derived from a yaw rate gyroscope. Let us assume that with the automatic control system engaged, the pilot requires to turn the helicopter onto a new heading. He will do so by depressing a foot pedal in the appropriate direction and through a mechanical couling to a hydraulic servo system will cause the system to change the pitch of the tail rotor blades and thereby initiate the turn. At the same time, one or other of the micro-switches referred to above, will be actuated to de-energise a relay contained within the yaw synchroniser unit. The compass system detects the desired heading change as a disturbance and so produces a porportional heading error signal in a CT synchro in the synchroniser unit, the synchro forming part of the transmission loop between the compass system and the tail rotor servo system. This signal must be nulled otherwise it will oppose the heading change by applying corrective control through the servo system. Through the action of the de-energised relay the signal is therefore coupled to a turn amplifier in the synchroniser unit, and after amplification, it is supplied to a motor which drives the CT synchro to continuously null the error signal during the heading change. When the helicopter reaches the desired heading, the pilot releases control at the foot pedals thereby causing the relay to energise and to disconnect the nulling loop circuit; thus both the desired and actual attitudes are in synchronism. The forego ng nulling operation also takes place when the automatic control system is not in use so that as in the case of a fixed-wing aircraft system it can be engaged without snatching of the controls (see also Synchronising, page 151).

In the event of a disturbance in yaw subsequently occurring, the magnetic field produced in the heading synchro of the compass system will rotate in the appropriate direction and will be transmitted to the yaw synchroniser CT synchro, to produce a rotor voltage of an amplitude proportional to the amount of heading change. After amplification by the yaw amplifier of the automatic control system, the output is applied to the servo system of the tail rotor the blades of which change pitch to restore the helicopter to the desired heading.

As noted earlier, the yaw rate gyroscope generates signals corresponding to the rate of helicopter displacement, and this is the case whether a turn is carried out manually or automatically. The signal generated is always in opposition to any change in heading error so that the heading error supplied to the tail rotor servo system is the algebraic sum of the displacement signal produced by the compass system and the rate signal. It also performs a damping function similar to that of the rate circuit adopted in the pitch and roll channels.

In order to permit the yaw channel to introduce larger corrections and/or allow for power changes which require a new tail rotor pitch to maintain a desired heading, a device known as an open-loop spring is incorporated in the yaw servo system. The spring adjustment is such that it places the yaw channel in an open-loop condition, and limits the mechanical feedback from the yaw servo causing the latter to move the pilot's foot pedals (unlike the pitch and roll channels in which automatic control inputs do not move the cyclic stick) at a rate proportional to the input signal. The pilot can override the displacement of the pedals in this condition. During a manually controlled turn, the rate gyroscope signal being in opposition, creates an open-loop condition on the yaw servo, and because the foot pedals are moved by the servo then the pilot is provided with an artificial 'feel' assisting him to establish a desired rate of turn.

The pilot can also change heading of the helicopter by means of a Yaw Trim Control provided on the automatic control system control panel. The control dial is graduated in one degree increments and one complete rotation corresponds to 72 degrees of heading change. In operation, it displaces the rotor of a yaw trim synchro which is coupled as a differential between the compass system and the yaw synchroniser unit. Thus the actual heading signal from the compass system is modified resulting in a change in the synchroniser CT synchro output which is applied to the tail rotor servo system. As the helicopter changes heading, the yaw trim signal is opposed by the changing signal from the compass system until the helicopter has turned through the number of degrees selected, at which stage, the trim signal is zeroed and the automatic control system stabilises the helicopter at the new heading.

Radio-coupled systems

Unlike fixed-wing aircraft, the progression of automatic control from basic stability augmentation to full control, under the guidance of outer-loop signal sources (VOR, ILS, altitude hold, etc.) and with little or no intervention on the part of the pilot, has not been quite as straight-forward. The fundamental reason for this was that airworthiness authorities were reluctant to certificate a type of aircraft which does after all, have varying levels of inherent instability, for operation under the conditions imposed by Instrument Flight Rules (IFR). Apart from the matter of instability, other factors considered were the pilot's high workload, the lack of adequate back-up systems and hardware redundancy essential to helicopter flight safety. The whole question of helicopter IFR operation, particularly single-pilot operation, became somewhat controversial and it was a long time before approval came to fruition. The manufacturer's of helicopters had however, made substantial inroads to instability problems, and likewise the manufacturers of automatic flight control systems from their experience in the fixed-wing aircraft field, had foreseen full automatic flight guidance for helicopters as a logical development, and so designed and produced systems accordingly. As a result, the capabilities of several types of helicopter/automatic control system combinations under IFR conditions were proven and ultimately attained the requisite certification.

Various types of control system having IFR or 'radio-coupled' capability as it is generally known, are currently in use in a number of helicopter types. The units are their interconnection of one example based on the Sperry 'Helipilot' system adopted in the Bell 212 helicopter, are illustrated schematically in fig. 8.4. In order to satisfy system redundancy requirements, two completely independent control systems are employed, each utilising actual attitude signal inputs from separate gyroscopic type attitude sensor units. The control system is integrated with a Flight Director (FD) system (see chapter 9) which, as will be noted, consists of a single computer, Attitude Direction Indicator (ADI) and a Horizontal Situation Indicator (HSI). The FD computer does, in fact, form the heart of the whole system since it processes heading, radio navigation, attitude, altitude, airspeed and vertical speed information to supply computed commands to the FD and the automatic control computers for automated flight path following.

Unit duplication also applies to the pitch and roll linear actuators which are mounted in pairs, and in series, each one being supplied from the appropriate control channels of its own automatic control computer. Thus in the event of failure of one or other of the computers, control can still be effectively applied by one or other actuator of both channels. An automatic gain programming circuit comes into operation to double the authority of the remaining actuator so that feel and response remain unchanged. Yaw control is effected by a single linear actuator supplied with signals from only one automatic computer. All the actuators are of the extending screw-jack type and are powered by d.c. motors. They are connected into the control linkages of the main and tail rotor systems such that they control the hydraulic supply to 'boost' actuators or servos. In some other automatic control/helicopter configurations, control of the rotor systems may be of the type whereby the actuators are connected directly to the controls. Position feedback signals are supplied from a linear voltage differential transformer operated by the screw-jack mechanism. Damping of actuator movements is provided by processing position signals through a rate feedback circuit before supplying them to the motors. In some types of automatic control system actuators, a synchro may be used for producing feedback signals.

As in the case of fixed-wing aircraft control systems, selection of the various outer-loop control modes is effected by means of a mode selector or controller unit. As will be noted from fig. 8.4, the controller is connected directly to the FD computer, and in this example, it provides for the selection of seven modes by push-in, push-off switches the buttons of which illuminate to annunciate the appropriate mode. Arming of the Vertical Speed (VS). Altitude, Airspeed (AS) and Heading (HDG) modes for signal processing by the computer is accomplished by pressing the appropriate switch buttons. Arming of the navigation modes, i.e. Reverse Course, ILS (Glide Slope), VOR/Localiser, and Auxiliary Navigation (used for additional back-up from say an area navigation system) is accomplished by means of a rotary selector switch. After selecting any one of these four modes, the NAV switch button is pressed. The GS button is pressed when it is required to initiate manual capture of the glide slope beam anytime after localiser beam capture and when the aircraft is below the beam.

The Engage Controller as the name implies, provides the necessary switching facilities for engaging each of the automatic control systems, yaw stability augmentation, stability augmentation only, or IFR mode. As in the case of the Mode controller, switches are of the push and annunciating type.

Other units peripheral to the integrated system are a radio altimeter, vertical speed indicator, a force trim release switch mounted on the cyclic stick, a 'go-around' switch, and an airspeed slew switch; these last named switches are mounted on the collective pitch lever (see page 61). The positions of the linear actuators relative to their centres of travel, are indicated by independent actuator position indicators located on the helicopter's instrument panel.

System operation

The control system operates in two basic modes: (i) stability augmentation (SAS) in which it assists the pilot when flying 'hands-on' to stabilise the helicopter against outside disturbances, and (ii) IFR in which the control system is coupled to the FD system and commanded to control the helicopter 'hands-off' in FD modes selected on the Mode Controller.

SAS mode

In this mode, system operation is fundamentally similar to that of the S61 helicopter stability augmentation system already described, i.e. desired attitude signals are produced by cyclic stick and foot pedal sensor units, and are compared with actual attitude signals produced by gyroscopically-controlled sensor units. Any resulting error signals, which also pass through a rate circuit, are however, applied as command signals to linear actuators as opposed to hydraulic servo valves. The mode is engaged by pressing the engage switches of both automatic control systems, and the SAS ONLY switch on the controller unit.

IFR or coupled mode

With both automatic control systems engaged, the IFR mode of operation is obtained by pressing the IFR switch on the engage controller, and then selecting any mode on the mode selector. Thus the pitch and roll channels of the control computers are coupled to the FD computer so that it provides the lateral and vertical guidance commands to which the control system will respond in addition to performing its normal stabilising function. Visual indications (or 'cues' as they are called) of the helicopter's attitude are presented at the ADI by corresponding positions of the pitch and roll command bars; commands are satisfied when the bars are centred. If either bar should display a large displacement from centre (which happens when control actuators do not have enough authority or travel to maintain attitude) the pilot must re-trim the helicopter's attitude. This is done by pressing the force trim release switch so that the cyclic stick may be re-positioned without having to overcome the force normally exerted by the actuators. The appropriate stick sensor then supplies an error correcting signal to the automatic control computers at a summing point to which attitude sensor unit, and FD computer signals, are supplied. After processing, the signal then drives the relevant actuator so that it is re-centered and changes the helicopter's attitude accordingly. As the attitude sensing unit responds to the change, its signal starts nulling out the stick sensor signal, and at the same time supplies its signal to the FDC which then starts re-centering the ADI command bar appropriate to the control axis affected.

If an invalid signal condition exists, as evidenced by a command bar being biased out of view, the control channel affected is automatically de-coupled so that the channel reverts to maintaining the attitude which existed at the time of engagement (known as attitude retention). Coupling is automatically resumed when the appropriate command bar signal is again valid. In addition to displacement of the ADI command bars, indication that re-trimming is required, and that actuator re-centering takes place, is provided by displacements of the pitch and roll actuator position indicator pointers. The indicators are supplied with signals from the position feedback circuits of the linear voltage differential transformers driven by the actuators.

The yaw control channel of the system functions solely as a yaw damper in that it has no long-term hold capability. This is accomplished by a circuit that 'washes out' all inputs after a suitable control period (typically seven seconds). The channel is controlled by only one of the automatic control system computers and application of control to the tail rotor system is by a single linear actuator. Its signal circuit is integrated with those of both roll and channels for the purpose of ensuring turn co-ordination. The channel is engaged by pressing the push button switch corresponding to the system controlling yaw (usually the No. 1) and also a YAW SAS switch.

Changes in yaw attitude are sensed as heading changes by a directional gyroscope and synchro forming part of the main attitude sensor unit. The

Automatic Flight Control

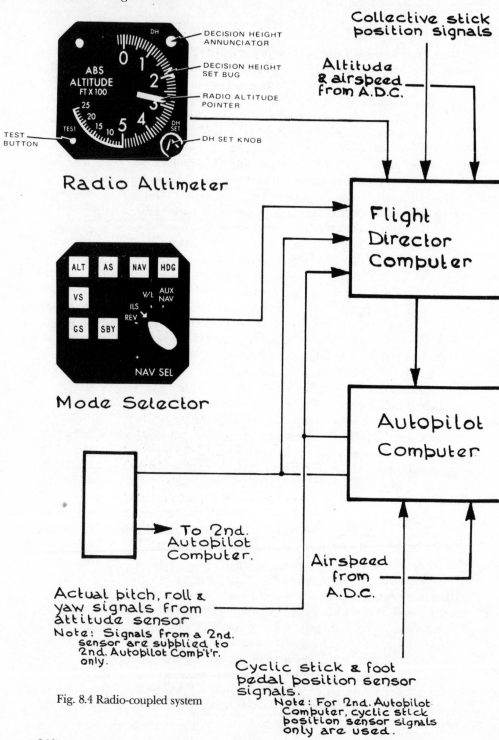

Radio Altimeter

Mode Selector

To 2nd. Autopilot Computer.

Actual pitch, roll & yaw signals from attitude sensor

Note: Signals from a 2nd. sensor are supplied to 2nd. Autopilot Comb't'r. only.

Collective stick position signals

Altitude & airspeed from A.D.C.

Flight Director Computer

Autopilot Computer

Airspeed from A.D.C.

Cyclic stick & foot pedal position sensor signals.

Note: For 2nd. Autopilot Computer, cyclic stick position sensor signals only are used.

Fig. 8.4 Radio-coupled system

240

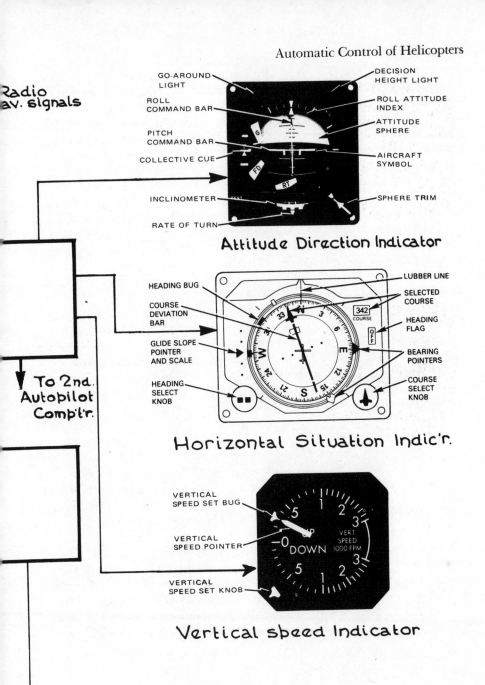

Radio
av. signals

GO-AROUND
LIGHT

ROLL
COMMAND BAR

PITCH
COMMAND BAR

COLLECTIVE CUE

INCLINOMETER

RATE OF TURN

DECISION
HEIGHT LIGHT

ROLL ATTITUDE
INDEX

ATTITUDE
SPHERE

AIRCRAFT
SYMBOL

SPHERE TRIM

Attitude Direction Indicator

HEADING BUG

COURSE
DEVIATION
BAR

GLIDE SLOPE
POINTER
AND SCALE

HEADING
SELECT
KNOB

LUBBER LINE

SELECTED
COURSE

HEADING
FLAG

BEARING
POINTERS

COURSE
SELECT
KNOB

342
COURSE

OFF

Horizontal Situation Indic'r.

To 2nd.
Autopilot
Comp't'r.

VERTICAL
SPEED SET BUG

VERTICAL
SPEED POINTER

VERTICAL
SPEED SET KNOB

DOWN

VERT.
SPEED
1000 FPM

Vertical speed Indicator

Control signals to pitch, roll &
yaw linear actuators.

Note: 2nd. Autopilot
Computer supplies
only pitch and roll
signals.

synchro output is applied to a rate generator circuit in the computer and is converted from an angular displacement signal to a derived rate of turn signal. After amplification it is applied to a circuit which drives the rate of turn pointer in the ADI (see fig. 8.4). The signal is also summed with a computed rate of turn signal composed of a roll attitude signal which is scaled and divided by an airspeed gain programming and switching circuit activated at speeds specific to helicopter type, by the airspeed sensor of an air data computer. The resultant signal is then scaled to provide a computed turn rate signal for the purpose of turn co-ordination. Any difference between computed rate and derived rate signals is processed to drive the yaw actuator through its power amplifier. The function and operation of the foregoing section of the yaw control channel is fundamentally the same as that used for turn co-ordination in some fixed-wing aircraft systems, an example of which has already been described on pages 120 and 124.

If the pilot wishes to control yawing motion by moving the foot pedals, the displacement of the pedal position synchro applies a signal to the control computer which is simultaneously summed with the derived rate of turn signal originating as already mentioned, from the directional gyroscope sensor. The signals however, are of opposite polarity and so cancel each other to prevent movement of the actuator; control of the tail rotor is therefore directly from the foot pedals.

Collective or power axis modes

This mode of command controls the vertical path of the helicopter through direct lift control, and is designated as three-cue operation (the other two cues being related to pitch and lateral control). The mode functions associated with collective command are glide-slope, vertical speed, altitude hold, flare, and go-around; the first three functions drive the collective cue only when airspeed hold is engaged, and coupled to the cyclic stick. Commands are displayed by a cue indicator which is brought into view on the ADI of the flight director when a collective mode function is selected (see fig. 8.4). Three-cue command signals are processed by the FD compuer, and when present, commands must be satisfied by manual control of the collective stick.

TEST QUESTIONS

1 From the point of view of stability augmentation only, in what way does a helicopter automatic flight control system differ from that used in a fixed-wing aircraft?

2 What are the functions of position sensors?

3 What methods are adopted to obtain rate of displacement signals?

4 The signal produced by a centre of gravity trim control system is algebraically combined with the:

    (a) actual attitude signal,

    (b) desired attitude signal,

    (c) rate of displacement signal.

5 In the system adopted in the S61 helicopter, how is 'zeroing' about a selected desired attitude obtained?

6 Describe two methods of control damping to prevent overshoot.

7 In systems using centre of gravity trim control, why are correction signals applied only to system pitch control channels?

8 In the S61 helicopter control system, the signals controlling the servo valve are:

    (a) rate signals only,

    (b) attitude error signals,

    (c) rate plus displacement signals.

9 What are the principal units which comprise a typical radio-coupled automatic control system of a helicopter?

10 Explain how linear actuators are connected into a control system.

11 How are desired attitude signals produced when a radio-coupled automatic control system is operating in the SAS mode?

12 What is the purpose of a force-trim release facility, and under what condition would it be used?

13 How are indications given of the necessity for re-trimming the attitude of a helicopter under automatic control?

14 Explain how turn co-ordination may be achieved.

9
Flight Director and Integrated Flight Control Systems

Flight instrument evolution has followed a pattern of divergent display complexity with advancing technology followed by consolidation of the displays as human capabilities of data interpretation were exceeded. Initially, instrument panel space was devoted to the minimum instrumentation needed for the control of the aircraft, i.e. the turn and slip indicator and the airspeed indicator. Also present were essential engine data displays, and the fundamental attitude data displays provided by the gyro horizon, the barometric type altimeter, vertical speed indicator, and the magnetic compass. Even at this low level of complexity, problems asssoicated with interpretation of displayed data, scanning of instruments and accuracy were mainifest. Many diverse panel arrangements came into use, reflecting the vagaries of particular instrument manufacturers, of demands on panel shape and size, and of the experience of particular pilots under instrument flying conditions.

Although the minimum instrumentation referred to above provided the essential data to manoeuvre and control the aircraft, instrument flight was feasible only as an emergency measure for relatively short periods. However point-to-point navigation, with the precision needed for both military and public transport operations, required the development of new flight instruments and navigational aids. This eventually came about with the progressive development of such radio navigation systems as automatic direction finder (ADF), ILS, VOR, and distance measuring equipment. While it was possible, and practical, to navigate by the earlier developed systems, a high degree of pilot proficiency was nevertheless demanded. This was particularly evident during the terminal manoeuvring and approach-to-landing phase, where the most precise flight path control is required coincident with the performance of many other tasks preparatory to landing.

In order to ease the pilot's workload, and to achieve greater precision of flight guidance and control, the idea of presenting data in the form of control commands was conceived, and this led ultimately to the application of servomechanism design principles to systems known as flight directors.

Flight directors

A pioneer flight director system (FDS) was the Zero Reader (developed by Sperry) which sensed not only flight path deviation, but also such control parameters as aircraft attitude, attitude rate, and deviation rate. Control command signals were computed and presented on an indicator not unlike that of the ILS. Although the pilot no longer had to assemble basic control data from a number of instruments, it was still necessary for him to monitor continuously other instruments as an assurance that all parameters were consistent and compatible with the desired flight objective.

It was logical, therefore, in the next stage of development, to integrate functions of a flight director with those of the complementary instruments, so that essential data could be displayed on fewer instuments thereby reducing scanning time. With small variations from one application to another, and from one aircraft operator to another, this basic integration concept is adopted in a majority of today's aircraft, despite the added demands stemming from the progress in operating under reduced visibility, and in the development of new navigation equipment. The lowering of weather minima (see page 277) directly affects instruments complexity as a result of the need for additional display functions, such as redundant and expanded flight path deviation, airspeed deviation, radio altitude, de-crab and roll-out command data, and integration of turn-and-slip data into the primary display. The advancement to lower weather minima created the need for display integrity; this, in turn, required that nearly all the functions of the instruments be monitored, and that provision be made for the warning of faulty display functions. The demands created by the development of new navigation equipment result from technical innovation and added flexibility. There is a need to assimilate navigational data not previously available or which is now available in a new form. Furthermore, there is a need to indicate which type of system is generating the displayed information, in which mode that system is operating, which of serveral redundant sets of that type of equipment is connected, and in what co-ordinates the data is displayed.

In the field of automatic control, the development of control systems was also strongly influenced by the demands imposed on flight director systems, particularly for control in all phases of flight. The principal reason for this is that much of the basic attitude and navigational data is common to both systems. It was also logical, therefore, to expand on the concept of integration, such that data and servomechanism links could be shared so that a flight director system could provide guidance commands for an automatic flight control system and monitor its performance, and be available for reversion to effective manual control if fully automatic control should be lost. Because so much of the basic data and system hardware can be shared, flight director systems are usually developed and made available as a natural complement to each manufacturer's automatic flight control system.

A flight director system developed in this manner comprises two principal display units; they are variously called (i) attitude direction indicator, flight director, or an approach horizon; and (ii) horizontal situation indicator or a course deviation indicator. A number of display configurations may be adopted dependent on a particular manufacturer's design, and on the extent of the functions to be integrated. However, there are certain features which are of a common nature and these may be highlighted by considering the two units shown in figs. 9.1 and 9.2.

Attitude direction indicator

This indicator presents aircraft attitude and direction information in the form of a three-dimensional display. Attitude is displayed by the relationship of a stationary delta-shaped symbol representing the aircraft, with respect to roll and pitch commands displayed by two pointers, or command bars flanking the aircraft symbol, and also by a horizon bar. The command bars form a shallow inverted 'V', and are driven by separate servomotors within the indicator such that they move up and down to command a change in pitch, and rotate clockwise and anti-clockwise to command a change of roll attitude. The outputs of the two servos are combined mechanically so as to provide an integrated pitch and roll command. Sensing with respect to the aircraft symbol is such that the pilot is always directed to 'fly into the V'. When a command has been satisfied, the command bars are aligned with the edges of the aircraft symbol.

The horizon bar is carried on a flexible tape which is also driven by separate pitch and roll servomotors within the indicator. Freedom of tape movement in pitch is ±90°, and 360° in roll. The upper and lower sections of the tape are coloured to represent the sky and ground respectively, and they also have index marks on them to indicate pitch angles. In some types of flight director, the lower section of the moving tape is also marked with lines converging on the centre of the indicator display thereby enhancing its 'forward view' effect. Roll angle is displayed by a pointer which rotates with the flexible tape, and is referenced against a fixed scale. The servomotors are supplied with signals from a vertical gyroscope unit located at a remote point.

Deviations from the ILS glide slope beam (see also page 176) are shown by vertical displacements of a pointer over a scale at the left-hand side of the indicator display. Each of the inner dots on the scale represents a ¼° displacement from the beam centre line, while the outer dots each represents a ½° displacement. The pointer is driven by a d.c. meter movement and, when not in use, is deflected out of view at the top of the scale. A pointer at the lower part of the display indicates deviations from the localiser beam, and is shaped to symbolise a view of a runway during an approach. The reference dots on the localiser or runway scale, indicate approximately 1¼° displacement from

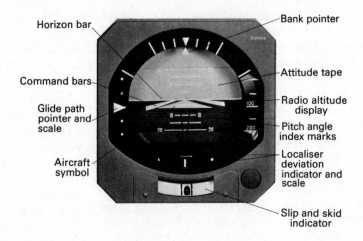

Horizon bar

Bank pointer

Command bars

Attitude tape

Glide path pointer and scale

Radio altitude display

Pitch angle index marks

Aircraft symbol

Localiser deviation indicator and scale

Slip and skid indicator

Fig. 9.1 Attitude direction indicator

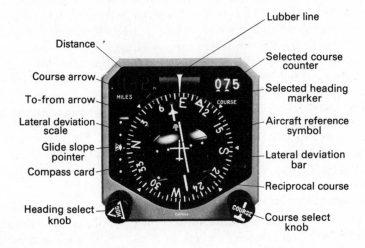

Lubber line

Distance

Selected course counter

Course arrow

Selected heading marker

To-from arrow

Lateral deviation scale

Aircraft reference symbol

Glide slope pointer

Lateral deviation bar

Compass card

Reciprocal course

Heading select knob

Course select knob

Fig. 9.2 Horizontal situation indicator

the beam centre line. The pointer is also driven by a d.c. meter movement, and, when not in use, is obscured by a black warning flag as shown in fig. 9.1. In some types of indicator, the localiser pointer, or runway symbol is also displaced in response to signals from a radio altimeter so that during the last 200 feet of descent, the pointer moves up to the fixed aircraft symbol thereby presenting a 'rising runway' display of the approach. This radio altitude display concept is also adopted in the indicator shown in fig. 9.1, but, in this case, it is effected by a pointer moving over a fixed altitude scale.

Indications of slip and skid are provided by an inclinometer similar to that adopted in conventional turn and slip indicators. In addition, some flight directors have a rate of turn pointer incorporated in the display, the pointer being actuated by signals from a rate gyroscope sensor unit.

Another command function which may be displayed in some attitude direction indicators is that related to the speed of an aircraft when executing a go-around manoeuvre following a missed approach. The display comprises a vertical scale and a pointer which is actuated in response to signals corresponding to the difference between indicated airspeed and a pre-determined go-around speed obtained from a speed computing system external to the flight director. The scale has several graduations ranging from the computed speed at the centre, to 'fast' and 'slow' at the top and bottom of the scale respectively. In order to achieve the correct go-around speed, engine power is adjusted so as to maintain the pointer at the centre of the scale. The pilot selects the go-around mode by pressing a button switch on the control wheel, the selection being indicated by the illumination of an annunciator light marked 'GA', and by displacement of the flight director command bars to command a wings-level climb attitude. In association with the go-around mode, a second annunciator light marked 'MDA' (minimum decision altitude) is provided. The light illuminates when the aircraft has descended to the preset radio altitude at which the decision whether to land or go-around must be made. If a flight director system is supplying guidance commands to an automatic flight control system during an approach, the latter system (with the exception of one having automatic landing capability) is caused to disengage when the 'GA' mode is selected.

The internal circuit arrangement of a representative type attitude direction indicator is shown in fig. 9.3.

Horizontal situation indicator

This indicator presents a pictorial display of navigation situation and, as will be noted from fig. 9.2, the situation is shown as a plan view of the aircraft's position and heading with respect to a selected heading and course. In addition to magnetic heading data signals, the indicator is also supplied with signal inputs corresponding to deviations from an ILS localiser beam, and VOR radial, and from a glide path beam. Indication of flight either to or from a VOR station is also provided. Selector knobs at the bottom corners of the indicator permit the setting of a desired magnetic heading and a VOR or localiser course. The aircraft reference symbol is fixed at the centre of the display and it indicates the position and heading of the aircraft in relation to the compass or azimuth card, and the lateral deviation bar. The compass card is synchronous-linked with the aircraft's magnetic compass system, and when changes in aircraft heading take place a position error signal is produced in a control transformer synchro within the indicator. After amplification by a servo amplifier in the instrument ampliflier unit, the signal is supplied to a

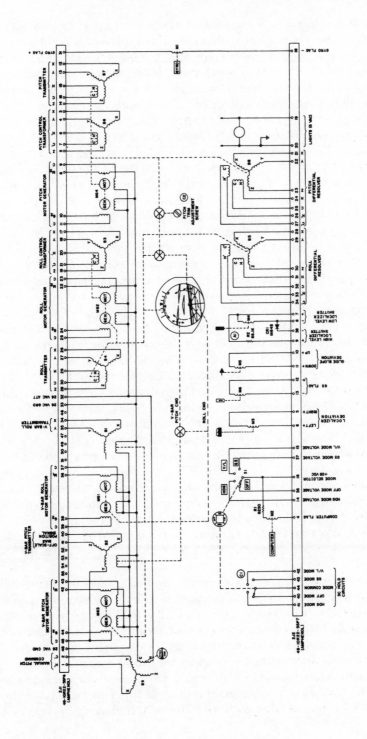

Fig. 9.3 Attitude direction indicator circuit arrangement

servomotor which, by means of a gear train system, drives the compass card to indicate the new heading with reference to a lubber line at the top centre of the indicator. Card movement is damped by means of a rate feedback signal produced by a rate generator which is driven by the motor. Feedback signals are mixed with position error signals, and the composite signal is amplified and supplied to the control phase of the servomotor.

At the same time, the servomotor drives the control transformer synchro rotor to the null position corresponding to the new heading. The lateral deviation bar is a movable centre section of the course arrow, and represents the centre line of the selected localiser course or VOR radial. The bar is deflected to the left or right by a d.c. meter movement to indicate the appropriate commands necessary for beam interception and capture, and it also rotates with the compass card as changes in aircraft heading take place. When operating in the localiser mode initial movement of the deviation bar begins when the aircraft is approximately 4° from the localiser beam centre, and the dots on the deviation scale represent approximately $1\frac{1}{4}°$ and $2\frac{1}{2}°$ from beam centre. In the VOR mode, initial movement of the bar begins when the aircraft is approximately 16° from radial centre, and the deviation scale dots then represent approximately 5° and 10° from radial centre.

Selection of a desired localiser course or VOR radial, is carried out by rotating the course selector knob until the course arrow coincides with the desired value on the compass card. The lateral deviation bar and deviation scale also rotate with the course arrow through the gear train system driven by the selector knob. At the same time a digital type of course counter is driven to the corresponding course indication; in fig. 9.2, this is displayed as 075°. Once set, the course arrow rotates with the compass card as aircraft heading changes. The gear train system also positions the rotors of a course resolver synchro associated with the VOR/LOC navigation receiver, and of a course datum control transformer synchro. When the course resolver synchro rotor position is changed, it shifts the phase of the reference 30 Hz signal in a phase shift circuit of the VOR instrumentation unit. The signal is then compared with the variable 30 Hz signal in a phase comparator, the output of which is supplied to the meter movement controlling the lateral deviation bar. When the output is such that it centres the deviation bar the aircraft is on the course selected.

When the aircraft deviates from the selected course, the phase-shifted reference signal is maintained at the angle determined by the resolver synchro rotor, but the variable signal phase received by the VOR navigation receiver is changed. The phase comparator will then produce an output which deflects the deviation bar to the left or right of the selected VOR course. The to–from arrow is positioned by a meter movement which is supplied with the corresponding signals from the radio navigation receiver and via a phase comparator in the instrumentation unit of the flight director system. In fig. 9.2 a 'fly to' command is displayed. In the LOC mode of operation, the deviation bar is similarly controlled by changes in resolver synchro rotor position, except that the output to the meter movement results from amplitude comparison of the signals either side of localiser beam centre. The to–from arrows remain out of view since no to–from signals are transmitted in the localiser mode.

Changes in the position of the course datum control transformer synchro rotor produces a position error signal in the stator windings. The signal is proportional to the difference between the selected course and the actual heading of the aircraft and is transmitted to the roll control channel of a steering computer or a flight director computer as a turn command to capture the selected VOR/LOC course. The signal is also transmitted to the automatic flight control system and if this system is coupled to the flight director, it will, of course, turn the aircraft automatically. The output from the appropriate computer is supplied to a roll command servo amplifer contained in an instrument amplifier unit, and after amplification it is fed to the roll servomotor coupled to the command bars of the flight director. Thus, the bars rotate to indicate the direction of roll required to capture the VOR/LOC course. The servomotor also drives a rate generator which produces a rate feedback signal for the purpose of damping display movements.

The selection of any desired magnetic heading is accomplished by positioning a triangular-shaped heading marker over the compass card, by means of the heading selector knob and its associated shaft and gear train system. At the same time, the rotor of a heading error control transformer synchro is rotated inside its stator, from its null position, and this produces a position error signal proportional to the difference between the selected heading and the aircraft heading sensed by the compass system. In fig. 9.2, the headings displayed are respectively 110° and 085°. The signal is processed in the same manner as that produced by the course datum control transformer synchro, and therefore results in the flight director command bars indicating the direction of roll required to fly on the desired heading. The circuit arrangement of a representative type of course indicator is illustrated in fig. 9.4.

Warning flags

As noted earlier, provision must be made for the warning of faulty display functions. In practice, warnings are effected by monitoring the command signals produced, so that when they are lost or are too weak to provide reliable information small red flags appear at appropriate parts of the flight director indicator and course indicator displays. The flags are actuated by d.c. meter mechanisms which are connected to the relevant signal sources.

In the case of flight director indicators there are, primarily, three warning flags labelled 'GS', 'GYRO' and 'COMPUTER' and respectively they indicate malfunctions of the glide-slope receiver or signal, and vertical gyroscope and atttiude display systems, and the director or steering computer and command display systems. The GS flag, when indicating a malfunction, obscures the glide slope pointer and scale to prevent its use. If the system is not being operated in the glide slope mode, the GS flag and pointer are biassed off-scale. Indication of localiser signal malfunction and/or localiser mode not selected, is also provided and generally takes the form of a black shutter which obscures the localiser pointer and scale (see fig. 9.1).

Other warning flags may be provided depending on any additional functions displayed; for example, a flag is provided to give warning of malfunctions in the circuit of a speed control display associated with a go-around manoeuvre.

In the case of a course indicator, there are also three primary warning flags and these are labelled 'GS', 'COMPASS' and 'VOR/LOC'. The GS flag operates in the same manner as that provided in the flight director indicator, while the compass flag indicates malfunctions of the magnetic heading signal circuit of the compass system. The VOR/LOC flag serves the dual function of warning of VOR radial signal and localiser signal malfunction. Warning flag operation is summarised in the table on page 255.

Pitch command facility

In some types of flight director systems, a pitch command facility is provided which permits the pilot to preselect a fixed climb or descent command under certain modes of operation. Selection is carried out by means of a selector knob which, in some cases, is located in the bottom left-hand corner of an attitude director indicator (see fig. 9.5) and in others is located on a separate flight director mode selector panel. The selector knob is mechanically coupled to the rotor of a control transformer synchro, and after the knob is rotated a signal is induced in the synchro. After amplification, this signal is transmitted to the pitch servomotor/generator which drives the command bars to the selected position. The aircraft attitude is then changed by 'flying the aircraft symbol into the command bars'. In addition to pitch command, a pitch trim adjustment is provided as a means of altering the position of the flight director horizon bar with respect to the aircraft symbol. The adjustment is purely mechanical in operation and is used for aligning the attitude display during installation of a flight director.

Operating modes

A number of flight director systems incorporate facilities for selecting various modes of operation, such facilities being comparable in function to the outer loop control of an automatic flight control system. This being so, it is possible for mode selection to be used on a common basis in cases where a flight director system is employed in combination with an automatic flight

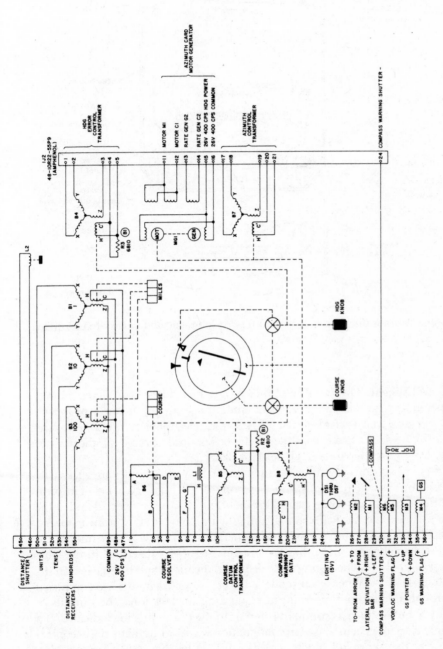

Fig. 9.4 Horizontal situation indicator circuit arrangement

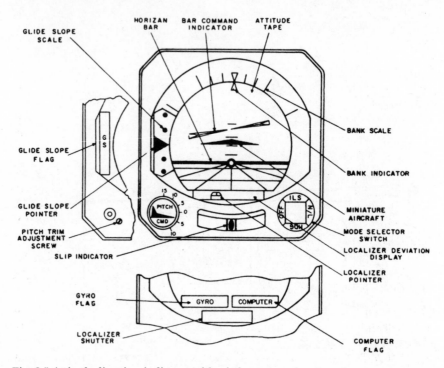

Fig. 9.5 Attitude direction indicator with pitch command and mode select facilities

control system. The number of modes vary dependent on specific aircraft operating requirements, and for a similar reason, the method by which modes are selected can also vary; for example, selection may be effected by the control knob of a rotary selector switch on an attitude direction indicator (see fig. 9.5) or on a separate mode selector panel (see fig. 9.6).

In some versions of a control panel, shown in fig. 9.7, modes are selected by push buttons which are push-on/push-off solenoid-hold switches. The push buttons illuminate when their corresponding modes are selected and at the same time a mechanically-actuated flag with the word 'ON' appears over a portion of each button engaged. The operating modes which are fundamental to some typical flight director systems, are briefly described in the table opposite, while some appropriate display indications are summarised in the table page 256. When each mode is selected, signal circuits are completed through the appropriate computer and amplifier sections, the outputs of which are supplied as command signals to the flight director indicator. If a flight director system is used in combination with an automatic flight control system, the command signals are also utilised by this system for applying control in the sense necessary to satisfy the relevant commands.

ATTITUDE DIRECTION INDICATOR

MODE	ROLL	PITCH	HORIZON ATTITUDE DISPLAY	GLIDE-SLOPE DEVIATION POINTER	LOCALIZER DEVIATION POINTER	GLIDE-SLOPE (flag)	LOCALIZER (flag)	GYRO (flag)	COMPUTER (flag)
OFF	BIASED OUT OF VIEW		SHOWS PITCH & ROLL	OUT OF VIEW UNLESS TUNED TO ILS – THEN SHOWS GLIDE-SLOPE DEVIATION	COVERED BY FLAG	OUT OF VIEW UNLESS TUNED TO ILS – THEN MONITORS ILS RADIO	COVERS DISPLAY	MONITORS GYRO + SERVO POWER + SERVO ERROR	BIASED OUT OF VIEW
HDG	HEADING ERROR + BANK ATTITUDE	PITCH COMMAND + PITCH ATTITUDE							MONITORS COMPASS + GYRO + VOR RADIO + COMPUTER
VOR/LOC RADIO TUNED TO VOR	VOR RADIO DEVIATION + BANK + COURSE DATUM								MONITORS COMPASS + GYRO + LOC RADIO + COMPUTER
VOR/LOC RADIO TUNED TO LOC	LOCALIZER RADIO DEVIATION + BANK + COURSE DATUM								
GS	LOCALIZER RADIO DEVIATION + BANK + COURSE DATUM	PITCH ATTITUDE + GLIDE-SLOPE RADIO DEVIATION		INDICATES GLIDE-SLOPE DEVIATION	INDICATES LOCALIZER DEVIATION	MONITORS GLIDE-SLOPE RADIO	MONITORS LOCALIZER RADIO		MONITORS COMPASS + GYRO + LOC RADIO + GS RADIO + COMPUTER

HORIZONTAL SITUATION INDICATOR

MODE	GLIDE-SLOPE DEVIATION POINTER	VOR/LOC DEVIATION BAR	GLIDE-SLOPE (flag)	VOR/LOC (flag)	COMPASS (flag)	TO-FROM ARROW
OFF	OUT OF VIEW UNLESS TUNED TO ILS – THEN SHOWS GLIDE-SLOPE DEVIATION					OUT OF VIEW UNLESS RADIO TUNED TO VOR – THEN DISPLAYS TO-FROM
HDG					MONITORS COMPASS + SERVO POWER + SERVO ERROR	
VOR/LOC RADIO TUNED TO VOR	OUT OF VIEW	DISPLAYS VOR/LOC DEVIATION	OUT OF VIEW UNLESS TUNED TO ILS – THEN MONITORS ILS RADIO	MONITORS NAV RADIO		DISPLAYS TO-FROM
VOR/LOC RADIO TUNED TO LOC						
GS	INDICATES GLIDE-SLOPE DEVIATION		MONITORS GLIDE-SLOPE RADIO			OUT OF VIEW

Fig. 9.6 Mode selector panel

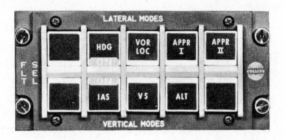

Fig. 9.7 Push-button type mode selctor

Fundamental Operating Modes

OFF   Command bars deflected out of sight, and flight director indicator used as an attitude reference only.

HDG   Command bars provide lateral guidance to achieve and maintain a compass heading, as selected on the course indicator. Vertical guidance is from a preselected pitch attitude.

VOR(NAV)/LOC   Command bars provide lateral guidance to capture and track a VOR radial or localiser beam. Vertical guidance is the same as in HDG mode.

GS   Command bars provide lateral and vertical

256

guidance to capture and track the localiser and glide slope beams respectivly. The GS and LOC pointers monitor aircraft deviations of the beam.

GS AUTO	As for GS except that interception and capture of glide slope takes place automatically after the localiser beam has been captured.
ALT	Command bars provide vertical guidance to hold the aircraft at the desired altitude.
APPR I	Selected for capture and tracking of GS and LOC beams on ILS approaches to Category I standards (see page 279). Command bars provide lateral and vertical guidance.
APPR II	As for APPR I but produces tighter tracking of beams to meet higher precision requirements of a Category II ILS approach (see page 279).
GA	Selected for a go-around manoeuvre after a missed approach, and after selecting either one of the approach modes. The command bars command a wings-level, pitch-up attitude. HDG and IAS modes may be selected after go-around power settings and airspeed are established.
IAS	Selected to maintain a particular indicated airspeed during climbout after take-off, and during letdown over a VOR station. The command bars provide vertical guidance.
V/S	Selected to maintain a particular vertical speed, i.e. rate of climb or descent. The command bars provide vertical guidance.
MACH	As for IAS mode but selected at higher altitudes.

Computer and amplifier units

As already noted in the foregoing brief descriptions of attitude direction indicator and horizontal situation indicator operation, the appropriate command signals are processed by computer and instrument amplifier units. The primary function of a computer unit is to provide all the computation necessary for determining any position or attitude errors, and to develop the signals necessary to command position or attitude changes. When a flight director system is integrated with an automatic flight control system, the computed signals are also utilised for the application of control. A computer may in some cases be a single unit containing solid-state signal circuits for both lateral and vertical guidance information, while for some director systems separate computer units are utilised. In addition to the signal circuits, a logic network is incorporated, its purpose being to provide correct analogue scaling of signals, and to adjust computer gains and logic to suit specific types of aircraft. All signal and power supply circuits are on printed circuit boards which are arranged as separate functional plug-in modules.

The primary function of an instrument amplifier is to supply servo-actuating power for the display mechanisms of the flight director and course indicators. The unit also contains separate plug-in module circuit boards which, as shown in the overall signal flow diagram of a representative system (fig. 9.8) correspond to five servo channels, two signal convertor channels, and three flag alarm circuits. If additional warnings are required the number of alarm circuits is increased accordingly. The converter channels accept d.c. input signals and convert them to 400 Hz signals for use by the pitch and roll command servo channels. The convertors receive pitch and roll steering signals from the computer, position error signal information from the pitch and roll command control transformer synchros in the flight director, and rate feedback signals from the pitch and roll command servomotor/generators. These signals are mixed and, after filtering, the composite signals provide the input for the appropriate command servo amplifier.

The continuing development of flight director systems, notably in the reduction of separate components, is typified by the example shown in fig. 9.9. In this case both indicators and the amplifier and computer units are housed in a single panel-mounted unit.

Electronic flight instrument system

This system, commonly referred to as 'EFIS', is a highly sophisticated type of flight director system in which flight operating and navigational data is processed by high-storage capacity digital computers, and then presented to the flight crew in video form. EFIS has two display units that correspond to the attitude director indicator and the horizontal situation indicator of a conventional flight director system, but whereas the latter requires electromechanically controlled elements for the presentation of data, EFIS display units utilise colour cathode ray tubes. Movements of horizon lines, pointers, command bars, etc., are effected by circuits which, in response to the

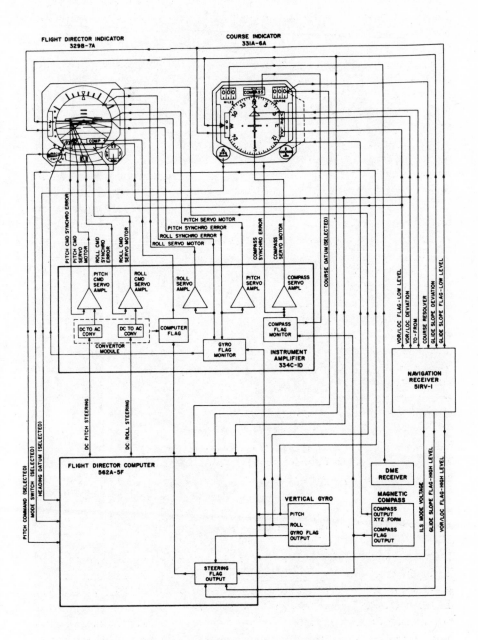

Fig. 9.8 Signal flow diagram of a representative flight director system

Fig. 9.9 Combined flight director system units

appropriate data signals, deflict electron beams within the tubes to appropriate matrix locations on the active surfaces of the tubes.

A single system is provided for each pilot, and as will be noted from fig. 9.10, a system is comprised of a symbol generator, a control panel, and the two indicators. The symbol generator is comprised of microprocessors, memories, and the circuits necessary for generating the displays of vital information. It receives data from a data bus which is supplied with signals from all the relevant systems of an aircraft and their computers. The system abbreviations indicated in fig. 9.10 are defined in Appendix 3.

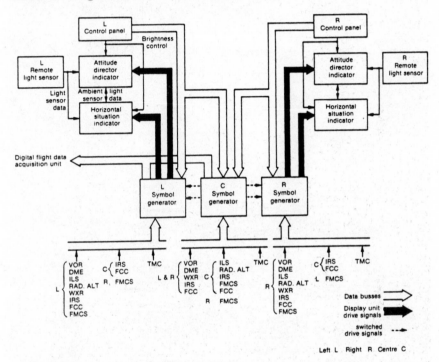

Fig. 9.10 EFIS units and signal interfacing

In a complete installation, three symbol generators are required; the third (centre) generator is a 'standby' one so that in the event that either of the other two should fail, its drive signals may be switched to the appropriate display units. Switching is done via electromechanical relays that are under the control of selector switches mounted on each of two control panels.

Control panel

Each pilot is provided with a control panel, and as may be seen from fig. 9.11,

261

Automatic Flight Control

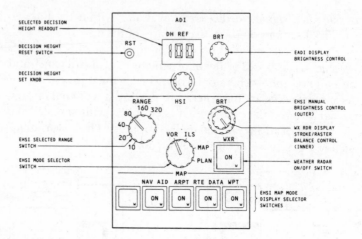

Fig. 9.11 EFIS control panel

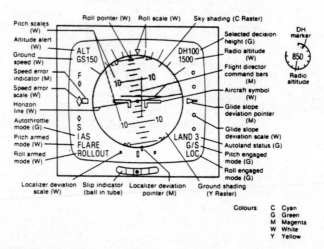

Fig. 9.12 EFIS attitude director indicator

the control switches are grouped appropriate to each of the display units.

Attitude director indicator

This unit displays traditional pitch and roll information, flight director commands, ILS localiser and glide slope deviations, selected airspeed, ground speed, automatic flight control and auto-throttle modes, radio altitude and decision height. As far as pitch and roll attitude information is concerned, the unit is an example of one utilising inertial references (see pages 124 and 186.

All information is displayed on an approximately five-inch square screen, and to convey some idea of the extent of this information and the colours in which it is displayed, fig. 9.12 illustrates the display presentation representing an aircraft making an automatically controlled approach to land. If during the approach the aircraft deviates beyond the normal ILS glide slope and/or localiser limits, the flight crew are alerted by the respective deviation pointers changing colour from white to amber; the pointers also start flashing. The alert condition ceases when the deviations return to within their normal limits.

It will also be noted from fig. 9.12 that pitch and roll information is referenced against a shaded background which, as in the case of the indicator used in conventional flight director systems, represents the sky and the ground. The sky shading is in the colour cyan (light blue) and the ground shading in yellow, both being produced by *raster scanning*; this is the term used to denote the manner in which an electron beam generated within a cathode ray tube is deflected back and forth to produce a solid image on the screen of the tube. All other symbols and characters are produced by a digital stroke pulsing technique known as *stroke scanning*. Each method of scanning is produced by individual generators contained within the symbol generators.

Radio altitude is digitally displayed during an approach, and when the aircraft is 2,500 and 1,000 feet above ground level. Below 1,000 feet the display automatically changes to a white circular scale calibrated in 100-foot increments, and the selected decision height changes from a digital readout to a magenta-coloured marker on the scale. As the aircraft descends, segments of the circular scale are simultaneously 'erased' so that the scale length is continuously decreased in an anti-clockwise direction.

At the pre-selected decision height (plus 50 feet) an aural warning is sounded and continues at an increasing rate until the decision height is reached. At this point, the colour of the circular height scale changes from white to amber; both the scale and marker flash for several seconds. A reset button is provided on the control panel and when pressed the flashing is stopped and the scale and marker are changed back to their normal colours.

During operation, the indicator generates a fair amount of heat, and therefore air from an equipment cooling system is circulated through it at a controlled rate. Temperature-sensing units are provided which are set at low and high values approximately 20°C apart. If the lower value is exceeded, a signal is transmitted to the symbol generator which causes the rastered data (i.e. sky/ground shading) to be turned off, thus alerting the flight crew. The

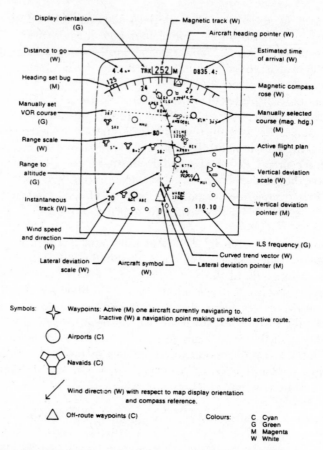

Fig 9.13 EFIS horizontal situation indicator in 'map' mode

display is restored when the temperature drops 5°C below the 'shutdown' value. If the higher value is exceeded, the whole display is switched off. Normal operation (minus the rastered data) is restored when the temperature drops 6°C below the 'shutdown' value.

Horizontal situation indicator

This unit presents a dynamic display of flight progress and plan view orientation, in four difference display modes which may be selected on the system control panel. The modes are MAP, PLAN, ILS and VOR.

The normally used MAP mode display colours and symbol identification are illustrated in fig. 9.13. In conjunction with a flight plan programmed into the flight management computer (FMC) the indicator displays information against a moving map background (hence the term dynamic display) with all elements to a common scale. The symbol representing the aircraft is at the lower part of the display and an arc of a compass scale is at the upper part. As in the case of pitch and roll information, heading data is supplied from an inertial reference system; it may be selected as either magnetic or true heading.

The tuned VOR/DME stations, airports and their identification letters, and the programmed flight plan, are all correctly oriented with respect to the position and track of the aircraft, and to the range scale (nautical miles/inch) selected on the control panel. Thus, with 80 selected as shown in fig. 9.11, the same number will be displayed alongside the instantaneous track line as indicated in the figure. If the weather radar has been selected on from the control panel, the radar 'returns' are also displayed at the same scale and orientation as the map mode. Indications of other data such as wind speed and direction, lateral and vertical deviations from the selected flight profile, distance to waypoints, estimated time of arrival, etc., are also displayed.

Typical examples of the other modes are shown in fig. 9.14. In the PLAN mode, a static map background with route data corresponding to the FMC flight plan is displayed together with track and heading information. If the flight crew wish to make any changes to the route, they first select them on the keyboard of the FMC display unit so that they can be checked as they appear on the screen of the horizontal situation indicator, before entering them into the FMC.

In the VOR and ILS modes heading orientation of the aircraft is displayed against either an expanded or a full compass scale. Selected range, wind information, and the name of the system from which signals are being supplied, are also displayed. If the weather radar has been switched on, radar 'returns' are also displayed when in these modes, but only if an expanded compass scale is presented.

A horizontal situation indicator display unit is cooled and temperature controlled in the same manner as the attitude director indicator.

Light sensors

In order to ensure that the light intensity of the displays is compatible with ambient light conditions in the flight deck, light sensors of the photo-diode type are provided to adjust the intensity automatically. Two sensors are mounted so that they respond directly to light coming in through the flight deck windshields, and there is one in the front of each display unit to respond to light in the area of the instrument panel.

Failure annunciations

As in the case of convential flight director system indicators it is also necessary for failure of data signals from such systems as the ILS and radio altimeter to be annunciated. In EFIS indicators annunciation takes the form of yellow

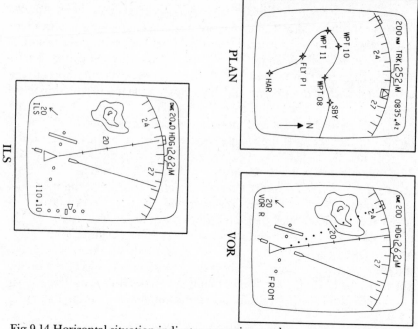

Fig 9.14 Horizontal situation indicator operating modes

flags 'painted' at specific matrix locations on the diplay unit screens (see fig. 9.14). In addition, fault messages may also be displayed, e.g. if the associated FMC and weather radar disagree with the control panel range data, the discrepancy message 'WXR/MAP RANGE DISAGREE' appears on the screen of the horizontal situation indicator.

TEST QUESTIONS

1 What information is displayed on a typical flight director unit? Describe a method of display presentation.

2 What type of signal is applied to the glide slope and localiser meters of flight director system indicators?

3 What is the significance of the reference dots on the scales of glide slope and localiser meters?

4 How is the 'go-around' mode selected, and what happens if the flight director system is supplying approach guidance commands to the automatic control system at the moment of selection?

5 Under what conditions will the 'MDA' light be illuminated?

6 What indications are provided by the lateral deviation bar of an HSI?

7 The TO-FROM indicator of an HSI is in operation when:

  (a) either the VOR or LOC mode is selected.

  (b) only the VOR mode is selected.

(c) a heading change is selected.

8 To which automatic flight control channels are Flight Director system signals supplied?

9 How are desired magnetic heading changes selected and transmitted?

10 How are system malfunctions indicated, and to which operating conditions can they be related.

11 What arrangement is provided in some Flight Director systems to permit the pre-selection of a fixed climb or descent?

12 Under what conditions would the modes 'GS AUTO' and 'APPR I' be selected?

13 Name the main units that comprise an electronic flight instrument system.

14 What is the function of the third symbol generator in a dual system?

15 Under what flight conditions do the glide slope and localiser deviation pointers of the EFIS attitude director indicator change from white to amber?

16 Name the four modes that can be displayed on the EFIS horizontal situation indicator, and state how they are selected.

17 Can weather radar 'returns' be displayed in all four modes?

18 When failure of data signals occurs, indication is given on EFIS display units by flags displayed in:

   (a) red

   (b) magenta

   (c) yellow

10
Logic Circuits and Diagrams

The operation of the majority of units comprising automatic flight control systems is based on the application of solid-state circuit technology, i.e. components such as resistors, rectifiers, and internal switches that are normally interconnected as separate discrete components, are all 'embedded' in micro-size sections of semiconductor material. Apart from the vast reduction in dimensions, this form of integration also makes possible the production of circuit 'packs' capable of performing a vast number of individual dedicated functions. Thus, in knowing the operating parameters of a system overall, and the functions that constituent units are required to perform, the complete circuitry of a system is built up by interconnecting selected functional packs. The packs consist of basic decision-making elements referred to as *logic gates*, each performing combinational operations on their inputs and so determining the state of their outputs.

As far as diagrammatic presentation of the foregoing circuits is concerned, greater use is made of a schematic form depicting interconnected blocks and a variety of special logic symbols, each representing a specific circuit network 'hidden away' in the semiconductor material. The study of a system's operation is therefore based more on the interpretation of symbols and the logic state of signal functions at the various interconnections of the circuit, rather than tracing through diagrams that depict all internal circuit details in pure theoretical form.

Logic gates

Logic gates are of a binary nature, i.e. the inputs and the outputs are in one of two states expressed by the digital notation 1 or 0. Other corresponding expressions are also frequently used, as follows:

> 1 – on; true; high (H); closed; engaged
> 0 – off; false; low (L); open; disengaged

The 1 and 0 state designations are arbitrary. For example, if the states are

268

represented by voltage levels, one may be positive and the other 0V; one may be negative and the other 0V; one may be positive and the other negative; both may be positive, or both may be negative. The applications of logic to a system or device may therefore be further defined as follows:

1. positive logic, when the more positive potential (high) is consistently selected as the 1 state.
2. negative logic, when the less positive potential (low) is consistently selected as the 1 state.
3. hybrid or mixed logic, when both positive or both negative logic is used.

The inherent function of a logic gate is equivalent to that of a conventional switch which can be referred to as a 'two-state' device, and this may be illustrated by considering the theoretical circuit of a simple motor control system shown in fig. 10.1 (a). In the 'off' position of the switch, the whole circuit is open, and is in an inactive or logic 0 state. In the 'on' position, the switch closes the relay coil circuit causing positive d.c. to pass through the coil. Since the input voltage at 'A' is at a high level with respect to ground, the input to the relay coil is of a logic 1 state and so the coil is energised. The input voltage at 'B' is also high and so operates the motor from the logic 1 state existing at point 'C' by closing of the relay contacts. The circuit may therefore be considered as a positive logic function circuit.

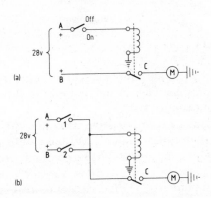

Fig. 10.1 Logic switching

As a further illustration of logic switching, let us consider the motor control circuit shown in fig. 10.1 (b). In this case control is effected by selecting either of two parallel-connected switches located remotely from each other. If it is required to operate the motor from, say, the switch 1 location, the circuit from input 'A' to the relay coil is closed by placing the switch at the 'on' position, thereby producing an active logic 1 state in the coil circuit and at the output 'C'. Switch 2 remains open so that the circuit from

269

input 'B' is in the logic 0 state. The converse would be true were the motor to be operated from the switch 2 position and with switch 1 off. The circuit is also an example of positive logic.

Gates and symbols

The circuits to which digital logic is applied are combinations of three basic gates performing functions referred to as 'AND', 'OR' and 'NOT': the latter being an inverting function and giving rise to two other gates referred to as 'NAND' and 'NOR'.

Gate circuits are designed so that switching is carried out by either junction diodes, or transistors, or by a combination of both. In order to simplify diagrams as much as possible, the internal circuit arrangements are omitted, and the gates are represented by corresponding distinctively-shaped symbols which conform to accepted standards. The three basic gate symbols are shown in fig. 10.2.

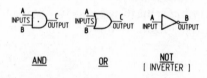

Fig. 10.2 Basic gate symbols

Variations in the symbol shapes adopted will be found in some literature, but those shown here are adopted in the majority of manuals relating to aircraft automatic flight control systems.

All possible combinations of input logic states and their corresponding output states in terms of the binary digits (bits) 0 and 1 are displayed by means of truth tables. The tables appropriate to the gates referred to thus far are given in Appendix 4, and to illustrate how they are constructed, let us consider the one shown in fig. 10.3. This corresponds to an AND gate and, as

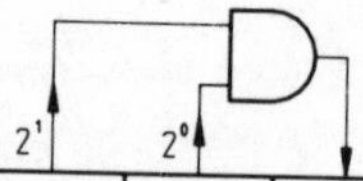

A	B	C
0	0	0
0	1	0
1	0	0
1	1	1

Fig. 10.3 Truth table

will be noted, the table is a rectangular co-ordinate presentation, the columns representing the inputs and the rows representing the logic combinations.

The number of different possible combinations is expressed by 2^n, where n is the number of inputs. Thus, for a basic 2-input gate the possible combinations are $2^n = 2^2 = 4$, and so the table has two input columns and four rows. For a 3-input gate there would be eight possible combinations, and so on. The sequencing of the 0s and the 1s which make up the logic combinations is based on identfying the inputs with 2s which are raised to a power based upon the input positions in a table. The table in fig. 10.3 has two input columns, and working from right to left (this sequence always applies) column B is identified with 2^0 and column A with 2^1. Since 2 raised to zero power equals 1, then one 0 and one 1 are alternately placed in each row of column B. Two raised to the power of 1 equals 2; therefore two 1s are alternately placed in each row of column A. From column C it will therefore be noted that an AND gate can only produce an output when the input combination is in the logic 1 state; for this reason, the gate is often referred to as an 'all or nothing' gate.

The same input combinations apply to an OR gate, but as reference to its truth table in Appendix 4 shows, it will produce an output when the inputs, either singly, or in combination, are in the logic 1 state; the gate is therefore referred to as an 'any or all' gate.

As an illustration of how gate functions may be related to theoretical circuits, let us again refer to fig. 10.1. In order for the motor shown in diagram (a) to operate it must have a logic 1 input supplied to it, and since this can only be obtained when both the switch *and* relay contacts are closed, then the circuit corresponds to an AND function and may be represented by the appropriate symbol, as in fig. 10.4. For the motor at diagram (b) to operate, the logic 1 input can be supplied to it when either switch 1 *or* switch 2 is closed; thus, the circuit corresponds to an OR function and may be represented by the appropriate symbol.

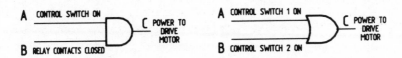

Fig. 10.4 Gate functions

The NOT function logic gate is used in circuits that require the state of a signal to be changed without having a voltage at the output every time there is one at the input, or vice versa. In other words, the function of its circuit is to invert the input signal such that the output signal is always of the opposite state. The symbol for an inverter is the same at that adopted for an amplifier but with the addition of a small circle (called a 'state indicator') drawn at either

271

the input or output side. When the circle is at the input side, it means that the input signal must be 'low' for it to be an activating signal; when at the output side an activated output function is 'low'. In many cases, the NOT function is used in conjunction with the input to an AND or OR gate as in fig. 10.5;

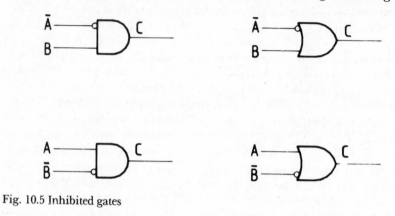

Fig. 10.5 Inhibited gates

the gate is then said to be *inhibited* or *negated*. In order to exphasize the inversion, a line is drawn over the letter designating the inverted input. The truth tables are also given in Appendix 4 and should be compared with those of the AND and OR gates.

The addition of an inverter at the output of an AND gate and of an OR gate changes their functions and they are then known respectively as NAND (a contraction of Not and AND) and NOR (a contraction of Not OR) gates. They are identified by the symbols shown in fig. 10.6.

Fig. 10.6 NAND and NOR gates

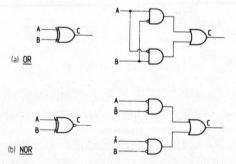

Fig. 10.7 Exclusive gates

272

Fig. 10.7 illustrates the symbols of two logic gates called exclusive OR and exclusive NOR, each being a combination of two inhibited AND gates and an OR gate.

In some cases, the inputs to AND and OR gates may be connected together in the configurations known as 'wired AND' and 'wired OR'. They are symbolised as shown in Appendix 4.

Practical logic diagrams

As pointed out earlier in this chapter, a study of systems operation is based on the interpretation of symbols and logic states of signal functions depicted in diagrams of schematic form. From the details given thus far, it would perhaps appear that such interpretation is not that easy. This may be the case initially, but once a working knowledge of the symbols and their associated logic states has been acquired, it will be found that practical logic diagrams overall can present far less difficulty in interpretation than those depicting circuits in the more conventional theoretical form. In this connection, we may consider the example diagram of fig. 10.8. This relates to an annunciator system associated with one type of automatic flight control system, and it depicts the signal states appropriate to capture of the localiser (LOC) beam during the landing approach mode.

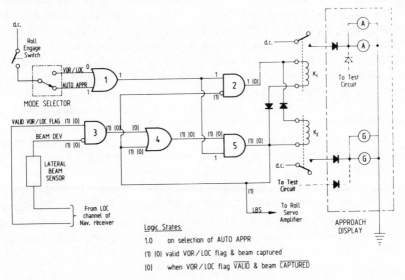

Fig. 10.8 Logic diagram – approach mode annunciator system

Selection of the AUTO APPR mode is made on the control panel of the system, and as will be noted, a logic 1 input is applied to OR gate 1. Since the VOR/LOC position of the switch is open, a logic 0 is applied as the other

273

input to gate 1 and it produces a logic 1 state at its output, which is then applied to NAND gate 2. Sensing of any deviations from the LOC beam is effected in the relevant channel of the aircraft's navigation receiver, and for the operation of the circuit shown, two inputs from the receiver are required; the deviation signal, and a signal for the actuation of a VOR/LOC flag provided in the horizontal situation indicator of the flight director system associated with the automatic flight control system. The deviation signal is applied to a lateral beam sensor within the roll control channel, and then as an input to NAND gate 3. The flag actuating signal is applied as the second input to gate 3.

When the values of the corresponding signals are below those required to actuate the VOR/LOC flag and to initiate capture of the LOC beam, then the inputs to gate 3 are logic 0. Gate 3 assumes a logic 0 output state and applies this to OR gate 4, and because this gate now has two logic 0 inputs, its output applied to AND gate 5 is also logic 0. Together with the logic 1 input from OR gate 1, the output state of gate 5 is logic 0, and since this provides a ground for the logic 1 output state of NAND gate 2, then relay K_1 is energised to illuminate the amber lights of the approach display unit. The lights therefore indicate that selection of the AUTO APPR mode is established, and also that the system is armed in readiness for capture of the LOC beam.

When the lateral beam sensor senses beam capture, a logic 1 is applied to gate 3. The flag actuating signal applied as a second input to gate 3 will also be logic 1, signifying that the beam signal strength is valid for control. The output state of gate 3 is therefore logic 1 and is applied to OR gate 4; the other input is momentarily logic 0 and so its output is logic 1 which, on being applied to AND gate 5, also produces a logic 1 output state at this gate. This output is supplied to relay K_2 and also back to OR gate 4 and to the inverted input of NAND gate 2, causing its output state to revert to logic 0; relay K_1 will be now be de-energised and thereby extinguish the amber lights. The logic 0 from gate 2 provides a ground for relay K_2 and so it is energised to illuminate the green lights to indicate that the LOC beam has been captured. The relay is 'latched' in the engerised condition by the logic 1 input supplied to OR gate 4.

Lateral control of the aircraft after beam capture, and ultimately onto the beam centre, is effected by also applying the logic 1 output state from gate 5 as the lateral beam sensor signal to the amplifier which controls the application of power to the roll servomotor of the automatic flight control system.

TEST QUESTIONS

1 Name the functions performed by the three basic logic gates.

2 The logic symbol shown represents:

(a) an AND gate.
(b) a NAND gate.
(c) an OR gate.

3 The logic equivalent of the switching arrangement shown would be:

(a) an AND gate.
(b) a NOR gate.
(c) an OR gate.

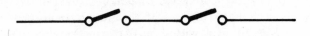

4 For the logic circuit shown, an output at logic 1 will be obtained with:

(a) both inputs at logic 1.
(b) only one input at logic 1.
(c) both inputs at logic 0.

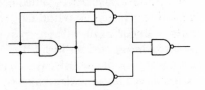

5 What is the purpose of a truth table?

6 The truth table shown corresponds to:

	A	B	C
(a) a NAND gate.	0	0	0
(b) an OR gate.	0	1	0
(c) an AND gate.	1	0	0
	1	1	1

7 What is the significance of a line drawn over a letter or signal function when related to the input or output of a logic gate?

11
Automatic Landing

The fundamental landing requirement

In order to achieve a safe landing, an aircraft has to be so controlled that its wheels make contact with the ground comfortably within the paved surface of the runway, within fairly narrow longitudinal limits along it, and at a sinking speed not greatly in excess of an optimum value of about 1 to 2 feet per second. The speed at touch-down should have been reduced from the approach margin of about 30% above the stall to about half this value, by progressive reduction of engine power during the landing flare. Finally, the wings should have been levelled prior to the actual landing, and the aircraft yawed to bring its longitudinal axis parallel to the runway centre-line to remove any drift angle due to cross-wind; the latter manoeuvre being known as decrabbing, or drift 'kick-off'. Control of the aircraft is needed about all three axes simultaneously, as well as the control of airspeed through engine power changes; it will be appreciated, therefore, that the approach and landing manoeuvre is the most difficult one demanded of the pilot. Add to this the unfortunate fact that in aircraft operations a large percentage of all accidents can be attributed to the approach and landing phase of a flight, and it is self-evident that systems designed to carry out automatic landings under all visibility conditions must provide guidance and control better than that provided by the pilot looking at the outside world. Accident rate statistics figure largely in the formulation of the requirements for automatic landing systems, and this led to the adoption (by the United Kingdom certification authorities) of a minimum reliability value of 1 in 10^7; in other words, that a system should not cause a fatal accident more often than one in ten million landings.

The control function during the approach and landing manoeuvre is required on a highly repetitive basis, and although a number of parameters are to be controlled simultaneously, such control is only necessary for a comparatively short period of time, and is therefore most suited to automatic means.

As a prelude to 'blind landing', automatic landing has always been the ultimate aim of control systems designers and aircraft operators, throughout the development of automatic flight control systems. The history of such developments, the attendant problems, and the attainment of the requisite high safety levels have been so well documented over the past two decades that even a brief summary would constitute a volume in itself. However, in making a broad analysis of available data, it will be found that the many problems which have had to be solved in the development of systems in current use, and having autolanding capability, can be grouped in the following three main areas:

1. Achieving the highest integrity and reliability of systems bearing in mind that they need to be entrusted with very considerable authority over the controls of an aircraft, including the throttles, and in the presence of the ground.

2. The provision of adequate monitoring information on the progress of the approach and landing manoeuvre, and which will enable the pilot to take over under the most critical conditions of a system malfunction in the presence of the ground.

3. The substitution of the pilot's direct vision with an automatic ground guidance system, having an integrity and reliability of the same high order as that demanded of the 'on board' system.

Weather minima

In low visibility operations, the weather limits for landing are given in the following terms.

1. *Runway visual range* (RVR) which is an instrumentally derived value that represents the range at which high-intensity lights can be seen in the direction of landing along the runway. Its readings are transmitted to the air traffic controller who can inform the pilot of the very latest visibility conditions.

2. *Decision height* is the wheel height above the runway elevation by which a go-round must be initiated by the pilot unless adequate visual reference has been established, and the position and approach path of the aircraft have been visually assessed as satisfactory to safely continue the approach or landing.

Minimum values of these two quantities (known as 'weather minima') are specified by the national licensing authorities for various types of aircraft, and for various airports. When the traffic controller advises that RVR is above the specified minimum the pilot may descend to the specified decision height, and if by then he has sighted a sufficiently large segment of the ground to enable him to be confident of his judgement, he may carry on and land; otherwise he must overshoot, and either enter the holding pattern pending another approach, or divert to an alternative airport. During the approach,

277

the pilot's line of sight is down the glidepath and not along the runway, and this gives rise to another factor, called 'slant visual range', which a pilot must take into account in order to avoid misinterpretation of visual cues.

ICAO categorisation

The foregoing terms are related in a system of categorisation adopted by ICAO, and which describes low-visibility landing capabilities based on the principle that the probability of having adequate short visual reference, for the range of permitted decision heights, should be as high as possible. The definitions of the main categories are graphically illustrated in fig. 11.1.

The three categories also serve as an indication of the stages through which automaic approach and automatic landing development progresses, and thereby designate the capabilities of individual automatic flight control systems. In addition, they designate the standards of efficiency of the ground guidance equipment available at airports, namely ILS localiser and glide path, and approach, runway and taxiway lighting.

In connection with automatic landing systems, and in describing low weather minima, the term 'all weather operations' is frequently used; a term which can, and sometimes is, taken to mean that there are no weather conditions that can prevent an aircraft from taking-off and landing successfully. This is not the case, because no automatic system can, for example, perform the landing task in wind conditions in excess of those for which the aircraft has been certificated, this being primarily governed by the controllability characteristics and strength factors of the aircraft. Similarly, no automatic system can land an aircraft on a runway the surface of which, because of water, slush or ice, is not fit for such an operation.

System reliability and redundancy

In chapter 7 (page 217) details were given of the purpose and operation of devices designed to limit the authority of automatic control systems in the event of 'runaway' conditions resulting from malfunctions. While such devices may be incorporated in the more conventional control systems, and thereby be generally effective for the intended purpose down to 'break-off' heights, i.e. approach heights at which a control system is disengaged, this would not satisfy the requirements for systems designed for autolanding. For example, if an aircraft is on the glide path and a 'runaway' occurs in the pitch control channel causing a nose-down attitude then obviously height will be lost, and in using a torque limiting device having a preset value, the aircraft could be well below the glide path before recovery can commence. Thus, there is a minimum altitude to which the device can be used.

The height lost following a malfunction could be reduced by a more severe

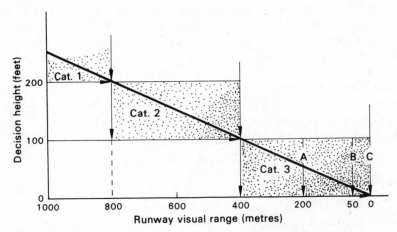

Category 1: Operation down to minima of 200 ft decision height and runway visual range of 800 m with a high probability of approach success.

Category 2: Operation down to minima below 200 ft decision height and runway visual range of 800 m, and to as low as 100 ft decision height and runway visual range of 400 m with a high probability of approach success.

Category 3A: Operation down to and along the surface of the runway, with external visual reference during the final phase of the landing down to runway visual range minima of 200 m.

Category 3B: Operation to and along the surface of the runway and taxiways with visibility sufficient only for visual taxiing comparable to runway visual range value in the order of 50 m.

Category 3C: Operation to and along the surface of the runway and taxiways without external visual reference.

Fig. 11.1 Categories of low-visibility landings

limiting of control system authority. However, in cases where the flight path may be subject to disturbances resulting from turbulence and wind shear, the situation arises of having to apply rapid correction to the flight path leading to a demand for servomotor torque greater than that allowed by the safety devices. Thus, the setting of safety devices is dictated by two conflicting requirements.

1. They must limit the effect of a 'runaway' such that safe recovery can be effected by the pilot;

2. They must allow sufficient authority to the control system so that the required flight path can be followed accurately in the presence of disturbances.

Even with a compromise setting of a safety device, there is the possibility of a height loss under 'runaway conditions', which during an automatic landing would be unacceptable.

279

A further factor which limits the application of safety devices in the manner of conventional control systems, is their inability to protect against passive failures. While not producing flight path changes directly, these failures would nevertheless mean that the predetermined and accurate flight manoeuvre of automatic landing could not be maintained and so set up an equally dangerous situation.

It follows therefore, that to achieve the objective of automatic landing, the operation of an automatic flight control system must be of such a nature that it will:

1. not disturb the flight path as a result of an active malfunction;

2. have adequate authority for sufficiently accurate control along the required flight path;

3. warn of a passive failure;

4. not fail to complete the intended flight manoeuvre following an active or a passive failure.

In order to resolve the problems which would otherwise have been associated with the application of the more conventional flight control systems, it was considered necessary to adopt the concept of 'system redundancy', i.e. to utilise multiple systems operating in such a manner that a single failure within a system will have an insignificant effect on the aircraft's performance during the approach and landing operation.

In describing failures and the system redundancy concept, it is inevitable that certain terminology must be adopted. It is therefore relevant at this point to review the accepted definitions.

Fail-soft is used to describe the ability of a system to withstand a failure without endangering passenger safety, and without producing excessive deviations from the flight path. An equivalent term adopted in the U.S.A. is *fail-passive*.

Fail-operational. This describes a system in which one failure (sometimes more) can occur, but leaves the overall system still functioning, and without causing degradation of performance beyond the limits required for automatic landing and roll-out. Alternative terms are: *fail-active* and *fail-survival*.

Simplex. This term is usually used to define a single automatic control system and its appropriate number of sub-channels. Although various elements of the system may be duplicated, a single failure elsewhere will result in complete unserviceability. In the U.S.A., the equivalent term *single (non-redundant)* is used.

Multiplex. This term is applied to a system comprising two or more sensibly independent simplex systems and sub-channels used collectively so that, in the event of a failure of a system or sub-channel, the remaining systems are alone capable of performing the controlling function. The number of systems and sub-channels adopted is qualified by the terms duplex, triplex and quadruplex as appropriate.

Duplex system is a system of two complete systems or channels which are interconnected, and which together provide continuous control. If comparison monitoring is provided, a duplex system can provide fail-operational capability. The term should not be confused with the terms duplicate-monitored or duplicate-redundancy. An equivalent term adopted in the U.S.A. is *dual active with passive monitoring*.

Triplex system is a fail-operational system of three complete systems or channels which are interconnected and which together provide continuous control. In the event of failure of one of the systems or channels, that system or channel is outvoted by the other two and is automatically disengaged; control is therefore continued in duplex. In the event of a further fault in either of the two remaining systems or channels, they will both disconnect, and the aircraft is returned to the pilot in a trimmed and safe attitude. An equivalent term used in the U.S.A. is *triple-redundant*.

Duplicate-monitored. This refers to a system comprising two systems in parallel and with separate power supplies. The components of both are designed to be either self-monitoring or to have their outputs checked by parallel comparator circuits. Only one system is engaged at any particular time, the other system being in a follow-up mode, and thereby serving as an active standby. In the event of a fault being shown up by the self-monitors or comparators of either of the systems, control is automatically changed over to the standby system.

Dual-dual. This term is used by some manufacturers to define a twin fail-operational control system having twin passive monitoring systems. It should not be considered synonymous to a duplex system, since the control systems may or may not be active simultaneously. In the event of a monitor detecting a failure in its associated system, the second system with its monitor is switched in.

Monitoring. In its strictest sense and, in particular, when applied to multiplex systems, this term defines the process of making comparisons either between two or more outputs (or inputs) or between an output (or input) and a selected datum. The monitoring process can also assume a limiting function; e.g. when it is set up to cause a system to disconnect whenever an output (or input) exceeds a prescribed limit.

Comparison monitor (or Comparator) is one which operates on data supplied from comparable stages in two or more similar systems.

Equaliser. This is a device which adjusts the performance of the sub-systems in multiplex systems to remove differences between sub-system outputs that may arise other than as a result of fault conditions. Two devices are normally adopted, one called a *gain equaliser* which adjusts the amplitude of response of sub-systems, and the other called a *datum equaliser* which adjusts the steady state output of sub-systems.

Automatic landing sequence

The profile of an automatic approach, flare and landing sequence is illustrated in fig. 11.2 and is based on a system that utilises triple digital flight control computer channels, allowing for redundancy to operate in the fail operational and fail passive conditions already defined. Depending upon the number of channels that are armed and engaged, the system performs what are termed a 'LAND 2' status or 'LAND 3' status autoland. Thus, 'LAND 2' signifies there is dual redundancy of engaged flight control computers, sensors and servos (fail passive operation) while 'LAND 3' signifies triple redundancy of power sources, engaged flight control computers, sensors and servos (fail operational). Each status is displayed on an autoland status annunciator.

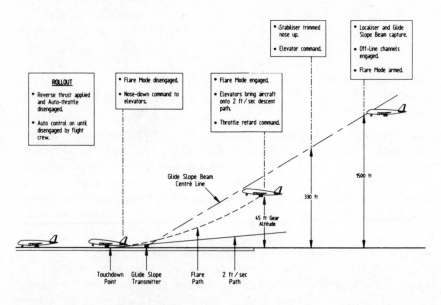

Fig. 11.2 Automatic approach, flare and land

During cruise and initial stages of approach to land, the control system operates as a single channel system, controlling the aircraft about its pitch and roll axes and providing the appropriate flight director commands. Since multichannel operation is required for an automatic landing, at a certain stage of the approach, the remaining two channels are armed by pressing an 'APPR' switch on the flight control panel. The operation of this switch also arms the localiser and glide slope modes. Both of the 'off-line' channels are continually supplied with the relevant outer loop control signals and operate on a comparative basis the whole time.

Altitude information essential for vertical guidance to touchdown is always provided by signals from a radio altimeter which becomes effective as soon as the aircraft's altitude is within the altimeter's operating range (typically 2,500 feet).

When the aircraft has descended to 1,500 feet radio altitude, the localiser and glide slope beams are captured, and the armed 'off-line' control channels are then automatically engaged. The localiser and glide slope beam signals control the aircraft about the roll and pitch axes so that any deviations are automatically corrected to maintain alignment with the runway. At the same time, the autoland status annunciator displays 'LAND 2' or 'LAND 3', depending upon the number of channels 'voted into operation' for landing the aircraft, and computerised control of flare is also armed.

At a radio altitude of 330 feet, the aircraft's horizontal stabiliser is automatically repositioned to begin trimming the aircraft to a nose-up attitude. The elevators are also deflected to counter the trim and to provide subsequent pitch control in the trimmed attitude.

When an altitude is reached at which the landing gear is 45 feet above the ground (referred to as gear altitude) the flare mode is automatically engaged. The gear altitude calculation, which is pre-programmed into the computer, is based upon radio altitude, pitch attitude, and the known distance between the landing gear, the fuselage and the radio altimeter antenna. The flare mode takes over pitch attitude control from the glide slope, and generates a pitch command to bring the aircraft onto a 2 feet/second descent path. At the same time, a 'throttle retard' command signal is supplied to the autothrottle system to reduce engine thrust to the limits compatible with the flare path.

Prior to touchdown, and about 5 feet gear altitude, the flare mode is disengaged and there is transition to the touchdown and roll-out mode. At about 1 foot gear altitude, the pitch attitude of the aircraft is decreased to 2°, and at touchdown, a command signal is supplied to the elevators to lower the aircraft's nose and so bring the nose landing gear wheels in contact with the runway and hold them there during the rollout. When reverse thrust is applied, the autothrottle system is automatically disengaged. The automatic flight control system remains on until disengaged by the flight crew.

Autothrottle system

An autothrottle system serves the dual purpose of maintaining constant airspeed during automatic approach and landing phases by adjustments of engine power, and closing the throttles at a constant rate during an autoflare phase. A typical throttle control system is schematically illustrated in fig. 11.3.

Airspeed information is supplied from an air data computer via a control transformer link, the actual speed values being compared with a datum airspeed, this being the one at which the system was engaged. Differences between the two values produce error signals which are fed to the servo amplifiers and, after amplification, to the throttle servomotors. Thus, assuming that an error signal is produced in response to a decrease in airspeed, the servomotors will be activated to cause the throttles to open by an amount proportional to the error signal amplitude. As the airspeed of the aircraft slowly increases, the error signals are reduced and the throttles moved to the closed position. The throttles are not returned to the original positions, since a higher amount of thrust is required to overcome the drag resulting from the higher airspeed.

As in any servo system, the error signals must be balanced by feedback signals, the signals in this case, being relevant to throttle servomotor position and rate of position change. Thus, the total input to the servo amplifiers is reduced to zero and a point is reached at which throttle actuation ceases, but some airspeed error remains. The residual error is corrected by passing the signal through an integrator circuit. Changes in airspeed resulting from changes in pitch attitude are anticipated by means of a rate-of-pitch-attitude-change signal which is applied to the servo amplifiers by a pitch rate gyroscope.

In a number of current types of public transport category aircraft, autothrottle systems have been introduced the operation of which is directed principally towards the conservation of fuel. The elements and data sources for one such system (employed in the Boeing 747) are shown schematically in fig. 11.4. In conjunction with a Total Air Temperature/Engine Pressure Ratio limit system (TAT/EPR) the complete autothrottle system provides three primary control modes: (i) EPR control; (ii) Mach hold; and (iii) speed control. In the first of these, the autothrottle commands the engine thrust levers so that the engine with the highest EPR, i.e. the ratio of engine inlet pressure to exhaust gas pressure, acquires and maintains the EPR limit value for the selected mode minus any increment of EPR decrease selected. The computer continuously compares all four engine EPRs and selects the one with the highest value as the controlling unit. The EPR mode is used during take-off, climb and go-around, and can also be used for maximum continuous thrust, and for cruise flight.

In the Mach hold function, which is used during cruise flight, the Mach number is held at the value at which the system was engaged. The speed control mode is used to acquire and maintain a selected airspeed, normally for descent, holding, approach and landing. The speed is indicated on a fast/slow speed scale of the attitude direction indicator of the flight director

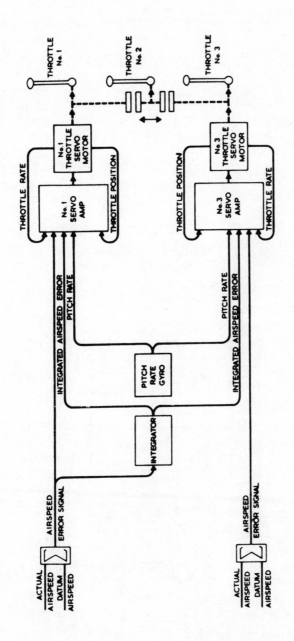

Fig. 11.3 Autothrottle system

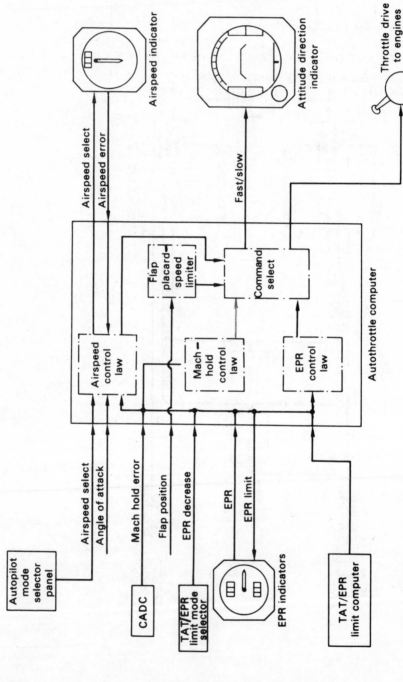

Fig. 11.4 Element and data sources of TAT/EPR autothrottle system

system. The selected value is indicated on the mode selector panel of the automatic flight control system, and also by a 'bug' on the captain's and first officer's airspeed indicators.

Sub-modes are also available to provide additional control or protection, including take-off, overboost protection, minimum speed protection (provided by angle of attack sensors) and flap speed limit protection which automatically limits the maximum speed that can be commanded by the autothrottle system to a value determined by flap position.

TEST QUESTIONS

1 What is meant by the abbreviations RVR and DH?
2 What are the categories of automatic approach and landing?
3 A system in which a failure occurs but leaves the overall system still functioning and without degradation of performance has:
  (a) fail-passive ability
  (b) fail-soft ability
  (c) fail-operational ability
4 In what manner does a duplicate-monitored system differ from a duplex system?
5 From which source are altitude signals derived during automatic approach and flare.?
6 What are the parameters required to be monitored by an autothrottle system?

Appendix 1: Fixed-wing Aircraft/Autopilot Combinations

Aerostar 601	King KRC 200; Century IV; Bendix FCS810
Airbus A300; 310	SFENA
BAC 1-11 201 AC/300 series	Bendix PB20; Elliot E2000/E2000
400series/500 series	Bendix PB2000/E2000,E2100,E2200
Beechcraft Baron 55,58	Bendix FCS810; Century IV; Century III; King KFC 200, KFC 250; Collins AP107
95-B55	Century III; Century IV; Beech B-5, H14
Queenair 65-80/70/A65	Brittain B4; Beech H14/Bendix M4/Bendix M4
Duchess 76	Century II; Century IV
Duke 60	Century IV
King Air 90	Sperry SPZ200; Centrury IV; Collins AP106; Bendix M4 series
King Air A100/200	Collins AP105; Beech H14/Collins APS80, Collins AP105; King KFC 300
Bonanza A36	Bendix FCS810; Century I
C23	Beech Navomatic
F33A	Century III; King KFC 200
Boeing 707 series/720 series	Bendix PB20/PB120
727 100 series/200 series	Sperry SP50/SP150
737/-236	Sperry SP77/SP177
747	Sperry SPZ1
757	Collins FCS-700
767	
Britannia	Smiths SEP2
Britten-Norman Islander/Trislander	Brittain B5; Collins AP107; Century I/Collins AP107
Bristol 170	Sperry A3
Canadair CL-44	Bendix PB20
Cessna 172 series, 177, 182 series,	Navomatic 200, 300 series; Century I, II

288

Appendix 1: Fixed-wing Aircraft/Autopilot Combinations

U2 06F, T337H
  series 210, 310, 330 — Navomatic 400 series
  series 340 — Navomatic 400 series; King KFC 200
  series 400/500 — Navomatic 800, 1000 series; King KFC 200/Sperry SPZ200, SPZ500

DHC Twin Otter/Dash 7 — Collins AP106/Sperry SPZ700

Douglas DC-3/DC-6/DC-8 — Sperry A-3/A12/SP30
DC-9/DC-10 — Sperry SP50G/Bendix PB100

Embraer Bandeirante — Bendix M4 Series
  Brazilia — King KFC300
  Xingu — Sperry SPZ200

Falcon 20E/20F/50 — Collins AP104, 109/Collins 105/Sperry SPZ600

Fokker F27 200 and 400/F28 4000 — Smiths SEP2/SEP6

Grumman AA/Traveller — Century I
  5A Cheetah
  5B Tiger — Century I, II
  GA7 Couger — Century III
  G159 Gulfstream I — Collins AP104, 105
  G1159 Gulfstream II — Sperry SP50G

Herald 100, 200, 400 series — Sperry AL30

HP Jetstream – I/200/300 — Bendix M4 series; Smiths SEP10/Bendix M4 series/Sperry SPZ500

HS Trident — Smiths SEP5
  748-1/-2A/-2B — Smiths SEP2/SEP2, SEP6; Sperry SPZ500/SEP2
  125-1, 1B, 3B
  -400 series — Collins AP103, 104
  -600 series/700 series — Collins AP104/AP103; APS180
  146 — Smiths SEP10

Learjet 35A, 36A — Bendix FCS200

Lockheed – 1011 Tristar — Collins FCS-110

Mooney M20 Series — Brittain B2C, B5; Century 21; King KFC200

Partenavia P68B/P68C — Century I; King KFC200/Century III

Piper PA23-160/-250 — Century I, Altimatic II, III, V; Bendix FCS810
  24-180 — Century I
  28 series — Altimatic III; Century I, 21; Mitchell Autocontrol II, III; Piper Autoflite II
  30/31 series/32 series — Altimatic III; Century II; Autocontrol III/Altimatic III, V, X; Bendix FCS 810, 870; King KAP 200, KFC 200,

289

	KFC 250, Century 41; King KAP 200, KFC 200; Autocontrol III
34 series	Altimatic III; King KAP 200, KFC 200
39/42	Altimatic III/King KFC 300
Rallye TB10/235	Century I/Badin Crouzet
Rockwell 112/114/500	Century I, II, III/Century I; Altimatic III; King KFC 200/Century III
685/690/840	Bendix FCS810; M4/Bendix M4; Collins AP106/Collins AP106
Sabre 65	Collins APS 80
Short Skyvan/Belfast	Bendix M4/Smiths SEP5
Socata TB10	Century I, III
Swearingen SA 226T (B)	Collins APS 80
Viscount 700 series/800 series	Bendix PB10; Collins AP101/PB10; Smiths SEP2

Appendix 2: Helicopter/Autopilot Combinations

Aerospatiale: Dauphin	SFIM 145
AS330J Puma/	
AS332L Tiger	SFIM PA137/SFIM PA155
AS330B Ecuriell	SFIM PA85E3
Augusta A109	Sperry Helipilot I, II; Sperry SHZ-109
Bell 206A/206B/206L-1	SFENA 400/Collins APS 841H; Ferranti FAS/2/Collins APS 841H
212/222	SFENA 400; Sperry Helipilot I/ Sperry Helipilot I
214 ST	Bell system
Boeing Vertol 234 LR	Hamilton Standard
Bolkow B0105	Ferranti FAS/2 Autostab
Sikorsky S61N	Hamilton Standard
S76A	Hamilton Standard; Sperry Helipilot I
Westland Wessex 60-1	Ferranti FAS2W
Lynx 88	MEASL Mk 34
WG 30	Newmark FLN 400

Appendix 3: Acronyms and Abbreviations Associated With Automatic Flight Control Systems, Equipment and Controlling Signal Functions

ACCEL	ACCELerometer
ACQ	ACQuire (prefixed by a condition, e.g., ALT ACQ)
A/D	Analogue to Digital
ADC	Air Data Computer
ADI	Attitude Director Indicator
AFCS	Automatic Flight Control System
AFS	Automatic Flight System
AGC	Automatic Gain Control
AGS	Automatic Gain Stabilisation
AHRS	Attitude and Heading Reference System
ALG ARM	Align Arm
ANN	ANNunciator
AOSS	After Over Station Sensor
AP, A/P	AutoPilot (suffixed by condition, e.g., ENG, DISC)
APFDS	AutoPilot and Flight Director System
APMS	Automatic Performance and Management System
APPR OC	APProach ON Course
APS	Altitude PreSelect
APSB	APS Bracket
ARINC	Aeronautical Radio INCorporated
ARM	ARMed (prefixed by condition, e.g., LOC ARM, VOR ARM)
AS, A/S	Airspeed
ASA	Autoland Status Annunciator
AT	AutoThrottle
ATS	AutoThrottle System
AT/SC	AutoThrottle/Speed Control
ATT	ATTitude (may be followed by condition, e.g., ATT HOLD)
ATT ERR	ATTitude ERRor
AUTO APPR	AUTOmatic APProach

B/A	Bank Angle
BARO	BAROmetric
BB	Bar Bias
B/B	Back Beam
B/C, BC, B/CRS	Back Course
B/D	Bottom of Descent
BITE	Built-In Test Equipment
BRG	BeaRinG
CADC	Central Air Data Computer
CAP	CAPture (prefixed by a condition, e.g., LOC CAP, NAV CAP)
CBB	Collective Bar Bias
CDU	Control and Display Unit
CE	Course Error
CLK	CLocK
CMD	CoMmanD (prefixed by another abbreviation, e.g., FD CMD)
CP	Control Panel
CPL	CouPLed (prefixed by condition, e.g., ROLL, PITCH, APPR)
CRS	CouRSe
CT	Control Transformer
CW	Caution and Warning
CWS	Control Wheel Steering
D/A	Digital to Analogue
DADC	Digital Air Data Computer
DEVN	DEViatioN
DES	DESired (suffixed by condition, e.g., DES TRK, DES CRS)
DG	Directional Gyroscope
DH	Decision Height
DIFCS	Digital Integrated Flight Control System
DISC	DISConnect
DISP	DISPlacement
DLC	Direct Lift Control
DME	Distance Measuring Equipment
DMUX	DeMUltipleXer
DSR TK	DeSiRed TracK
DTG	Distance-To-Go
DU	Display Unit
EADI	Electronic Attitude Direction Indicator

EFCU	Electronic Flight Control Unit
EFIS	Electronic Flight Instrument System
EHSI	Electronic Horizontal Situation Indicator
EHSV	Electro-Hydraulic Servo Valve
ENG	ENGage
EO	Easy-On
EX LOX	EXpanded LOCaliser
FAC	Flight Augmentation Computer
FAWP	Final Approach WayPoint
FCC	Flight Control Computer
FCEU	Flight Control Electronic Unit
FCU	Flight Control Unit
FCES	Flight Control Electronic System
FD, F/D	Flight Director
FGS	Flight Guidance System
FIS	Flight Instrument System
FL CH	Flight Level CHange
FMA	Flight Mode Annunciator
FMC	Flight Management Computer
FMCS	Flight Management Computer System
FMS	Flight Management System
FODTS	Fibre-Optic Data Transmission System
FS	Fast Slew
FTR	Force Trim Release
GA, G/A	Go-Around
GS, G/S	Glide Slope
HARS	Heading and Attitude Reference System
HDG	HeaDinG (can be suffixed by condition, e.g., HDG HOLD, HDG SELect)
HLD	HoLD
HSI	Horizontal Situation Indicator
IAS	Indicated AirSpeed
IAWP	Initial Approach WayPoint
ICU	Instrument Comparator Unit
ILS OC	Instrument Landing System On Course
INS	Inertial Navigation System
INTLK	INTerLocK
INWP	INtermediate WayPoint
IRS	Inertial Reference System
IRU	Inertial Reference Unit

IVS	Instantaneous Vertical Speed
IVV	Instantaneous Vertical Velocity
LAU	Linear Accelerometer Unit
LBS	Lateral Beam Sensor
LNAV	Lateral NAVigation
LOC	LOCaliser
LRRA	Low-Range Radar Altimeter
LRU	Line Replaceable Unit
LSSAS	Longitudinal Static Stability Augmentation System
LSU	Logic Switching Unit
LVDT	Linear Voltage Differential (also Displacement) Transformer
MADGE	Microwave Aircraft Digital Guidance Equipment
MALU	Mode Aunnunciation Logic Unit
MAN	Manual
MAP	Mode Annunciator Panel
MAWP	Missed Approach WayPoint
MCDP	Maintenance Control Display Panel
MCP	Mode Control Panel
MDA	Minimum Descent Altitude
MM	Middle Marker
MPU	Microprocessor Unit
MSU	Mode Selector Unit
MUX	Multiplexer
NCD	No Computed Data
NCU	Navigation Computer Unit
ND	Navigation Display
NDB	Non Directional Beacon
NOC	NAV On Course
OC,O/C	On Course
OD	Out of Detent (may be prefixed, e.g., CWS OD)
OM	Outer Marker
OSS	Over Station Sensor
P ATT	Pitch ATTitude
PBB	Pitch Bar Bias
PCA	Power Control Actuator
PCPL	Pitch CouPLed
PCWS	Pitch Control Wheel Steering
PECO	Pitch Erection Cut-Off

PFD	Primary Flight Display
P HOLD	Pitch HOLD
PSAS	Pitch Stability Augmentation System
PSM	Power Supply Module
PSO	Phase Shift Oscillator
P SYNC	Pitch SYNChronisation
RA, R/A	Radio (Radar) Altimeter
RBB	Roll Bar Bias
RCPL	Roll CouPLed
RCWS	Roll Control Wheel Steering
REF	REFerence
REV/C	REVerse Course (same as Back Course)
RG	Raster Generator
R/HOLD	Roll HOLD
RLS	Remote Light Sensor
RMI	Radio Magnetic Indicator
RN, RNAV	Area NAVigation
RN/APPR	Area Navigation APPRoach
RSAS	Roll Stability Augmentaion System
RTE DATA	RouTE Data
RVDT	Rotary Voltage Differential Transmitter
SAM	Stabiliser Aileron Module
SAS	Stability Augmentation System
SBY	StandBY
S/C	Step Climb
SCAT	Speed Command of Altitude and Thrust
SCM	Spoiler/Speedbrake Control Module
SEL	Select
SFCC	Slat/Flap Control Computer
SID	Standard Instrument Departure
SG	Symbol Generator (Stroke Generator)
SGU	Symbol Generator Unit
SPD	SPeeD (Airspeed or Mach hold)
SRP	Selected Reference Point
SS	Slow Slew
SSEC	Static Source Error Correction
STAR	Standard Terminal Arrival Route
STS	STatuS (prefixed by a function, e.g., TRACK STS)
STCM	Stabiliser Trim Control Module
TACAN	TACtical Air Navigation
TAS	True Air Speed

T/C	Top of Climb
TCC	Thrust Control Computer
TCS	Touch Control Steering
T/D	Top of Descent
TKE	TracK angle Error
TK CH	TracK CHange
TMC	Thrust Management Computer
TMS	Thrust Management System
TMSP	Thrust Mode Select Panel
TRP	Thrust Rating Panel
TTG	Time To Go
TTL	Tuned To Localiser
TURB	TURBulence
VAR	VARiable
VBS	Vertical Beam Sensor
VGU	Vertical Gyro Unit
VLD	VaLiD (usually suffixing a condition, e.g., VG VLD, FLAG VLD)
VNAV	Vertical NAVigation
VOR	Very-high-frequency Omnidirectional Range
VOR APPR	VOR APPRoach
VOR OC	VOR On Course
VORTAC	VOR TACtical (Air navigation)
VS	Vertical Speed
WO, W/O	WashOut
WPT	WayPoinT
WXR	Weather Radar transceiver
XTK DEV	Cross TracK DEViation
XTR	TRansmitter
YD, Y/D	Yaw Damper
YDM	Yaw Damper Module

Appendix 4: Logic Gates and Truth Tables

AND

A	B	C
0	0	0
0	1	0
1	0	0
1	1	1

OR

A	B	C
0	0	0
0	1	1
1	0	1
1	1	1

INVERTER

A	B
0	1

A	B
1	0

NAND

A	B	C
0	0	1
0	1	1
1	0	1
1	1	0

NOR

A	B	C
0	0	1
0	1	0
1	0	0
1	1	0

NEGATED AND ($\bar{A}$)

$\bar{A}$	B	C
1	0	0
1	1	0
0	0	1
0	1	0

NEGATED AND ($\bar{B}$)

A	$\bar{B}$	C
0	1	0
0	0	0
1	1	1
1	0	0

NEGATED OR

A	$\bar{B}$	C
0	1	1
0	0	0
1	1	1
1	0	1

$\bar{A}$	B	C
1	0	1
1	1	1
0	0	0
0	1	1

EXCLUSIVE GATES

NOR

A	B	C
0	0	1
0	1	0
1	0	0
1	1	1

OR

A	B	C
0	0	0
0	1	1
1	0	1
1	1	0

WIRED GATES

AND

OR

Appendix 5: Solutions to Multi-choice Questions

Chapter 1	4(b), 9(b), 14(b), 21(b), 27(c), 28(a)
Chapter 3	4(b), 7(c)
Chapter 5	1(c), 2(b)
Chapter 6	8(c), 10(b), 14(c)
Chapter 7	1(c)
Chapter 8	4(b), 8(c)
Chapter 9	7(b), 18(c)
Chapter 10	2(b), 3(a), 4(b), 6(c)
Chapter 11	3(c)

Index

300

Index